Series preface

Volume 1 - Levels 4, 5 and 6

Volume 2 - Levels 7 and 8

Volume 3 - Levels 9 and 10

This is a totally new series written to meet all the requirements of the National Curriculum Key Stage 4, which also gives pupils the necessary preparation for the revised GCSE (1994).

The tests at the end of Key Stage 4, ie GCSE, mark the end of compulsory schooling. For very many pupils, these tests will be the evidence of their education that they will take with them into the adult world. It is important that during those last two years at school pupils acquire the following:

❑ Mathematical skills required for success in adult life.

❑ Recognition of the applications of Mathematics in everyday life.

❑ Appreciation of Mathematics as a source of interest in its own right.

How does the series work?

There are three books in the series, which cover the mathematical material for all but a small minority of the school population in this age group. There is some degree of overlap between the books, as it is important not to cater for too narrow an ability range. The books are in line with the achievement levels 4-10, though not rigidly: the National Curriculum stratification of the curriculum into levels is used as a framework round which to structure a course of study.

Each volume contains the following:

25 Chapters

The chapters cover the material specified by the National Curriculum. They are largely self-contained (ie it is not assumed that pupils will have covered all previous topics), thereby ensuring greater flexibility.

A variety of exercises

Many different types of exercise are included, to fulfil the National Curriculum criterion that pupils should become expert at a variety of tasks. The books of this series contain exercises of different lengths, as follows:

❑ Short questions in contexts *relevant to this age of pupil* (with answers at the back of the book – to be removed if desired).

❑ Longer, end of chapter questions, which may incorporate material from other parts of the syllabus. These questions might occupy *one or two class periods* and provide something for faster learners to do while the other pupils catch up.

❑ Guidelines for four extended tasks which could occupy *two or three weeks* and are concerned with the *use and application of mathematics*.

❑ Problems which can be solved using *spreadsheet programs*.

❑ *Puzzles* and *paradoxes* which demonstrate that mathematics is not as unambiguous as it may seem.

The extended tasks and many of the longer questions at chapter ends are open-ended, to give scope for exploration by pupils. A *balance* is maintained between questions which arise from *outside mathematics* and those which are part of the *internal development of mathematics*.

These tasks and questions have been taken from a wide variety of sources. One particularly fruitful source has been the history of mathematics, from Egypt, India, China, etc, as well as from Greece and modern Europe. It is hoped that pupils will learn to appreciate the long history and wide diffusion of mathematics.

Four consolidation sections

Spaced regularly throughout the books are consolidation sections containing the following:

A cross curriculum topic
This is taken from contexts from Science, Politics, History, etc. and is chosen to demonstrate the usefulness of mathematics across many subjects. They will serve as a useful basis for discussion, and provide interesting and readable interludes in the teaching text. The four topics between them touch upon much of the material of the book. By reference to the appropriate chapters they will help pupils see the application and source of the principles they are studying.

An extended task (as described above)

Exercises
There are miscellaneous exercises which are separated into Group A, containing questions *similar to those in the chapters,* Group B containing *challenge* questions, and Group C of *longer* questions.

Puzzles and paradoxes
These will demonstrate that mathematics is not as straightforward as it may seem!

Material on using computers

The National Curriculum Council stresses that every advantage should be taken of computers and calculators. Spreadsheets provide an ideal environment within which to explore mathematics, and each book includes a chapter containing problems which can be investigated with a spreadsheet.

Graded revision examples, test papers and GCSE examination papers

There are sets of *revision examples* and *revision tests* to ensure that students refresh and maintain their knowledge of previous material, and also *four examination papers* modelled on the new sample questions released by the *GCSE boards* in *April 1992*.

Free teachers' guide

There is a *free* Teachers' Guide to accompany each volume for teachers using the books as class texts. The guides contain *keys* to connect the material in the books with the *levels* of the National Curriculum. *Solutions* and *notes* on the longer exercises and the extended tasks are given, along with suggestions for how they could be developed by talented pupils.

Mathematics

y Stage 4
corporating GCSE

lume 2

ermediate tier (Levels 7 & 8)

C. Solomon

blications Ltd
e Place
OON W12 8AW

Acknowledgements

We are grateful to the following for permission to reproduce illustrations:

Casio Electronics Co Ltd

The Hulton Picture Library

The photograph on page 1 is reproduced by courtesy of the Trustees of the British Museum

A CIP catalogue record for this book is available from the British Library

ISBN 1 873981 22 8
Copyright R.C. Solomon © 1992

First edition 1992
Reprinted 1992, 1993

Typeset by
Kai typesetting and DP Publications Ltd
Illustration by Cath Chadwick

Printed in Great Britain by
Bath Press Ltd, Bath

What about the author?

Bob Solomon has spent many years teaching and writing mathematics at this level. His GCSE Mathematics book is widely recommended as a revision course text in sixth form colleges and colleges of further education; his 'Higher' level book for GCSE has been described as 'the very best practice by the very best teachers'. Theta said of his A-Level revision text that it was 'clearly the result of many years of teaching experience'.

Fits the National Curriculum and GCSE

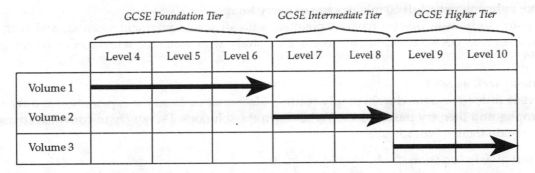

| | GCSE Foundation Tier | | | GCSE Intermediate Tier | | GCSE Higher Tier | |
	Level 4	Level 5	Level 6	Level 7	Level 8	Level 9	Level 10
Volume 1							
Volume 2							
Volume 3							

Preface for Volume II

This is the *second* book in the series, and covers Levels 7 and 8 of the Mathematics syllabus. It can be used either to take the pupil up to the testing at Key Stage 4 at those levels, or as preparation for those pupils who will be progressing to levels 9 and 10.

RC Solomon
June 1992

Study and examination hints

1. Study hints

This book has been written to help you understand the material of Levels 7 and 8 of National Curriculum Mathematics. Of course it must be used in an efficient way. The following hints will help you make good use of your study time.

A good rule to follow is: *Little but often*
An hour a day for seven days is more useful than seven hours of work on a single day.

Make sure you get a full 60 minutes out of every hour
Do your study in as quiet a room as possible, with all your equipment to hand, and with as few distractions as possible. Do not try to combine study with watching television or listening to the radio.

Write as well as read
There is little to be gained from simply reading Mathematics. Read the explanation and the worked examples and then try the exercises. Write down the solutions. Do not try to convince yourself that you can do them in your head.

Do not give in too soon
There are answers at the back of the book, but use them for checking that you are right, rather than for finding out how to do a problem.

At the end of the book are four exams and two mental tests. You are allowed a calculator for these exams. Make sure you are confident in its use. For the mental tests, get someone to read out the questions to you, repeating them once, and taking 20 minutes over each test. You are not allowed a calculator in these tests.

2. Examination hints

How well you do in an exam depends mainly on how well you have prepared for it. But many candidates do poorly because of bad examination technique. The following hints will help you make the most of your examination time.

Read the question carefully
Very many marks are lost by candidates who have misunderstood a question. Not only do they lose the marks for that question, but they also lose time because the question is made more complicated by their mistake.

Do not spend too much time on one question
There is little or no point in spending a third of the time on a question that carries a twentieth of the marks. Leave that question, and come back to it later if you have time at the end of the exam.

Show your working
If you obtain a wrong answer just because of a slight slip, then you will not lose many marks provided that you show all your working. If you put down a wrong answer without any explanation then you will get no marks at all.

Try to make your solutions neat

Use enough paper to ensure that your answer can be read easily. But do not spend too much time on this – there is no point in spending five minutes on a beautiful diagram for a question which is only worth 2 marks.

Recognise what each question is about

Many candidates find that they can answer a question when they are doing an exercise consisting of several similar problems, but can not answer the same question when it occurs in a test paper surrounded by different questions. Read each question carefully, and identify the topic or topics of the question. The examiners are not trying to 'catch you out'. They are trying to test that you have studied each part of the syllabus and are able to answer questions on it.

Recognise combinations of topics

Many questions start with a problem in one area of mathematics, and then require you to apply your answer to another, related, area. Make sure you appreciate what the examiners are looking for.

Above all: *Make good use of your time!*

During the months that you are preparing yourself for the examination make sure that each hour of learning or revision is well spent. During the actual examination, make the best use of the short time available.

Contents

Chapter 1

Whole numbers and fractions

In 1865 the British Museum acquired an Egyptian scroll of leather, dating from about 1,650 B.C. It was so old and so tightly rolled that 60 years passed before it was unrolled.

What they found were rows of numbers. The modern numerals are below. The bars above the numbers make them into fractions, so that $\bar{6} = \frac{1}{6}$. What do the rows mean?

Fig 1.1

1.1 Whole numbers

Composites and primes

We can factorize a number like 15, by writing it as $15 = 3 \times 5$. But 3 and 5 cannot be factorized any further.

A number like 15, which can be written as the product of smaller numbers, is called composite. Numbers like 3 or 5, which cannot be split up any further, are called prime.

We could choose 1 to be either prime or not. By convention it is not prime. The first few primes are 2, 3, 5, 7, 11, 13 etc.

		$\overline{10}$	$\overline{40}$	$\overline{8}$
		$\overline{4}$	$\overline{12}$	$\overline{3}$
$\overline{25}$	$\overline{15}$	$\overline{75}$	$\overline{200}$	$\overline{8}$
	$\overline{7}$	$\overline{14}$	$\overline{28}$	$\overline{4}$
	$\overline{18}$	$\overline{27}$	$\overline{54}$	$\overline{9}$
	$\overline{26}$	$\overline{39}$	$\overline{78}$	$\overline{13}$

Numbers can be expressed as the product of primes. For example:

$60 = 2 \times 2 \times 3 \times 5 = 2^2 \times 3 \times 5$

1.1.1 Example

Express 360 as the product of primes.

Solution　　Obviously 2 is a factor. Keep on dividing by 2 until we get an odd number.

$360 = 2 \times 2 \times 2 \times 45$

45 is divisible by 5, giving 9.

$360 = 2^3 \times 9 \times 5$

Recognize that 9 is 3×3.

$360 = 2^3 \times 3^2 \times 5$

1.1.2 Exercises

1) Express the following as products of primes.

　　a) 30　　　　b) 100　　　　c) 56　　　　d) 110　　　　e) 52　　　　f) 720

1

2) How can you tell quickly whether a number is divisible by 2?

3) How can you tell quickly whether a number is divisible by 5?

4) A number is divisible by 3 if the sum of its digits is divisible by 3. Use this result to tell quickly which of the following are divisible by 3:

    a) 3453   b) 111   c) 10,008   d) 1010

5) What is the largest odd number which divides 120?

6) What is the largest power of 2 which divides 360?

1.2 HCF and LCM

Highest common factor

The factors of 12 are 1, 2, 3, 4, 6 and 12 itself. The factors of 15 are 1, 3, 5 and 15 itself. 3 is the highest number which is a factor of both 12 and 15.

The Highest Common Factor or H.C.F of two numbers is the largest number which will divide into both of them.

Least common multiple

The multiples of 12 are 12, 24, 36, 48, 60 etc. The multiples of 15 are 15, 30, 45, 60 etc. 60 is the least number which is a multiple of both 12 and 15.

The Least Common Multiple or L.C.M of two numbers is the smallest number which they will both divide into.

One way to find the H.C.F or LCM of two numbers is to write them both as the product of primes. For the HCF we take all the prime factors which occur in both. For the LCM we take all the prime factors which occur in either of the numbers.

1.2.1 Example

On the left side of the road the lamp-posts are 4 metres apart, and on the right side they are 6 metres apart. At the bottom of the road they are directly opposite each other. How far up the road are they next directly opposite each other?

Solution   There will be a lamp-post on the left after every 4 metres, and on the right after every 6 metres. There will be a lamp-post on both sides after the LCM of 4 and 6 metres.

             Write 4 and 6 in terms of primes.

             $4 = 2^2, 6 = 2 \times 3$. The LCM is $2^2 \times 3$

             The lamp-posts will be opposite after 12 metres

1.2.2 Exercises

1) Find the HCF for the following pairs of numbers:

    a) 6 & 10   b) 4 & 14   c) 9 & 15   d) 12 & 30   e) 14 & 15

2) Find the LCM for the pairs of numbers in Question 5.

3) For the pairs of numbers in Question 1, find

    a) The product of the numbers   b) the product of the HCF and the LCM.

        What do you notice?

4) You have several 2p coins and several 5p coins. What is the least sum of money that can be made up either from 2p coins or from 5p coins?

5) You have a 3 pint jug and a 5 pint jug. What is the least volume that can be made up using either the 3 pint jug only or the 5 pint jug only?

6) Two hands move round a dial: the faster moves round in 6 seconds, the slower in 8 seconds. If they start together at the top of the dial when are they next together at the top of the dial?

7) A committee decides to meet every 6 days, provided that this day is a Saturday. The first meeting is on Saturday 4th January. When will the next meeting be?

8) A rectangular area of 150 cm by 120 cm is to be covered with square tiles. We want to use the largest tiles possible, without cutting any. How big should the tiles be?

1.3 Arithmetic of fractions

Mixed numbers

A number like $2\frac{3}{4}$, containing both whole numbers and fractions, is called a mixed number. If a mixed number is written as a fraction the top will be bigger than the bottom. This is called a vulgar fraction.

$$2\frac{3}{4} = \frac{11}{4}$$

Multiplication and division

When fractions are multiplied, the tops are multiplied together and the bottoms are multiplied together.

$$\frac{3}{7} \times \frac{5}{8} = \frac{3 \times 5}{7 \times 8} = \frac{15}{56}$$

To divide by a fraction $\frac{5}{8}$, multiply by $\frac{8}{5}$.

$$\frac{3}{7} \div \frac{5}{8} = \frac{3}{7} \times \frac{8}{5} = \frac{3 \times 8}{7 \times 5} = \frac{24}{35}$$

When multiplying or dividing by a mixed number, first convert it to a vulgar fraction.

$$\frac{1}{9} \times 2\frac{3}{4} = \frac{1}{9} \times \frac{11}{4} = \frac{11}{36}$$

Addition and subtraction

When fractions are added or subtracted, they must first be put over the same denominator.

$$\frac{3}{7} + \frac{5}{8} = \frac{3 \times 8}{7 \times 8} + \frac{5 \times 7}{8 \times 7} = \frac{24 + 35}{56} = \frac{59}{56} = 1\frac{3}{56}$$

1.3.1 Example

1) Evaluate   a) $1\frac{3}{4} \times \frac{2}{5}$ b) $\frac{3}{4} \div \frac{2}{5}$.

     Solution   a)   First express $1\frac{3}{4}$ as a vulgar fraction. $1\frac{3}{4} = \frac{7}{4}$.

                Multiply the tops together and the bottoms together.

$$\frac{7}{4} \times \frac{2}{5} = \frac{14}{20} = \frac{7}{10}$$

            b)   To divide by $\frac{2}{5}$ is to multiply by $\frac{5}{2}$.

$$\frac{3}{4} \div \frac{2}{5} = \frac{3}{4} \times \frac{5}{2} = \frac{15}{8} = 1\frac{7}{8}$$

2) Evaluate $\frac{2}{5} + \frac{1}{4}$, leaving your answer as a fraction.

Solution   Write both the fractions with a denominator of 20.

$$\frac{2}{5} + \frac{1}{4} = \frac{8}{20} + \frac{5}{20} = \frac{13}{20}$$

1.3.2 Exercises

1) Convert the following to vulgar fractions:

   a) $1\frac{2}{3}$
   b) $2\frac{3}{5}$
   c) $3\frac{3}{10}$
   d) $1\frac{2}{7}$

2) Convert the following to mixed numbers:

   a) $\frac{12}{5}$
   b) $\frac{20}{7}$
   c) $\frac{31}{8}$
   d) $\frac{100}{13}$

3) Evaluate the following, leaving your answers as fractions.

   a) $\frac{2}{3} \times \frac{4}{7}$
   b) $\frac{5}{6} \times \frac{2}{15}$
   c) $\frac{3}{2} \times \frac{3}{5}$
   d) $\frac{2}{7} \times \frac{5}{3}$

   e) $1\frac{1}{3} \times \frac{1}{10}$
   f) $2\frac{3}{7} \times \frac{4}{5}$
   g) $1\frac{5}{6} \times 2\frac{3}{7}$
   h) $\frac{2}{3} + \frac{4}{7}$

   i) $\frac{1}{2} + \frac{3}{5}$
   j) $\frac{5}{9} + 3$
   k) $\frac{11}{20} + \frac{1}{40}$
   l) $1\frac{2}{3} + \frac{4}{7}$

   m) $\frac{1}{3} + 2\frac{4}{5}$
   n) $1\frac{2}{7} + 2\frac{1}{3}$

4) Evaluate the following, leaving your answers as fractions.

   a) $\frac{1}{3} + \frac{1}{4}$
   b) $\frac{3}{5} + \frac{1}{6}$
   c) $\frac{1}{7} + \frac{2}{3}$
   d) $\frac{2}{3} - \frac{2}{5}$

   e) $1\frac{1}{4} + \frac{1}{2}$
   f) $2\frac{1}{9} + 3\frac{1}{4}$
   g) $1\frac{5}{7} - \frac{1}{10}$

5) George buys $1\frac{3}{4}$ yards of wire, and cuts off $\frac{1}{3}$ of a yard. How much does he have left?

6) $2\frac{1}{4}$ pints are poured from a 15 pint container. How much is left?

7) A man has three children: in his will he leaves half his estate to his wife, a quarter to his eldest child and a fifth to the middle child. What fraction does the youngest child get?

8) How many $\frac{1}{2}$ pint jugs can be filled from a 20 pint container?

9) I buy a batch of 32 apples, of which a quarter are bad. How many are good?

10) A ship sails at $12\frac{1}{2}$ km/hr. How long will it take to cover 75 km.?

11) Michael walks one quarter of the distance to school, and then takes the bus. If the bus ride is $1\frac{1}{2}$ miles, how far does he walk?

12) Gabriel takes $1\frac{1}{2}$ minutes to peel an apple. How many apples can he peel in 9 minutes?

13) The profit of a firm is divided equally between its three partners. Each partner then has to pay three-tenths of his share in tax. What fraction of the original profit does each partner keep?

14) A cook uses eleven twelfths of a pound of flour to make 20 cakes. How much flour does each cake contain?

15) The only fractions used by Egyptian Mathematicians were unit fractions, i.e. those with 1 on top. The text at the beginning of the chapter is about conversion to unit fractions. See if you can write $\frac{2}{5}$, $\frac{3}{5}$ and $\frac{4}{5}$ in terms of unit fractions, without repeating any.

1.4 Longer exercises

A. Factorization

1) Take any 2 digit number and put it alongside itself to obtain a 4 digit number. Factorize this number. So if you started with 54, you would get $5454 = 2 \times 3^3 \times 101$.

2) Repeat with some other 2 digit numbers. What do you notice about the factorization? Can you show why it works?

3) Take any 3 digit number and put it alongside itself. Show that 7, 11 and 13 are factors of the number. So if you chose 354, you will find that 354354 is divisible by 7, 11 and 13.

4) Can you show why the result of (3) works?

5) What happens if you choose a 4 digit number and put it alongside itself?

B. Composite numbers

Some numbers are more composite than others. 12 has 5 factors, though 15 has only 3 factors. (Not including the number itself).

1) A number is called highly composite if it has more factors than any previous number, i.e. if it sets a new record of numbers of factors. Find the highly composite numbers up to 100.

   A number is called abundant if its factors add up to more than the number itself. $1 + 2 + 3 + 4 + 6 > 12$, so 12 is abundant.

2) Find some other abundant numbers. Is every highly composite number abundant?

Multiple choice question *(Tick appropriate box)*

A firm employs two security guards. They meet at the factory gate at 9 pm. One guard takes exactly 25 minutes to do his round, the other takes exactly 30 minutes. They will next meet at the factory gate at:

a) 9.05 pm ☐

b) 11.30 pm ☐

c) 9.30 am ☐

d) 11.50 pm ☐

e) none of these ☐

Points to note

1) *Prime factors*

   When expressing a number in terms of primes, do not forget to show when a factor is repeated. 60 is equal to $2^2 \times 3 \times 5$, not $2 \times 3 \times 5$.

2) *HCF and LCM.*

   a) If a factor is repeated in both numbers, take account of this when working out the HCF.

   b) The product of two numbers is a common multiple of them, but it may not be the least common multiple. If both numbers have a common factor then there is no need to repeat it.

3) *Fractions*

   a) When adding fractions, do not add the numerators together and the denominators together.

   $\frac{2}{3} + \frac{4}{5} \neq \frac{6}{8}$.

   b) Do not invert fractions.

   $\frac{1}{3} + \frac{1}{6} = \frac{1}{2}$. But $3 + 6 \neq 2$.

Chapter 2

Calculation

> The picture on the right shows the display of a scientific calculator. You are probably familiar with many of the keys.
>
> Make two lists, one list of the functions which you know how to use and one of those which you don't.

2.1 Use of calculator

Probably you are skilful at using your calculator to perform the basic operations of +, −, × and ÷. With a scientific calculator you can handle more complicated calculations, without the need to write anything down on paper. This makes arithmetic quicker and more accurate.

Calculations are made easier with use of the memory and brackets buttons.

Memory

When you have made a calculation, the result can be stored in the memory. This is done by pressing the Min button (or STO on some brands). When you want to use the result press the MR button (or RCL). This is better than writing down the result and then having to key it in again.

To clear the memory, press AC and then Min .

Brackets

The standard order of operations is that × and ÷ take priority over + and −. For example:

"3 × 4 + 2" means:

> Multiply 3 and 4 and then add 2.

The answer is 14.

If we want to do + or − first, then brackets must be used.

"3 × (4 + 2)" means:

> Add 4 and 2 and then multiply by 3.

The answer is 18.

The same principle applies when using a calculator. The calculation above using brackets can be keyed in exactly as it is written.

2.1.1 Examples

1) Jane has £124.6 and Joan has £204.56. How much do they have in French Francs at 9.6 FF per £ or in Deutschmarks at 2.98 per £?

Solution   The total amount of British money is 124.6 + 204.56 = £329.16. We will use this total twice, so save it in the memory by pressing $\boxed{\text{Min}}$.

To convert to FF multiply by 9.6. To convert to DM, multiply by 2.98. The sequence of buttons is:

$\boxed{9}\,\boxed{.}\,\boxed{6}\,\boxed{\times}\,\boxed{\text{MR}}\,\boxed{=}$ or $\boxed{2}\,\boxed{.}\,\boxed{9}\,\boxed{8}\,\boxed{\times}\,\boxed{\text{MR}}\,\boxed{=}$

They have 3159.936 FF or 980.8968 DM

2) Evaluate the expression $(2 + 3(4 - 1))^2$.

Solution   Key in this expression in the order in which it is written. Be sure to press $\boxed{\times}$ after the 3.

$\boxed{(}\,\boxed{2}\,\boxed{+}\,\boxed{3}\,\boxed{\times}\,\boxed{(}\,\boxed{4}\,\boxed{-}\,\boxed{1}\,\boxed{)}\,\boxed{)}\,\boxed{x^2}\,\boxed{=}$

When you press the $\boxed{(}$ button, a sign (01 or (02 appears. This shows how many levels of brackets you are using. On many types of calculator you can have up to 6 levels of brackets nested inside each other.

The answer is 121

3) Evaluate $\dfrac{8.7}{2.9 + 3.4}$, giving your answer to 4 sig. figs.

Solution   This could be calculated in two ways.

Using memory, store the bottom line in the memory and then divide by it. The sequence is:

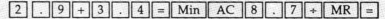

$\boxed{2}\,\boxed{.}\,\boxed{9}\,\boxed{+}\,\boxed{3}\,\boxed{.}\,\boxed{4}\,\boxed{=}\,\boxed{\text{Min}}\,\boxed{\text{AC}}\,\boxed{8}\,\boxed{.}\,\boxed{7}\,\boxed{\div}\,\boxed{\text{MR}}\,\boxed{=}$

Using brackets, be sure to put the bottom line in brackets when you divide by it. The sequence is:

$\boxed{8}\,\boxed{.}\,\boxed{7}\,\boxed{\div}\,\boxed{(}\,\boxed{2}\,\boxed{.}\,\boxed{9}\,\boxed{+}\,\boxed{3}\,\boxed{.}\,\boxed{4}\,\boxed{)}\,\boxed{=}$

The solution is 1.381

2.1.2 Exercises

In the following, calculate the expressions without writing anything down except the final answers. Give your answers to 3 decimal places.

1) Evaluate the following:

   a) $12 \times (3.4 + 5.4)$

   b) $(17 - 12.34) \div 3.6$

   c) $(2.22 + 3.84) \times (3.3 + 8.4)$

   d) $(1.38 - 1.83) \times (107 - 138)$

   e) $(0.12 + 0.27) \times (3.1 - 1.2)$

   f) $(3.9 - 1.2) \div (3.1 - 1.6)$

   g) $\dfrac{1.273}{1.32 + 2.57}$

   h) $\dfrac{4.3 + 8.3}{10.2 - 8.32}$

2) A room has a ceiling of 3 m by 4 m, and the walls are 2.9 m high. Find the total area of walls and ceiling. How much would it cost to decorate the room:

   a) with paint at £0.55 per m^2 b) with wallpaper at £0.85 per m^2?

3) 107 books are bought at £3.56 each. What is the total cost after a £44 discount? What is the total cost after a 10% discount?

4) Norah took £212 on holiday, and spent £14.32 during the journey. How much would she have left

   a) in Pesetas at 183 per £   b) in Escudos at 253 per £?

5) A man can row at 5.43 km per hour. He is rowing with a current, which adds 2.44 km/hour to his speed. How long will it take to row 23 km? How long will 17 km take?

2.2 Estimation

The time taken in learning to use memory and brackets on a calculator is time well spent. There are several advantages to performing calculations in one go, without writing anything down.

Speed. Time is saved by not having to write.

Fewer mistakes. A calculator will remember a number correctly. But if you write it down and then key it in again you may make a mistake.

Accuracy. If you are asked to give an answer to 3 significant figures, then it is necessary to do all the work to more than 3 significant figures. If all the working is done on a calculator, then it is done to 8 or more significant figures.

The disadvantage of doing all the work on a calculator is that you have no record of the calculations. In order to check that you have done the right things it is a good idea to make a rough estimate of the answer you expect to get.

The estimate can be made by taking each number to 1 significant figure and then working it out in your head.

2.2.1 Example

Make a rough estimate of $\frac{2.79 + 3.32}{8.45 - 6.21}$ and then perform the calculation accurate to 4 decimal places.

Solution   The top line is roughly equal to $3 + 3 = 6$. The bottom line is roughly $8 - 6 = 2$.

A rough estimate is $6 \div 2 = 3$

Work out the expression, using brackets or the memory on your calculator. Do the rounding at the end of the calculation.

The value to 4 decimal places is 2.7277

2.2.2 Exercises

1) For each of the following, make a rough estimate of the answer. Then perform the calculation accurate to 3 significant figures. Check your answers if they don't agree.

   a) 4.26513×6.94647 b) $98.34 \div 22.52$

   c) $23 \times (14.1 - 9.2)$ d) $(193 + 22.52) \times 1018$

e) $(2.13 + 1.93) \times (7.42 - 2.13)$ f) $(0.02 + 0.032) + (1.9 + 2.7)$

g) $\dfrac{107 + 282}{1.92 + 1.98}$ h) $\dfrac{0.00693 - 0.00216}{4.62 - 1.57}$

2)   What is the approximate total cost of 87 books at £4.99 each?

3)   The average weight of a can of beans is 0.632 kg. What is the approximate weight of 37 cans?

4)   In one year, the Fanshawe family spent £3,571 on food. What was the approximate expenditure per week?

5)   The total time taken to mark 37 exam papers was 62.3 hours. What was the rough average time per paper?

6)   You have £126 of holiday money, and there are approximately 2200 Lire to the £. How much, roughly, should you get?

7)   The four stages of a building project will take 103 hours, 47 hours, 18 hours and 28 hours. Approximately how long will the total project take? At 8 hours a day how many days will it take? If the builder charges £12.58 per hour how much will it cost?

8)   An area of land is 532 square miles. The town population is 127,000 and the country population is 68,000. What is the approximate density of people per square mile?

2.3 Longer exercises

A. Making the largest number

Here are three competitions to see who is most expert at the use of a calculator.

1)   "All the 2's". You can use four 2's in any combination, using any function of the calculator. Can you beat $2 \times 2 \times 2 \times 2$? See who can make the largest number.

2)   "Four buttons". See who can make the largest number, using just 4 buttons on the calculator.

3)   "Four fours". See how many of the numbers between 0 and 100 you can make, using four 4's in any combination. For example, $1 = \frac{4}{4} + 4 - 4$. $2 = \frac{4}{4} + \frac{4}{4}$.

B. Other functions

A scientific calculator has many functions on it which you will not need. The HYP and e^x buttons, for example, you will not meet unless you do A-level Mathematics. Here are some of the others.

1)   **x!.** Try 1!, 2!, 3!, 4! and so on. What is the rule for this function? What is the largest x for which this function works?

2)   **FIX.** Getting your calculator in the FIX mode will enable all calculations to be done to a fixed number of decimal places. On many calculators this is Mode 7. The sequence for 3 decimal places is:

$$\boxed{\text{Mode}} \quad \boxed{7} \quad \boxed{3}$$

From now on all numbers are expressed to 3 decimal places. Try some calculations.

Is the calculator working to only 3 decimal places, or is it working to more than 3 places and hiding them? See if you can find out.

To cancel FIX get into Mode NORM. (Mode 9 on many calculators).

3)   **a/b.** Some calculators can work in fractions. To enter $\frac{4}{7}$, for example, press the following:

4   a/b   7

You can also enter "mixed numbers" like $1\frac{4}{7}$, by the following:

1   a/b   4   a/b   7

Try some fraction calculations. How do you convert from fractions to decimals? Can you convert from decimals to fractions?

There is a limit to the size of the numerator and denominator. See if you can find out this limit.

4)   At the beginning of this chapter you were asked to list the functions of a calculator which you knew how to use. Has the list changed?

Multiple choice question *(Tick appropriate box)*

$\dfrac{4.17 + 8.71}{4.28 - 1.93}$, evaluated to 2 significant figures, is:

a)   1.1   ☐

b)   5.5   ☐

c)   5.4   ☐

d)   2.4   ☐

e)   7.9   ☐

Points to note

1)   *Use of calculator*

   a)   Be sure to press the ☐= button after a calculation. And don't press it twice – if you do so the results are unpredictable.

   b)   When working out a complicated fraction press ☐= after the top line.

   c)   When working out a complicated fraction, either use brackets for the bottom line or put it in the memory.

   d)   When working out something like 3(7.65 + 4.92) remember to press ☒ after the 3.

2)   *Estimation*

   a)   Checks of accuracy are very useful, but don't expect too much of them. They ensure, for example, that your answer is not 10 times too big or 10 times too small.

   b)   Save your rounding to the end of the calculation. If you round all the figures too soon then the errors will accumulate.

Chapter 3
Large numbers

You are worried about the threat of overpopulation to the planet. A friend tries to reassure you, by claiming that however many people there are in the world, they would all fit comfortably onto the Isle of Wight.

Is this true? The area of the Isle of Wight is 381 square km. If all the 5,000,000,000 people in the world were to go there, how much space would each person get?

3.1 Mental arithmetic of large numbers

Numbers bigger than 1

Suppose we have two numbers, like 6,000 and 30, each of which consists of a digit followed by 0's. When they are multiplied we multiply the digits and add the 0's. When they are divided we divide the digits and subtract the 0's.

$$6,000 \times 30 = 180,000$$

$$6,000 \div 30 = 200$$

Numbers less than 1

Suppose that one of the numbers is less than 1. 0.3 can be considered as $\frac{3}{10}$. So when we multiply by 0.3 we multiply the digits together as before, but remove one of the 0's.

$$6,000 \times 0.3 = 1,800$$

When we divide by 0.3 we divide the digits as before, but we put on an extra 0.

$$6,000 \div 0.3 = 20,000$$

The answers you get can always be checked with a calculator.

3.1.1 Exercises

Evaluate the following by mental arithmetic. You can then check your answer with the help of a calculator.

1) $200 \times 4,000$ 2) $5,000 \times 300$ 3) $7,000 \times 2,000$ 4) $4,000 \div 200$

5) $6,000 \div 200$ 6) $10,000 \div 100$ 7) $55,000 \times 200$ 8) $450 \times 40,000$

9) $2,200 \times 300$ 10) $50,000 \div 200$ 11) $20,000 \div 40$ 12) $60,000 \div 40$

13) 900×0.1 14) $4,000 \times 0.3$ 15) $60,000 \times 0.8$ 16) $4,000 \div 0.2$

17) $60,000 \div 0.3$ 18) $9,000 \div 0.3$

19) An object moves at 400 m/sec for 0.5 seconds. How far has it gone?

20) The density of a certain plastic is 0.3 grams/cm^3. What is the weight of 200 cm^3?

21) 20,000 people each contributed £0.7 to a charity. How much was raised in total?

22) Paperback books are 0.4 inches wide on average. What length of shelves is needed for 3,000 books?

23) What is the volume of 1,200 grams of wood, if its density is 0.6 grams/cm^3?

24) If it takes 0.3 hours to mark a script, how long will 600 scripts take to mark?

25) Slates are 0.4 cm in thickness. How many slates are there in a stack which is 200 cm high?

3.2 Standard form

A very large number will have many 0's in it. When counting the number of 0's it is easy to make a mistake. It is necessary to have a way of writing a number so that we can tell quickly how large it is.

Standard form is used for very large numbers. A number is in standard form when there is only one digit to the left of the decimal point. For example:

$$256,700 = 2.567 \times 10^5$$

Standard Form can also be used for very small numbers. In this case the power of 10 is negative.

$$0.000000123 = 1.23 \times 10^{-7}$$

Notice that the power of 10 tells us how far the decimal point has been moved. In the first example it was moved 5 places to the left. In the second example it was moved seven places to the right.

Sometimes numbers have to be adjusted to put them in standard form, by raising or lowering the power of 10. For example, $24 \times 10^6 = 2.4 \times 10^7$, and $0.24 \times 10^8 = 2.4 \times 10^7$

Use of calculator

To enter numbers in standard form on your calculator, use the $\boxed{\text{exp}}$ button. To enter 3×10^9, press the following:

$$\boxed{3} \boxed{\text{exp}} \boxed{9}$$

If the power of 10 is negative, press the $\pm$ button after the power. To enter 4×10^{-8}, press the following:

$$\boxed{4} \boxed{\text{exp}} \boxed{8} \boxed{\pm}$$

Do not rely too much on your calculator. You should be able to deal with numbers in standard form without its help.

3.2.1 Example

Write the following in standard form:

      a) 34,560,000   b) 0.000000045   c) 732×10^4

Solution   a)   Move the decimal point 7 places to the left. This is balanced by increasing the power of 10 by 7.

            3.456×10^7

      b)   Move the decimal point 8 places to the right. This is balanced by decreasing the power of 10 by 8.

            4.5×10^{-8}

      c)   Move the decimal point two places to the left, and increase the power of 10 by 2.

            $732 \times 10^4 = 7.32 \times 10^6$

3.2.2 Exercises

1)   Express the following in standard form:

   a)   23,000   b)   876,000,000   c)   0.000123   d)   0.000005

2)   Express the following as ordinary numbers:

   a) 2×10^6 b) 9.3×10^{10} c) 4.2×10^{-7}

3)   Adjust the following to standard form:

   a) 45×10^8 b) 99.2×10^{12} c) 935×10^4

   d) 0.3×10^9 e) 0.34×10^{23} f) 0.04×10^{23}

   g) 55×10^{-8} h) 836.2×10^{-12} i) 0.65×10^{-6}

4)   The profit of a firm is five hundred million pounds. Write this in standard form.

5)   The sun is a hundred and fifty million kilometres from Earth. Write this in standard form.

6)   A ship weighs fifty thousand tons. Write this in standard form.

7)   Life began on Earth about three thousand million years ago. Write this in standard form.

8)   The circumference of the Earth is forty million metres. Write this in standard form.

9)   The population of the U.S.A. is about two hundred and fifty million. Write this in standard form.

3.3 Multiplication and division

Multiplication

When two numbers in standard form are multiplied, then the first parts are multiplied, and the powers of 10 are added.

$$3 \times 10^7 \times 2 \times 10^4 = 6 \times 10^{11}$$

Division

When two numbers in standard form are divided, then the first parts are divided, and the powers of 10 are subtracted.

$$3 \times 10^7 \div 2 \times 10^4 = 1.5 \times 10^3$$

3.3.1 Example

Evaluate the following, leaving your answers in standard form.

   a) $3 \times 10^6 \times 4 \times 10^5$ b) $4 \times 10^9 \div 5 \times 10^3$

Solution   a)   Multiply the 3 and 4 together, and add the powers of 10.

   $$3 \times 4 \times 10^6 \times 10^5 = 12 \times 10^{11}$$

   This is numerically correct, but it is not in standard form.

   $$3 \times 10^6 \times 4 \times 10^5 = 1.2 \times 10^{12}$$

   b)   Divide the 4 by 5, and subtract the powers of 10.

   $$\tfrac{4}{5} \times 10^{9-3} = 0.8 \times 10^6$$

   $$4 \times 10^9 \div 5 \times 10^3 = 8 \times 10^5$$

3.3.2 Exercises

1) Evaluate the following, leaving your answer in standard form:

   a) $3,000 \times 100$

   b) $2 \times 10^4 \times 4 \times 10^4$

   c) $3 \times 10^8 \times 2 \times 10^9$

   d) $5 \times 10^8 \times 3$

   e) $5.2 \times 10^5 \times 2 \times 10^8$

   f) $8 \times 10^5 + 4 \times 10^2$

   g) $9 \times 10^8 + 6 \times 10^2$

   h) $4 \times 10^7 + 8 \times 10^3$

   i) $1 \times 10^8 + 4 \times 10^3$

2) Light travels at 1.86×10^5 miles per second. How far does it travel in an hour? How far does it travel in a year?

3) There are 5×10^{26} carbon atoms per gram. How many carbon atoms are there in 5,000 grams of pure carbon?

4) The radius of the Earth is 6.4×10^6 m. What is its circumference?

5) If a heart beats once every second, how many heart beats are there in a lifetime of 70 years?

6) A gram of water contains 30 drops. How many drops are needed to fill a tank of 1,000 kg?

7) Look again at the problem at the beginning of the chapter. Write the population of the world in standard form. There are 1×10^{10} cm^2 in 1 km^2: write the area of the Isle of Wight in standard form. If everyone was on the Isle of Wight, how many cm^2 would each person get?

3.4 Addition and subtraction

When two numbers in standard form are added or subtracted, we must first ensure that they have the same power of 10. The first parts are added, but the powers of 10 are left unchanged.

3.4.1 Examples

1) Evaluate $3 \times 10^8 + 9 \times 10^8$

   Solution   Add the first parts to obtain $3 \times 10^8 + 9 \times 10^8 = 12 \times 10^8$.

   Convert this to standard form:

   $$3 \times 10^8 + 9 \times 10^8 = 1.2 \times 10^9$$

2) The population of East Germany was 1.7×10^7, and of West Germany 6.1×10^7. What is the combined population after unification?

   Solution   Add together the two numbers.

   The total population is 7.8×10^7

3.4.2 Exercises

1) Evaluate the following, leaving your answer in standard form:

   a) $4 \times 10^8 + 5 \times 10^8$

   b) $3.3 \times 10^6 + 2.7 \times 10^6$

   c) $9.5 \times 10^5 + 8 \times 10^5$

   d) $7.2 \times 10^7 - 4 \times 10^7$

   e) $4 \times 10^9 - 2.8 \times 10^9$

   f) $9 \times 10^{12} - 8.8 \times 10^{12}$

2) A ship weighs 5×10^7 kg when it is empty. How much does it weigh when cargo of 2×10^7 kg has been added?

3) The Earth came from the sun 4.6×10^9 years ago. Life began on Earth 3×10^9 years ago. For how long was there no life on Earth?

4) The Earth is 1.5×10^8 km from the Sun. The planet Venus is 1.08×10^8 km from the Sun. When Earth and Venus are in line on opposite sides of the Sun, what is the distance between them? When they are in line on the same side of the Sun, what is the distance between them?

5) The population of a country is 6.4×10^7, of whom 4.1×10^7 are over 21. How many are under 21?

6) The national debt of a country is $\$5.3 \times 10^9$. How much is there left after $\$2.7 \times 10^9$ has been repaid?

3.5 Longer exercise

The Sand Reckoner

There are some, King Gelon, who think that the number of the sand is infinite. Again there are some who, without regarding it as infinite, yet think that no number has been named which is great enough to exceed its multitude. But I will try to show you that of the numbers named by me, some exceed the numbers of grains in a mass of sand equal in magnitude to the Earth ...

Archimedes. "The Sand Reckoner"

Archimedes, who lived from 287 to 212 BC, was the greatest Mathematician of the ancient world. The excerpt quoted above is from a letter in which he works out how many grains of sand would fill the Earth.

At his time there was no standard way of writing numbers bigger than 10,000. Archimedes produced a system for writing numbers up to any size.

With our modern number system it is easier to express large numbers. You can answer the question: "How many grains of sand would fill the Earth?"

1) The radius of the Earth is 6,400 km, which is 6,400,000 m. Write this in Standard Form.

2) The formula for the volume of a sphere is $V = \frac{4}{3}\pi r^3$. Use your answer to Question 1 to find the volume of the Earth, in m^3.

3) Now we have to find the number of grains of sand in a m^3. We have to estimate – say that a grain of sand is 0.5 mm in diameter. How many grains would stretch for a cm? how many for a m?

4) Use your answer to Question 3 to find the number of grains in a m^3.

5) From your answers to Questions 2 and 4 find how many grains would fill the whole Earth.

... I conceive that these things, King Gelon, will appear incredible to the great majority of people who have not studied Mathematics, but I thought the subject would be appropriate for your consideration.

(end of letter)

Multiple choice question *(Tick appropriate box)*

In standard form, $3 \times 10^8 + 4 \times 10^2$ is equal to:

a) 7.5×10^5 ☐

b) 7.5×10^3 ☐

c) 0.75×10^6 ☐

d) 7.5×10^9 ☐

Points to note

1) *Mental arithmetic*

   a) When multiplying large figures you add together the number of 0's. Do not multiply.

   b) When multiplying by a number smaller than 1 then the effect will be to decrease the original number. Make sure it does not increase. Similarly, when dividing by a number smaller than 1 the effect is to increase the original.

2) *Standard form*

   a) Be sure that there is only one digit to the left of the decimal point. If there is more or less than one then the number is not in standard form.

   b) When multiplying numbers in standard form you add the powers of 10. Do not multiply.

   $$2 \times 10^5 \times 3 \times 10^6 \neq 6 \times 10^{30}$$

   When adding numbers in standard form do not add the powers of 10.

   $$4 \times 10^6 + 5 \times 10^6 \neq 9 \times 10^{12}$$

   c) You can only add or subtract numbers in standard form when they have the same power of 10.

Chapter 4

Powers and reciprocals

The square of 2 is written 2^2. The cube of 2 is written 2^3. If we go on multiplying by 2 we get 2^4, 2^5, 2^6 and so on. Make up a table of the values:

2^2	2^3	2^4	2^5	2^6	2^7	2^8	2^9	2^{10}
4	8			64				

What happens when we multiply these numbers together? Try some: you should find for example that $2^3 \times 2^4 = 2^7$. What rule is there? What is the rule for division?

4.1 Powers of numbers

If a number is multiplied by itself several times, the result is a power of the number. Squares and cubes are examples of powers.

If 3 is multiplied by itself 5 times, the result is the 5th power of 3, and is written 3^5. 5 is called the index.

$$3 \times 3 \times 3 \times 3 \times 3 = 3^5$$

Multiplying and dividing powers

If we multiply the 5th power of 3 with its square, then the result is 5 + 2 = 7 threes all multiplied together. So we get the 7th power. This means that we have added the indices.

$$(3 \times 3 \times 3 \times 3 \times 3) \times (3 \times 3) = 3 \times 3 \times 3 \times 3 \times 3 \times 3 \times 3$$

$$3^5 \times 3^2 = 3^7$$

Going the other way, when we divide a power of 3 by another, then we subtract the indices.

$$\frac{3 \times 3 \times 3 \times 3 \times 3 \times 3 \times 3 \times 3 \times 3}{3 \times 3 \times 3 \times 3 \times 3} = 3 \times 3 \times 3 \times 3. \text{ So } \frac{3^9}{3^5} = 3^4$$

Use of calculator

A calculator can find powers directly, using the $\boxed{x^y}$ button. To find 3^5, key in the following:

The answer 243 will appear.

Order of operations

Taking powers has priority over multiplication.

5×2^3 means: take the cube of 2, then multiply by 5. The result is 40.

If we want to do the multiplication first, then it must be put in brackets.

$(5 \times 2)^3$ means: multiply 5 and 2, then take the 3rd power. The answer is 1,000.

The brackets can be expanded out.

$(5 \times 2)^3 = 5^3 \times 2^3$.

4.1.1 Examples

1) Evaluate 6×3^2.

   Solution Square 3 to obtain 9, then multiply by 6.

   $$6 \times 3^2 = 54$$

2) Simplify $2x^5 \times 3x^7$.

   Solution Multiply the powers of x, by adding the indices to obtain x^{12}.

   Multiply this by 2×3.

   $$2x^5 \times 3x^7 = 6x^{12}$$

4.1.2 Exercises

1) Evaluate the following:

   a) 2^5 b) 3^4 c) 7^3 d) 2×3^3

   e) $(2 \times 3)^3$ f) 7×3^2 g) $(7 \times 3)^2$ h) $2^2 \times 3^3$

   i) $2^3 \times 3^2$ j) $\frac{1}{2} \times 4^2$ k) $(\frac{1}{2} \times 4)^2$

2) Simplify the following:

   a) $x^3 \times x^8$ b) $y^4 \times y^9$ c) $(z^3)^2$ d) $w^8 \div w^3$

   e) $t^{12} \div t^4$ f) $2x^3 \times 4x^4$ g) $3y^3 \times 4y^8$ h) $(7z^4)^2$

   i) $(2t^3)^3$ j) $8w^7 \div 2w^2$ k) $9t^8 \div 3t^4$ l) $s^7 \div 4s^3$

3) Use your calculator to find the following:

   a) 3^6 b) 4^5 c) 1.5^3 d) 3.2^4

4) A square has side x cm. What is its area? If the side is doubled, what is the new side? What is the new area?

5) A cube has side y inches. What is its volume? If the side is tripled, what is the new side? What is the new volume?

6) In computer jargon, a byte is the unit of memory which can hold one letter or digit. A kilobyte or K is $2^{10} = 1024$ bytes.

   a) The Model A BBC computer has 16 K of memory. How many bytes does it have, expressed as a power of 2?

   b) The Amstrad PCW computer has 256 K of memory. How many bytes is this, expressed as a power of 2?

   c) A hard disk may have 32 megabytes of memory, where 1 megabyte = 1024 K. How much memory is this, expressed as a power of 2?

4.2 Powers and roots

The opposite operation to taking powers is taking roots.

9 is the square of 3, and so 3 is the square root of 9. This applies to all powers: 81 is the fourth power of 3, so 3 is the fourth root of 81.

$$3^4 = 81, \text{ so } \sqrt[4]{81} = 3$$

4.2.1 Examples

1) Find the fourth root of 625.

   Solution   Try fourth powers until we reach 625. $2^4 = 16, 3^4 = 81, 4^4 = 256, 5^4 = 625$.
   $$\sqrt[4]{625} = 5$$

2) Express the square root of x^6 in terms of a power of x.

   Solution   When a power of x is squared the index is doubled. So to find the square root of x^6 we halve the index.
   $$\sqrt{x^6} = x^3$$

4.2.2 Exercises

1) Find the following roots:

   a) $\sqrt{64}$
   b) $\sqrt[3]{1,000}$
   c) $\sqrt[4]{10,000}$
   d) $\sqrt[3]{125}$

   e) $\sqrt[5]{243}$
   f) $\sqrt[3]{343}$
   g) $\sqrt[4]{1,296}$
   h) $\sqrt[3]{64}$

   i) $\sqrt{9 \times 25}$
   j) $\sqrt[3]{8 \times 27}$
   k) $\sqrt{100 \times 4}$
   l) $\sqrt{\frac{25}{9}}$

   m) $\sqrt{\frac{4}{9}}$
   n) $\sqrt[3]{\frac{1}{8}}$
   o) $\sqrt[3]{\frac{8}{27}}$
   p) $\sqrt[3]{\frac{8}{1000}}$

2) Simplify the following:

   a) $\sqrt{x^8}$
   b) $\sqrt{y^{10}}$
   c) $\sqrt[3]{x^6}$
   d) $\sqrt[3]{8x^3}$

   e) $\sqrt{y^2 z^4}$
   f) $\sqrt[3]{27x^6}$
   g) $\sqrt[2]{(st)^4}$
   h) $\sqrt[3]{(8x^3)^2}$

3) Find a number, bigger than 1, whose square root and cube root are both whole numbers.

4) The area of a square is 64 cm^2. What is its side?

5) The volume of a cube is 216 m^3. What is its side?

6) The area of a square is $36z^2$ square inches. What is its side?

7) The volume of a cube is $1,000y^6$ cm^3. What is its side?

4.3 Reciprocals

The reciprocal of a number is 1 over the number.

The reciprocal of 3 is $\frac{1}{3}$.

If we have a fraction $\frac{a}{b}$, then its reciprocal is found by turning it upside down to obtain $\frac{b}{a}$.

The reciprocal of $\frac{2}{3}$ is $\frac{3}{2}$.

4.3.1 Example

Find the reciprocals of   a) 5   b) $2\frac{1}{3}$.

Solution   a)   Put 1 over 5.

The reciprocal of 5 is $\frac{1}{5}$

b)   First express $2\frac{1}{3}$ as a mixed number, $\frac{7}{3}$. Now turn this upside down.

The reciprocal of $2\frac{1}{3}$ is $\frac{3}{7}$

4.3.2 Exercises

1)   Find the reciprocals of the following:

a)   2   b)   4   c) $\frac{3}{4}$ d) $\frac{5}{7}$

e) $\frac{1}{4}$ f) $\frac{1}{12}$ g) $\frac{5}{4}$ h) $1\frac{1}{6}$

i) $2\frac{2}{7}$ j) x k) $\frac{1}{x}$ l) $\frac{x}{y}$

2)   Take any number, multiply it with its reciprocal. What do you get?

3)   Take any number, find its reciprocal, find the reciprocal of the reciprocal. What do you get?

4.4 Longer exercise

Logarithms

Before calculators became widespread a lot of calculation was done by logarithms. They were invented by a Scotsman, John Napier, in about 1610.

Finding a logarithm (log for short) is the opposite to finding a power of 10.

$10^2 = 100$, so log 100 = 2. $10^3 = 1,000$, so log 1,000 = 3.

1)   Find log 10,000, log 1,000,000, log 10.

2)   Logs can be defined for numbers other than powers of 10. Use a table of logs or your calculator to find log 2, log 3, log 6. What is the connection between them?

3)   Logs were used to multiply as follows. Suppose we want 3.124×2.532. Find the logs of the numbers. Add these logs. Then find the product by using the antilog table, or the 10^x button on your calculator. Check that the answer is correct.

4)   Do some other multiplications using logs. How do you do division?

5)   Find log 2, log 4, log 8. What is the connection? How would you use logs to find 2^{12}?

6)   Use logs to find 1.08^{20}, and check your answer.

7)   These logs are based on 10. We could also have logs based on 2, written $\log_2$. $2^4 = 16$, so $\log_2 16 = 4$. Find $\log_2$ for 4, 8, 16, 32, 64. How are these related to the table in the problem at the beginning of the chapter?

Multiple choice question *(Tick appropriate box)*

When simplified, $4x^2 \times 3x^3$ becomes:

a) $12x^6$ □

b) $7x^5$ □

c) $12x^5$ □

d) $432x^5$ □

e) $60x$ □

Points to note

1) *Powers*

   a) Do not confuse the 5th power of a number with 5 times that number.

   b) When multiplying powers, add the indices. Do not multiply.

2) *Order*

   Taking powers is done before multiplying or dividing, unless there are brackets. With an expression like 5×4^2, you square 4 and then multiply by 5.

3) *Roots*

   Do not confuse the 4th root of a number with a quarter of the number.

Chapter 5

Sequences

Three stages of building a house of cards are shown on the right. How many cards are used at each stage?

If you manage to build a house 6 storeys high, how many cards will you use? What is the tallest house you could build with 52 cards?

5.1 Number patterns

Fig 5.1

Suppose we have a sequence of numbers. There are two ways to obtain its terms.

Altering the previous term

Sometimes each number is given by some operation applied to the previous number. Suppose the sequence is 1, 4, 7, 10, 13, ... Then each term is found by adding 3 to the one before.

Values of a function

Sometimes the numbers are the values of a function. Consider the function $3n - 2$. When $n = 1$, this function is 1. When $n = 2$, it becomes 4. And so on – for $n = 1, 2, 3, 4, 5$ the function takes the values 1, 4, 7, 10, 13.

5.1.1 Examples

1) Find the next two terms of the sequence 2, 5, 8, 11, 14, ... Describe the rule which generates the sequence.

   Solution   Notice that each term is 3 greater than the one before. Apply this operation two more times:

   The next two terms are 17 and 20

   The way we found the next two terms tells us how the sequence is generated.

   Start at 2, and keep on adding 3

2) Describe the rule which gives the sequence 2, 6, 18, 54, 162, ...

   Solution   Notice that the ratio between successive terms is always 3. This gives us the rule for the sequence:

   Start with 2, and keep on multiplying by 3

3) Write down the first 4 terms of the sequence given by the formula $n^2 + n - 1$.

   Solution   Putting $n = 1$, we obtain $1^2 + 1 - 1 = 1$. Putting $n = 2$, we obtain $2^2 + 2 - 1 = 5$. The next two terms are found by putting $n = 3$ and $n = 4$.

   The first 4 terms are 1, 5, 11, 19

5.1.2 Exercises

1) Find the next two terms for each of the following sequences:

   a) $1, 3, 5, 7, 9$

   b) $2, 7, 12, 17, 22, \ldots$

   c) $11, 8, 5, 2$

   d) $-3, -5, -7, -9$

   e) $1\frac{1}{2}, 1\frac{3}{4}, 2, 2\frac{1}{4}, 2\frac{1}{2}$

   f) $3, 2\frac{2}{3}, 2\frac{1}{3}, 2$

   g) $3, 6, 12, 24$

   h) $81, 54, 36, 24$

   i) $\frac{1}{2}, \frac{2}{3}, \frac{3}{4}, \frac{4}{5}$

   j) $\frac{1}{2}, \frac{3}{4}, \frac{7}{8}, \frac{15}{16}$

2) Describe the rules which generate the sequences of Question 1.

3) The following expressions give the n'th term of a sequence. In each case write down the first 4 terms.

   a) $4n - 1$

   b) $3n + 1$

   c) $8 - n$

   d) $1 + \frac{1}{2}n$

   e) $n^2 + 1$

   f) $2n^2 + n + 1$

   g) $\frac{2}{n}$

   h) $\frac{n + 1}{2n + 1}$

   i) $1 - \frac{1}{n}$

4) Below is a table of the numbers 0 – 99.

0	1	2	3	4	5	6	7	8	9
10	11	12	13	14	15	16	17	18	19
20	21	22	23	24	25	26	27	28	29
30	31	32	33	34	35	36	37	38	39
40	41	42	43	44	45	46	47	48	49
50	51	52	53	54	55	56	57	58	59
60	61	62	63	64	65	66	67	68	69
70	71	72	73	74	75	76	77	78	79
80	81	82	83	84	85	86	87	88	89
90	91	92	93	94	95	96	97	98	99

   Describe the sequences:

   a) Down the third column

   b) Along the fourth row

   c) Down the diagonal from top left to bottom right

   d) Down the diagonal from top right to bottom left.

   What other sequences can you find within the table? Can you find a sequence which goes up in steps of 8?

5) Write down the first 5 terms of the sequence given by the formula $\frac{1}{2}n(n + 1)$. These are called triangular numbers. Can you show why?

6) The problem at the beginning of this chapter involved building a house of cards. The numbers of cards for each stage are 2, 7, 15, 26, 40, 57. Write down the differences between these terms. Continue the sequence of differences for two more terms. Hence continue the original sequence for two more terms.

5.2 Finding the formula

Suppose we want to find the 100'th term of a sequence. If we only have a rule for going from one term to the next then we will have to obtain the first 99 terms. But if we have a formula for the n'th term the 100th term can be written down immediately.

Consider the sequence 1, 5, 9, 13, ... Each term is 4 greater than the previous term. Write down the sequence given by the formula $4n$. This sequence can be adjusted by adding or subtracting to give the required sequence.

5.2.1 Examples

1) Find an expression for the n'th term of the sequence 1, 4, 7, 10, 13, ...

   Solution   Each term is 3 greater than the one before. Write down the numbers given by the formula $3n$: they are 3, 6, 9, 12, 15, ... Notice that these numbers are all 2 greater than the ones we want. So subtract 2 from $3n$ and the formula will be correct.

   The n'th term is $3n - 2$

2) Find the 100th term of the sequence which begins 1, 4, 9, 16, ...

   Solution   Notice that each term is a square.

   The n'th term is n^2

   Now it is easy to write down the 100th term.

   The 100th term is $100^2 = 10{,}000$

5.2.2 Exercises

1) Find expressions for the n'th terms of the following sequences:

   a)   1, 3, 5, 7, 9, ...

   b)   2, 5, 8, 11, 14, ...

   c)   10, 15, 20, 25, 30, ...

   d)   10, 9, 8, 7, ...

   e)   7, 5, 3, 1, –1, ...

   f) $2, 2\frac{1}{2}, 3, 3\frac{1}{2}, ...$

   g) $1\frac{1}{3}, 1\frac{2}{3}, 2, 2\frac{1}{3}, ...$

   h)   1, 8, 27, 64, ...

   i) $1, \frac{1}{2}, \frac{1}{3}, \frac{1}{4}, \frac{1}{5}, ...$

   j) $0, \frac{1}{2}, \frac{2}{3}, \frac{3}{4}, \frac{4}{5}, ...$

2) Write down the 50'th terms of the sequences in Question 1.

3) A sequence starts with 3, and each term is found by adding 2 to the previous term. Find an expression for the n'th term.

4) A sequence starts with 10, and each term is found by subtracting 3 from the previous term. Find an expression for the n'th term.

5) The sequence 3, 6, 11, 18, ... has n'th term given by $n^2 + k$. Find k.

6) The sequence 2, 4, 8, 14, 22, ... has n'th term $n^2 + an + b$. Find a and b.

7) The problem at the beginning of the chapter involved a House of Cards. For a house which is n storeys high a total of $an^2 + bn$ cards are needed. Find a and b.

5.3 Testing the rule

Suppose a rule is suggested for a sequence. We can test it by seeing whether it works for the first few terms.

5.3.1 Example

Several lines are drawn on a piece of paper, so that every line crosses every other line, and all the crossing places are different. Is it true that the number of regions will follow the sequence 2, 4, 8, 16, ... ?

Solution   With one line, there are two regions on either side of it. With two lines, there is a cross shape giving four regions. The third line adds an extra three regions, the fourth line adds an extra four, and so on.

The sequence of the number of regions is 2, 4, 7, 11, ...

The number of regions does not follow the sequence given

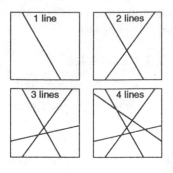

Fig 5.2

5.3.2 Exercises

1) Test to see whether the formula fits the sequence.

   a) $3, 5, 7, 9, ... 2n + 1$

   b) $-1, 3, 7, 11, ... n^2 - 2$

   c) $1, \frac{1}{2}, \frac{1}{3}, \frac{1}{4}, ... 2 \times \left(\frac{1}{2}\right)^n$

   d) $0, \frac{1}{2}, \frac{2}{3}, \frac{3}{4}, ... 1 - \frac{1}{n}$

In the following questions, test to see whether the claim is true or false.

2) 36 divides each term of the sequence 108, 1008, 10008, 100008, ..

3) An n-sided figure has $2n - 6$ diagonals.

4) The sequence with n'th term $n(n+1)(n+2)$ has terms which are all divisible by 6.

5) The sequence 1+2, 2+3, 3+4, ... consists of prime numbers.

6) The sequence with n'th term $n^2 + n + 11$ consists of prime numbers.

7) If n lines are drawn on a sheet of paper, each line crossing every other line, there will be $\frac{1}{2}n(n-1)$ crossing points.

8) A great circle of a sphere is a circle on its surface which is as large as possible.

   a) As great circles are drawn on a sphere, the number of crossing points follows the sequence 0, 2, 4, 6, 8, ...

   b) As great circles are drawn on a sphere, the number of regions of the sphere follows the sequence 2, 4, 8, 16, ...

5.4 Longer exercises

A. Man and dog

A man is 1,000 metres away from home. He walks home at 1 metre per second. His very energetic dog runs home at 4 m/sec, barks, then runs back to rejoin his master. The dog then rushes home again and so on.

Fig 5.3

1) How far will the master walk while the dog is first running home?

2) While the dog is running to rejoin its master, their combined speed is $4 + 1 = 5$ metres per sec. How long does the dog take to rejoin its master? How far will the man walk during this time?

3) Repeat (1) and (2), to find where the man is at each successive time that the dog rejoins him.

4) How far will the dog have run by the time the man gets home? How many times will it have run to and fro?

B. Exploring in the desert

An expedition is planned to a desert where there is no food or water. The explorers must carry their own supplies. Each explorer can carry enough supplies for one person for 4 days.

1) Suppose one explorer sets off alone. Show that he can travel 2 days journey into the desert before having to return.

2) Suppose two explorers set off together. After 1 day's journey one explorer returns to base, leaving behind supplies for two days. Show that it is now possible for the other explorer to penetrate a total of 3 days journey into the desert.

3) How could an explorer penetrate a distance of 4 days journey into the desert? How many people would be needed?

4) Can you find a general formula, for the number of explorers needed to carry supplies so that one of them can penetrate n days journey into the desert?

Multiple choice question *(Tick appropriate box)*

A sequence begins 2, 0.5, –1, –2.5, –4. The n'th term of the sequence could be:

a) $0.5 + 1.5n$ ☐

b) $-1.5n$ ☐

c) $3.5 - 1.5n$ ☐

d) $2 - 1.5n$ ☐

Points to note

1) *Finding the rule*

    a) Do not be too hasty when finding the rule for a sequence. There are many possible sequences which begin 1, 2, 4, … Look at further terms before deciding what the rule is.

    b) Be careful with fractional and negative numbers. If a sequence is going down, then each term is a certain amount less than the one before.

2) *Formulas*

    a) If a sequence has a constant increase of 5 say, then the n'th term is $5n$ + some constant. Do not forget this constant.

    b) If a sequence starts with 10 and goes up in steps of 2, then the formula will be $8 + 2n$, not $10 + 2n$.

Chapter 6

Spreadsheets

Alice likes to watch snooker on television, but Bryony and Charlene can't stand it. They insist she must video all the matches and watch them when they are not there.

During a tournament there are twelve programmes of snooker, three each of length 20 mins, 30 mins, 50 mins and 60 mins. Can they all be recorded on four 120 minute video cassettes, without breaking any of the programmes?

A spreadsheet provides a rich environment within which to do mathematics. This chapter contains some of the many situations which can be investigated with the aid of a spreadsheet. They involve material which occurs throughout the book.

Fig 6.1

Types of spreadsheet

There are many different spreadsheets available. In this chapter the instructions are given for Lotus 1-2-3 and for Excel. It is hoped they will work for many other spreadsheets as well. Some differences are as follows:

Formulas. A formula like A1+A2 must start with + in Lotus, as +A1+A2. In Excel it can be either +A1+A2 or =A1+A2.

If a formula begins with a number, then in Excel an = or a + sign must be put first, as in =3*A1.

Functions. A function begins with @ in Lotus, and either @ or = in Excel. If a range of values is given, it is defined using a . sign (Lotus) or a : sign (Excel). So for finding the sum of a range of numbers, we write @SUM(A1.A10) in Lotus and =SUM(A1:A10) in Excel.

Spreadsheet techniques

It is assumed that you are familiar with the entering of items in a spreadsheet, and with copying formulas from one group of cells to another. In particular, you should be familiar with relative addresses. In cell B4, the formula +3*A4 refers to the cell to the left. So when this formula is copied to D4, it will change to +3*C4.

6.1 Functions and sequences

The successive values of a function or a sequence can be shown on a spreadsheet.

Functions

Suppose we have the function $3x^2 + 3$, and wish to find the first 10 values. Fill the cells A1, B1, ... , J1 with 1, 2, ... , 10. In cell A2 put +3*A1^2+3. Copy this formula into cells B2, C2, ... , J2. The 2nd row will contain the values of the function.

29

Sequences

Suppose we have a sequence which starts with 3, and which increases by 2 at each step. Put the number 3 into cell A3. In cell B3 put the formula +A3+2. Copy this formula into cells C3, D3, ... , J3. The 3rd row will contain the values of the sequence.

6.1.1 Example

A sequence starts with 2, and goes up in steps of 3. Set up a spreadsheet which will find the function to give the n'th term of the sequence.

Solution Put 1, 2, ... , 10 in cells A1, B1, ... , J1. Put 2 in A2, and +A2+3 in B2. When this formula is copied to C2, D2, ... J2 the second row will contain the first 10 terms of the sequence.

For our first guess we might try $2n$. In A3 put +2*A1, and copy this across to B3, C3, ... , J3. Notice that this goes up in steps of 2 instead of 3.

Now try $3n$. Put this in the fourth row. Notice that all the terms of the fourth row are 1 greater than those in the second row.

If we put the formula $3n - 1$ in the fifth row, it will correspond exactly to the second row. The final spreadsheet is below.

	A	B	C	D	E	F	G	H	I	J
1	1	2	3	4	5	6	7	8	9	10
2	2	5	8	11	14	17	20	23	26	29
3	2	4	6	8	10	12	14	16	18	20
4	3	6	9	12	15	18	21	24	27	30
5	2	5	8	11	14	17	20	23	26	29

The function is $3n - 1$

6.1.2 Exercises

1) In the following, apply the methods of the example above, to find the function corresponding to the sequence. Enter 1, 2, ... , 10 in the first row. Enter the sequence in the second row as indicated. Make guesses for the formula, and enter them in the rows below.

   a) Put 5 in A2. Put +A2+2 in B2. Copy this across to J2.

   b) Put 2 in A2. Put +A2+0.5 in B2. Copy this across to J2.

   c) Put 8 in A2. Put +A2-3 in B2. Copy this across to J2.

2) In the following, enter 1, 2, 3, ... , 10 in the first row. Enter the function in the second row. Enter the first value in A3. Guess the rule which will enable you to go from one term to the next.

   a) $2n + 3$

   b) $5n - 3$

   c) $7 - 2n$

3) The following sequences correspond to functions of the form kc^n, where k and c are constant. Apply the methods of Question 1 to find the values of k and c. For example, if $k = 2$ and $c = 3$, enter +2*3^A1 in A3 and copy it across.

   a) Put 2 in A2. Put +A2*2 in B2. Copy this across to J2.

   b) Put 12 in A2. Put +A2*3 in B2. Copy this across to J2.

   c) Put 1 in A2. Put +A2*2 in B2. Copy this across to J2.

4) Choose a sequence of your own, and enter it in row 2. See if you can find the function corresponding to it.

6.2 Trial and improvement

Often equations can be solved by trial and improvement. A spreadsheet can be used to try different values until the equation is satisfied.

6.2.1 Example

Find integers x and y for which $7x - 9y = 1$.

Solution   Keep A1 for the value of x, and B1 for y. In cell A3 enter the formula +7*A1-9*B1. Initially the value will be 0.

      Enter values in A1 and B1, watching how A3 changes. If A1 contains 4 and B1 contains 3, then A3 will contain 1.

$$7 \times 4 - 9 \times 3 = 1$$

6.2.2 Exercises

1) Use a spreadsheet to find integers which satisfy the following:

   a) $5x - 7y = 1$ b) $12x - 7y = 1$ c) $15x - 26y = 1$

2) Use a spreadsheet to find integers x and y for which:

   a) $x^2 - 2y^2 = 1$ b) $x^2 - 5y^2 = 1$ c) $x^2 - 7y^2 = 1$

(Note: the equation of the form $x^2 - Ny^2 = 1$ has a long history in mathematics. It is called Pell's Equation, after an English mathematician of the 17th century. In fact it was studied by an Indian mathematician called Brahmagupta in the 6th century, and solved by another Indian called Bhaskara in the 12th century. Often the solutions are very big – the first solution of $x^2 - 61y^2 = 1$ is $x = 17,663,319,049$ and $y = 226,153,980$.)

3) It can be shown that every positive integer can be written as the sum of four squares. (Possibly including 0^2.) For example, $39 = 6^2 + 1^2 + 1^2 + 1^2$ and $33 = 4^2 + 4^2 + 1^2 + 0^2$. Use a spreadsheet to represent the following as the sum of four squares.

   a) 23   b) 67   c) 231   d) 391

6.3 Packing

Suppose we wish to put several items into containers, using as few containers as possible. This packing problem can be solved using a spreadsheet.

6.3.1 Example

We want to make a structure with the following lengths of wood.

> 8, 10, 10, 12, 12, 14, 14, 16, 16, 18, 18. (All in cm)

The lengths are to be cut from beams of length 30 cm. How can this be done using as few beams as possible?

Solution   Set up a spreadsheet by letting the first 7 columns represent the beams. In cell A5 put @SUM(A1.A4). (Or =SUM(A1:A4) for Excel). This adds up the first four numbers in the first column. Copy this across to B5, C5, ..., G5.

Initially the 5th row will contain 0's. Now "pack" the lengths into the A, B and C columns. You will find that A5, B5 and C5 may go over 30. Shift the lengths between the other columns, until all the 5'th row entries are less than or equal to 30. You might obtain the spreadsheet below:

	A	B	C	D	E	F	G
1	18	18	16	16	10		
2	12	12	14	14	10		
3					8		
4							
5	30	30	30	30	28	0	0

The lengths can be cut from 5 beams

6.3.2 Exercises

1) You want to record seven pieces of music lasting 5 mins, 10 mins, 10 mins, 15 mins, 20 mins, 25 mins, 25 mins. Each side of a cassette lasts 30 minutes. Use a spreadsheet to find the least number of cassette sides that you need.

2) Twelve items must be sent by air. They weigh, in kilograms, 3, 3, 4, 5, 6, 6, 7, 7, 8, 8, 10, 11. Each box must contain at most 20 kg. What is the least number of boxes that can be used?

3) A building job is broken into fifteen tasks. Each task must be done by a single worker, and they will take, in hours, 4, 8, 8, 10, 10, 10, 10, 12, 12, 12, 14, 16, 16, 20, 30. The whole job must be completed within 40 hours. What is the least number of workers that can be employed?

4) Look again at the problem at the beginning of the chapter. Use a spreadsheet to find the least number of video cassettes to hold all the programmes.

5) These problems are often easier to set than to solve. Make up a problem of this sort and give it to someone else to answer.

6.4 Statistics

Spreadsheets can be used to analyse large amounts of data and to draw statistical diagrams from them. In particular, they can draw the cumulative frequency graphs of Chapter 22.

6.4.1 Example

The monthly rainfall was measured for 100 months, with results given in the table below. Use a spreadsheet to draw a cumulative frequency graph.

rainfall to nearest inch	0	1	2	3	4	5	6	7
frequency		2	12	18	25	26	8	6	3

Solution   Use the first row of the spreadsheet for the rainfall, putting 0, 1, 2, ..., 7 in B1 up to I1. Put the frequencies in the second row, B2 up to I2.

In B3 put +A3+B2. When this is copied across the third row will contain the cumulative frequencies. The spreadsheet will look as below.

	A	B	C	D	E	F	G	H	I
1		0	1	2	3	4	5	6	7
2			2	12	18	25	26	8	6	3
3			2	14	32	57	83	91	97	100

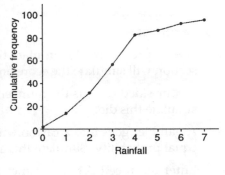

Fig 6.2

Draw a graph, selecting a line graph and using the first row for the x-values and the third row for the y-values. The result will be a cumulative frequency graph.

6.4.2 Exercises

22.3.2 of Chapter 22 contains many questions of cumulative frequency curves. Use the methods of the example above to draw these curves with a spreadsheet.

6.5 Probability

A spreadsheet contains a function which takes random values between 0 and 1. This can be used for probability experiments.

In Lotus the function is @RAND, and in Excel it is =RAND(). Below the Lotus notation is used.

Suppose we want to simulate the score on a die. @RAND*6 takes values between 0 and 6. @INT(@RAND*6+1) will take integer values between 1 and 6, with equal probability.

6.5.1 Example

A coin is spun 100 times. Simulate this on a spreadsheet, showing how the proportion of heads settles down to $\frac{1}{2}$.

Solution   First put the number of tosses in the first column, by putting 1 up to 100 in A2 up to A101. (We are keeping the first row empty). Let 0 represent Tails and 1 represent Heads. @INT(@RAND*2) will be either 0 or 1, with equal probability. Put this formula in B2 and copy it down to B101.

Use the C column to count the number of Heads. So in C2 put +B2+C1. (We wanted C1 empty for this). Copy this formula down to C101.

Use the D column for the proportion of Heads. In D2 put +C2/A2, and copy this formula down to D101.

Part of the spreadsheet is shown. Notice that the D column has approached 0.5.

A	B	C	D
95	1	51	0.536842
96	1	52	0.541666
97	0	52	0.536082
98	0	52	0.530612
99	1	53	0.535353
100	0	53	0.53

6.5.2 Exercises

1) Use a spreadsheet to simulate the rolling of a die 100 times. The formula at the beginning of the section will simulate the score on the die. Show how the average score settles down to 3.5.

2) A four-sided die has the numbers 1, 2, 3, 4 on its faces. Show how to adjust the @RAND function to simulate this die.

3) A gambler goes into a casino with £50. At each spin of the roulette wheel he wins or loses £10 with equal probability. Simulate this as follows.

Enter 50 in cell A1. The function 20*@INT(2*@RAND)-10 will be either +10 or –10 with equal probability. So in A2 put +A1+20*@INT(2*@RAND)-10. Copy this down the first column. Does the gambler lose all his money? After how many goes does this happen?

4) Suppose the odds are against the gambler, so that the probability of winning and losing are 0.49 and 0.51 respectively. This can be simulated by changing the formula of Question 3 to 20*@INT(@RAND/0.51)-10. Make this change in the spreadsheet, and see whether the gambler loses his money more quickly.

5) "Gambler's Ruin". Two gamblers A and B have £a and £b. They gamble £1 against each other by spinning a coin, until one of them is broke. Simulate this game, with $a = 10$ and $b = 5$.

Points to note

1) *Entering values*

A value will only be entered in a cell after you have pressed "enter" or have moved away from the cell.

2) *Notation*

Make sure you are familiar with the notation used by your spreadsheet, in particular with the way in which formulas and functions should be written. Don't forget the + or the = or the @.

3) *Multiplication*

If a formula involves multiplication, then write it as 3*A1, not as 3A1.

Chapter 7

Practical measurement

King Hieron II of Syracuse wanted a new crown. He gave an amount of gold to the craftsmen, but when the finished crown came back he suspected that some of the gold had been replaced by other cheaper metal.

The crown was passed over to Archimedes, the greatest scientist of the day. Gold is denser than other metals, and if other metals had been added to bring the crown up to the correct weight, the volume would be too big. How could he measure the volume, without melting down the crown?

One day Archimedes got into his bath and then leapt out again, shouting "Eureka!" (I have found it). What had he found? How did he measure the volume of the crown?

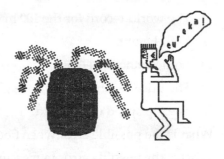

Fig 7.1

7.1 Error in measurement

Measurement is rarely exact. Two reasons for inexactness are:

1. The thing we are trying to measure might not be exactly defined. When we give the population of a town, we do not know who is a resident and who is a visitor.

2. However good our measuring instruments are, the results they give will always be slightly different from the true value.

It is important to recognize the possibility of error and to make allowances for it.

Below are some examples of measurement and the possible errors that might be involved.

Length. With a ruler lengths can be measured with an error of about 0.5 mm. Longer distances, such as the distance between two towns, could be measured with a possible error of 100 m.

Weight. With kitchen scales things can be weighed with a possible error of about 5 grams. A bathroom weighing machine can give your weight with an error of about 1 pound.

Time. With an ordinary watch with second hand, the time of a race can be measured with a possible error of about 0.5 seconds. With a stopwatch, the error might be 0.05 seconds.

7.1.1 Example

A man reckons that it takes him 13 minutes to walk to work. What would be the possible error in this measurement?

Solution   The time he takes would vary, depending on how he is feeling, how long it takes to cross roads and so on. He could be delayed by about a minute.

The possible error would be about 1 minute

7.1.2 Exercises

1) What could be the possible error in measuring the following:

    a) The distance from London to Paris.

    b) The distance between your home and school.

    c) The weight of your calculator.

    d) Your school record for the 100 m sprint.

    e) The world record for the 100 m sprint.

    f) Your height.

    g) Your mother's height.

    h) The price in January 1992 of a gallon of four-star petrol.

    i) The top speed of Concord.

2) What is the possible error when finding a length with a tape measure?

3) What is the possible error in measuring body temperature with a thermometer?

4) When measuring cloth, some people use the fact that the length from one's mouth to the end of one's arm is about a yard. What is the error in measuring a yard by this method?

5) When measuring time without a watch, one can count seconds by putting an elephant between them: "One elephant two elephant three elephant four …" What is the error in measuring 10 seconds by this method?

7.2 Errors in rounding

Suppose a length is measured with a ruler as shown below.

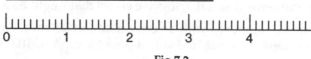

Fig 7.2

The nearest millimetre mark is at 3.4. So we say that the length is 3.4 cm to the nearest mm.

We claim that this figure is accurate. So the true value of the length cannot be less than 3.35 cm, otherwise it would have been closer to 3.3 cm. Similarly the length cannot be greater than 3.45 cm, otherwise it would have been closer to 3.5 cm. So we know that the true value of the length lies between 3.35 and 3.45 cm. The maximum error is therefore 0.05 cm.

When we give the results of a measurement, our value should show how accurate the measurement was. If it is given to 2 significant figures then those figures should be correct.

7.2.1 Examples

1) The weight of a stone is given as 8.36 grams, to 2 decimal places. What are the limits between which the weight must lie?

   Solution   Anything less than 8.355 would be rounded down to 8.35 or less, and anything greater than 8.365 would have been rounded up to 8.37 or more.

   The weight lies between 8.355 and 8.365 grams

2) A cake weighs 800 grams. It is divided into three equal portions. How much does each portion weigh?

   Solution   800 divided by 3 is 266.7 grams, to the nearest tenth of a gram. But the original cake would not be exactly 800 grams, and we could not hope to cut it very accurately. At best we should give the weight to the nearest 10 grams.

   Each portion weighs 270 grams

7.2.2 Exercises

1) A temperature is given as 34.3°, to one decimal place. Between what limits must the temperature lie?

2) The weight of a car is given as 910 kg, rounded to the nearest 10 kg. Between which limits does the weight lie?

3) The population of a town is given as 80,000, to the nearest 10,000. What are the limits between which the population lies?

4) The weight of a book is 0.54 kg, to 2 decimal places. What are the limits between which the weight lies?

5) The distance between two towns is given as 240 miles, to 2 significant figures. What are the limits between which the distance lies?

6) If six equal buns weigh 200 grams, how much does each weigh?

7) During a rainstorm 5 inches fell in 7 hours. What was the rainfall per hour?

8) The radius of the Earth is 6,400,000 metres, to 2 significant figures. What is the circumference of the Earth? (The circumference of a circle of radius r is $2\pi r$.)

7.3 Area and volume units

Correct units

The centimetre or cm is a unit of length. The square centimetre or cm^2 is a unit of area. The cubic centimetre or cm^3 is a unit of volume.

When giving measurements of length, area or volume be sure to use the correct units. Note the differences below:

Correct	Incorrect
An area of 5 cm^2	A length of 5 cm^2
A length of 3.2 metres	A volume of 3.2 metres
A volume of 7 m^3	An area of 7 m^3

37

Similarly, if x and y represent lengths:

$x + y$ represents a length

xy represents an area

xy^2 represents a volume

Fig 7.3

Changing units

Be careful when changing from one unit to another. There are 10 mm in a cm, but there are $10 \times 10 = 100$ mm² in a cm², as shown in Fig 7.3. There are $10 \times 10 \times 10 = 1,000$ mm³ in a cm³.

Similarly there are $100^2 = 10,000$ cm² in a square metre. There are $100^3 = 1,000,000$ cm³ in a cubic metre.

7.3.1 Examples

1) A volume is given as V m³, and an area as A m². What are the units of $V \div A$?

Solution   It might be that V is the volume of a cylinder, and that A is the area of its base. Then $V \div A$ is the height of the cylinder.

$V \div A$ is measured in metres

2) The density of a liquid is 0.9 grams per cm³. What is the weight in kilograms of a cubic metre of the liquid?

Solution   A cubic metre contains $100^3 = 1,000,000$ cubic centimetres. This weighs $0.9 \times 1,000,000 = 900,000$ grams. Divide by 1,000 to convert to kilograms.

The weight is 900 kg

7.3.2 Exercises

1) Below are the solutions to questions about measurement. Which are correct? Amend the incorrect ones.

a)   The volume is 83 cm³

b)   The area is 2,000 yards

c)   The length is 8 m³

d)   The volume is 10 cubic inches

e)   The area is 2 cubic feet

f)   The speed is 78 m/sec

2) x and y represent lengths, A represents an area and V represents a volume. Which of length, area or volume do the following represent?

a) y^2

b) Ax

c) $xy + A$

d) $2y + x$

e) $\dfrac{V}{x}$

f) $\dfrac{V}{xy}$

3) a)   How many cm² are there in a m²?

b)   How many mm² are there in a m²?

c)   How many mm³ are there in a m³?

d)   How many square inches are there in a square foot?

e)   How many cubic feet are there in a cubic yard?

4) Tiles which are 10 cm by 10 cm cost 20 p each. What will it cost to cover an area 4 m by 3 m?

5) If 1,000 cm³ of water weighs 1 kilogram, what is the weight of 1 m³?

6) 3 m^3 of a metal weighs 6,000 kg. What is the weight of 1 cm^3 of the metal?

7) If land costs £3 per m^2, what is the cost of a farm of 3 km^2?

8) An area of 1.2 square kilometres is sold for £4,800,000. What was the cost per square metre?

9) In the problem at the beginning of the chapter Archimedes was trying to find the density of a crown. The density of pure gold is 19,000 kg/m^3. The crown weighed 1,800 grams, and its volume (found from the volume of water displaced) was 110 cm^3. Had the King been cheated?

7.4 Longer exercises

A. Appropriate accuracy

Some questions in this chapter asked you to guess the accuracy of a measurement. With more time available you can find a more satisfactory answer. Investigate a measurement over a period of time, and see how much it varies. You will be able to state the measurement to a degree of accuracy which shows how much error should be allowed for. Suggestions of things to measure are:

a) Your weight. Weigh yourself everyday (at the same time of day) for a week.

b) The circulation of a newspaper. Newspaper often publish the number of copies that have been sold. Public libraries have back copies of newspapers. From them obtain the circulation figures of a newspaper over a period of time.

c) Your time to get to school. If you always go to school by the same method, time your journey every day for a week.

B. Length, area and volume units

In the metric system the units of area, cm^2 and m^2, and the volume units cm^3 and m^3, are easily obtained from the units of length. Conversion between the units is straightforward.

There are many other units of length, area and volume which people have found easier to use for various purposes. Some are metric, some are not. Find out about some of these units, and see how they compare. For example, find how many cubic inches there are in a gallon.

Length   Inch, foot, decimetre, dekametre, furlong, ell, mile, league, parasang, cubit, span.

Area   Hectare, acre, hide, quire, ream, perch, rood.

Volume   Litre, decilitre, pint, gallon, quart, gill, fluid ounce, Jeroboam, magnum, peck, bushel.

Multiple choice question *(Tick appropriate box)*

One cubic centimetre of metal weighs 2.02 grams. If we have roughly 1,000 kg of the metal, it will occupy a space of approximately:

a)   2 m^3 ☐

b)   0.5 m^3 ☐

c)   500,000 cm   ☐

d)   0.495 m^3 ☐

e)   5,000 m^3 ☐

Points to note

1) *Appropriate accuracy*

   Do not give your answer to too many decimal places or too many significant figures. If your answer is given to 2 decimal places, then the digits in those places should be correct.

2) *Rounding*

   If a value is rounded to 3.2, to one decimal place, then the original value must lie between 3.15 and 3.25. Do not say that it lies between 3.1 and 3.3.

3) *Units*

   a) Do not confuse the units for length, area and volume. If x and y are both lengths, then $x + y$ cannot be an area or a volume.

   b) Be careful when converting from cubic centimetres to cubic metres etc. There are $100^3 =$ 1,000,000 cm^3 in a m^3.

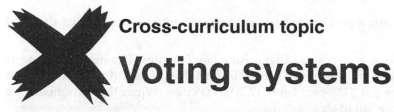

Cross-curriculum topic

Voting systems

At least every 5 years, there must be a general election in the U.K. All members of Parliament must resign, and their seats are contested. With a few exceptions, such as lunatics and peers, every citizen who is at least 18 is able to vote for one candidate.

After the election, the votes are counted and the seats in Parliament are decided. But are they shared fairly? Does the make-up of Parliament reflect the wishes of the population? Since the war there have been elections in which the party with the greatest number of votes did not receive the greatest number of seats, for example:

1951.		Labour	Conservative
	Votes	13,900,000	13,700,000
	Seats	295	321

Here the numbers are given rounded to the nearest 100,000. This means that the true value of the Conservative vote lies somewhere between 13,650,000 and 13,750,000. In fact it was 13,717,538.)

There are many different systems of voting. Here we shall look at some of them.

"First past the post"

The system in use in Britain today is straightforward. In each constituency each elector votes for one candidate: the votes are counted, and the candidate who receives most votes is the winner.

This system is like a horse-race. The candidates are like horses, and the one who passes the post first is the winner. So the system is called "First Past the Post". In a horse race it does not matter whether the winner was an inch ahead of the second horse or several yards. The same is true in this system – it does not matter whether the winning candidate is 1 vote or 20,000 votes ahead.

The system has many strange effects, which some people think are unfair.

Unfairness to small parties

The "First Past the Post" system is good for large parties and bad for small parties. A small party may have quite a large share of the vote, but if their share is spread evenly throughout the country they may win very few actual seats. Third parties have always complained about this. Here are the 1987 figures:

	Conservative	Labour	Alliance
Votes	13,760,583	10,029,807	7,341,633
Seats	376	229	22

Notice that the Alliance parties got almost 24% of the votes, but less than 4% of the seats in Parliament.

Another way of looking at it is to divide the number of votes by the number of seats.

	Conservative	Labour	Alliance
Voters per seat	37,000	44,000	334,000

We can see that each Liberal MP represents many more voters than a Labour or Conservative MP.

Exaggeration of majorities

Because of the "First Past the Post" system, a party may have only slightly more votes than its rival, yet get many more seats.

When the two top parties are very close, it is suggested that a cube law operates. The numbers of seats obtained are in the same ratio as the cubes of the votes obtained. In 1964 the Conservatives obtained 304 seats with 12,000,000 votes, and Labour got 317 seats from 12,200,000 votes. When these numbers are cubed they become very large, so they are put in standard form.

	Votes	Seats	Cube of votes
Conservative	12,000,000	304	1.728×10^{21}
Labour	12,200,000	317	1.816×10^{21}
Ratio	*0.984*	*0.959*	*0.952*

So the cube law works reasonably well here. For other elections, especially when the parties are widely separated, it does not work so well.

Majority systems

In the "First Past the Post" system the winner just has to beat the opponents individually. In a Majority System he or she has to beat all of them put together. That is, the election is only won when one candidate has more votes than all the other candidates put together.

On the first round of voting this may not happen. Usually the candidate with most votes does not have a clear majority over all other candidates combined. So another round of voting must take place. The candidates with least votes are forced to withdraw from the election. The system below is used in Australia.

The voters mark the paper twice, with their first choice and with a second choice. The first choices are counted, and if one candidate has a clear majority then he or she wins. If there is no clear majority, then all but the top two candidates are withdrawn and their second choices are counted. Now, because there are only two candidates, one must win.

This system prevents a candidate who is unpopular with a majority of the voters from winning. Suppose there are three candidates for a seat. The votes are as follows:

First choices   Smith 40%   Jones 31%   Brown 29%

On a "first past the post" system Smith would win. With a majority system, Brown withdraws from the election, and the second choices are counted. Out of Brown's 29% suppose 3% goes to Smith, and 26% to Jones. Now Smith has 43% and Jones 57%. Jones wins on second choices.

Proportional representation systems

The main objection to the "First Past the Post" system is that it gives an unfair representation of the parties. A Proportional Representation system tries to make the representation of each party in Parliament proportional to its support in the country. So if a party is supported by 30% of the voters, then it will have 30% of the seats in Parliament.

This is not always possible. It certainly cannot be done if each constituency returns only one representative, as in Britain. One way to get nearly Proportional Representation is to have the whole country as one constituency. This system is used in Israel.

In Israel there is only one constituency, the whole state. Electors vote for one party, and then the seats are shared out in proportion to the votes. Because there are many seats to be shared, this can be done fairly.

A disadvantage of this system is that it does not distinguish between different parts of the country. If it were adopted in Britain then the views of Scots voters would not be distinguished from those of Wales or England or Northern Ireland. So most countries with Proportional Representation have several constituencies, each with several members.

Largest remainder system

This system is in use in several European countries, in particular in Italy. Each constituency returns about 3 or 4 or 5 members. Suppose that there are 5 seats to be won, and that the total number of votes was 100,000. Then each seat represents 100,000 ÷ 5 = 20,000 votes. So certainly a party which gets 20,000 votes will win a seat, and a party which gets 40,000 votes will win two seats.

Of course, it is very unlikely that parties will win exactly 20,000 or 40,000 votes. There will be some votes left over after division by 20,000, the remainder. There will be seats left over. We see which parties have the largest remainders, and give them the extra seats.

Suppose that the votes cast were:

Party A 42,000   Party B 33,000   Party C 18,000   Party D 7,000

On division by 20,000 we obtain:

Party A: 2 seats,   remainder 2,000.

Party B: 1 seat,   remainder 13,000.

Party C: no seats, remainder 18,000.

Party D: no seats, remainder 7,000.

3 seats have been allocated, leaving 2 to go. The largest remainders are of Party B and Party C, who get one each. The final result is:

Party A	Party B	Party C	Party D
2 seats	2 seats	1 seat	0 seats

We can check to see that this is reasonably proportional to the number of votes cast.

Party	Proportion of votes	Proportion of seats
A	42%	40%
B	33%	40%
C	18%	20%
D	7%	0%

Highest average system

This system is in use in many European countries, in particular in Belgium. Suppose, as above, there are 5 members for a constituency. After the votes have been counted, there are several stages before the seats are allocated. At each stage, each party's average is calculated. If a party has obtained V votes, and has been allocated n seats, then the average is $V \div (n+1)$. (1 is added on to avoid dividing by zero.) The party with the highest average gets another seat, and the next stage takes place.

Let us see how this works with the figures above for parties A, B, C, D. Before any seats are allocated, the average for each party is just its number of votes.

Party	A	B	C	D
Seats won	0	0	0	0
Average	42,000	33,000	18,000	7,000

Here A has the highest average. It gets one seat. So now $n = 1$, and we divide A's votes by $1 + 1$.

Party	A	B	C	D
Seats won	1	0	0	0
Average	21,000	33,000	18,000	7,000

Now B has the highest average. It is awarded a seat, and its average goes down.

Party	A	B	C	D
Seats won	1	1	0	0
Average	21,000	16,500	18,000	7,000

A gets a second seat. A's average is now $42,000 \div (2+1) = 14,000$

Party	A	B	C	D
Seats won	2	1	0	0
Average	14,000	16,500	18,000	7,000

C wins its first seat.

Party	A	B	C	D
Seats won	2	1	1	0
Average	14,000	16,500	9,000	7,000

There is one seat to go: B now has the highest average and gets it. Notice that the final result is the same as with the "Largest Remainder" system.

STV systems

One disadvantage of the systems above is that one votes for a party not for a person. The voter has no chance to favour a particular candidate. A Proportional Representation system which allows one to vote for a person is the *Single Transferable Vote* system. It is in use in Ireland, and British Electoral Reform groups would like to see it used in this country.

In the last century Rowland Hill, the inventor of the postage stamp, was teaching in a school. The boys held an election for five members of a committee. The way that the election was held was for the candidates to stand in a row, and for the other boys to go and stand near the candidate they supported. Rowland Hill noticed two things.

a)   If a boy was very popular, i.e. had many more supporters than he needed, then some of his supporters went to back someone else.

b)   If a boy was unpopular, and had only few supporters, then those supporters would go and vote for someone else.

This school election ensured that the committee reflected what the pupils wanted. It is an example of STV in action.

At the election, each voter lists the candidates he wants to vote for, in order of preference. Suppose there are 4 members for the constituency, and 100,000 total votes.

Any candidate with more than $\frac{1}{5}$ of the total vote will be elected. (Because there cannot be 4 other candidates with more votes than he has.) He will probably get more than $\frac{1}{5}$ of the votes, and the surplus votes will be transferred to the second choices. This is like the operation (a) above.

Maybe now some other candidates have got more than $\frac{1}{5}$ of the votes. They will be elected, and their surplus votes distributed. We now look at the candidate with the least number of votes, and make him withdraw. His votes are now allocated to the second preferences on the ballot papers. This is like the operation (b) above.

These processes are repeated until all 4 seats have been filled. The result will be a selection in which most people have voted for one of the successful candidates, if not always as their first choice.

Which is best?

Several election systems have been described. If we want a Parliament which is an accurate reflection of the opinions of the country, then one of the Proportional Representation systems is best.

There are disadvantages to Proportional Representation. Frequently there is no clear winner of an election, so Parliament is ruled by a coalition of different parties. This often means that governments are continually changing, as the members of the coalition disagree with each other. This has often happened in Italy. Also it is common for one small party to hold the balance of power between two larger parties. The smaller party can then determine the government, by deciding whom to form a coalition with. This gives the small party power which is not proportional to its size. This has happened in Israel and in Ireland.

It is not obvious that the purpose of an election is to make a model of the whole country. Those who disagree with Proportional Representation say that it is more important to have a strong government with a clear majority. They would agree with Alexander Pope, who wrote in 1733:

> *For forms of government let fools contest*
>
> *Whate'er is best administer'd is best.*

The mathematics of voting systems

The analysis of voting systems involves much mathematics. Here material from Chapters 3, 4, 7, 9 and 21 has been touched upon.

Extended task. Proof by dissection

Introduction

A direct way of proving results about areas is to cut up one area and rearrange it so that it fits exactly into another area. This immediately convinces one that the two areas are equal.

The results of this investigation could be displayed on a board, as well as in a folder. Use a sheet of plywood as backing. Paste pieces of thick cardboard, with holes cut out for the areas which are to be shown equal. The geometric figures which are to be cut up could then be made of thinner cardboard, say the thickness of a postcard. A demonstration that the areas are equal is then to arrange the pieces in one hole, then to remove them and fit them in the other hole.

Areas of figures

1) **Parallelogram**. The area of a parallelogram is equal to the product of the base and the height. This can be shown by cutting up the parallelogram and rearranging it as a rectangle with the same height and base.

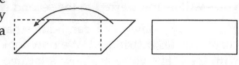

The two holes to be cut into the backing cardboard are of a rectangle and a parallelogram. The thinner cardboard is cut into a parallelogram, and is cut along the dotted line. You should find that the pieces will fit into both holes.

2) **Triangle**. The area of a triangle is equal to half the product of the height and base. This can be shown by cutting a parallelogram in half. It can also be shown by cutting up the triangle into three pieces which are arranged into a rectangle with the same base and half the height.

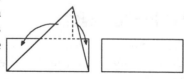

The holes for triangle and rectangle are shown. They have the same base, but the height of the rectangle is half that of the triangle. The triangle is cut along the dotted lines.

3) **Trapezium**. A trapezium has two parallel sides, a and b say. If the height of the trapezium is h, then the area is $\frac{1}{2}h(a + b)$. This can be shown by cutting the trapezium halfway up its height and rearranging the bits as a parallelogram

4) **Circle**. This dissection is more fiddly than the others, and the results are not exact. Still, if it is done carefully the result is convincing.

The circumference of a circle is $2\pi r$, and the area is πr^2. By a dissection show the circle has the same area as a rectangle which is πr by r.

Cut out a circle, and cut it into many equal sectors. When they are stacked with the pointed ends alternating they will be approximately rectangular in shape. So they will fit either into a circular hole or a rectangular hole.

Pythagoras

There are several ways of proving Pythagoras's theorem by means of rearranging areas. Here are a few.

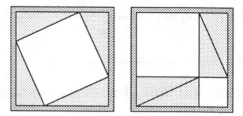

5) Get four sheets of the thinner cardboard and put then on top of each other. Cut across a corner, so that you have four congruent right-angled triangles.

Say the shorter sides of the triangle are a and b. Cut a square in the backing card of side $(a + b)$. The four triangles can be arranged in the hole in two ways. Why does it prove Pythagoras?

6) The two holes are as shown. The first hole consists of two squares, of side a and b. The thinner card is cut into the shape of the two squares, then mark a point X on AB so that AX = a. Cut along XD and XC.

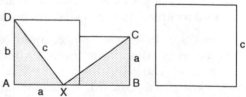

The right-angled triangle is AXD. The larger square hole has side XD. Show that the pieces can be put into the larger hole. Why does this prove Pythagoras?

7) For the next dissection we show the arrangement before and after. Beforehand make rough models with paper, so that you know what to do.

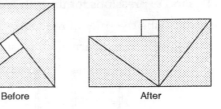

Before   After

Miscellaneous exercises

Group A

1) Express as powers of primes:

   a) 70   b) 64   c) 162

2) Find the HCF and LCM for the following pairs of numbers:

   a) 20 and 18   b) 5 and 7   c) 12 and 6

3) Use a calculator to evaluate the following to 3 significant figures, without writing down anything but the final answer:

   a) $(4.732 + 2.187) \times (3.192 - 2.128)$

   b) $27.3 \div (1.924 + 3.118)$

4) (Work out the following on a calculator, and do not write anything down except your final answers)

   A flat roof is 8.3 m by 5.2 m. What is its area? What would it cost to cover it at a price of £27.3 per m²? If the house below is 9.1 m high, what is the total volume of the house?

5) Make rough estimates for the results of the following calculations. Then perform the calculations exactly.

   a) $48 \times 27 \times 103$ b) $(8.32 + 1.8) \times (1.19 - 0.2)$

6) Evaluate the following without a calculator:

   a) 300×400 b) $20 \times 10{,}000$

   c) $0.2 \times 80{,}000$ d) $40{,}000 \div 0.2$

7) Express in Standard Form: a) 35,800,000   b) 0.00000052

8) Evaluate the following, giving your answers in Standard Form:

   a) $7 \times 10^5 \times 2 \times 10^8$ b) $4.6 \times 10^9 \div 2 \times 10^3$

   c) $1.4 \times 10^8 + 3 \times 10^8$ d) $2 \times 10^7 - 9 \times 10^7$

9) The population of a country is 8×10^7 people, and the average wealth is £4,000. What is the total wealth?

10) Evaluate the following:

   a) 5^4 b) 6^3 c) 2^7 d) 5×2^3 e) $(5 \times 2)^3$

11) Find the following roots:

   a) $\sqrt{256}$ b) $\sqrt[3]{64}$ c) $\sqrt[4]{1}$ d) $\sqrt{\frac{1}{9}}$ e) $\sqrt[3]{\frac{1}{8}}$

12) Find the reciprocals of:

   a) 7   b) $\frac{7}{11}$ c) $3\frac{2}{3}$ d) $\frac{1}{6}$

13) Find the next two terms for the following sequences:

   a) 1.2, 1.3, 1.4, 1.5, ...   b) 2.8, 2.5, 2.2, 1.9, ...

14) Find expressions for the n'th terms of the sequences in Question 13.

15) Describe the rules of the sequences in Question 13.

16) Below is a sequence of matchstick patterns. How many matches are there in the n'th pattern?

17) A time is given as 13.35 seconds to two decimal places. What are the limits between which the time lies?

18) Amelia reckons that next week she will spend about £20. What is the possible error in this?

19) There are 1,760 yards in a mile. How many square yards in a square mile?

20) Below are the answers given to a test. Which must be wrong?

   a)   The length of the stick is 3 m.

   b)   The cylinder holds 500 cm^2 of water.

   c)   A litre of paint covers 8 metres of wall.

Group B. Challenge questions

21) Another rule for finding the HCF of two numbers is as follows:

   > Subtract the smaller number from the larger. Replace the larger with the difference.
   > Repeat, until the two numbers are equal. This will then be equal to the HCF.

   Use this method to find the HCF for the pairs:

   a)   12 and 15   b)   25 and 35   c)   16 and 13.

22) By placing brackets in different ways, find how many different values you can obtain for $3 + 4 \times 7 - 2$.

23) What is the HCF of n and $n + 1$? What is the LCM?

24) See if you can devise a calculation which requires all the brackets on your calculator.

25) The movements of a concerto are in the ratio 5:2:3. If the total length is 20 minutes, how long are the movements?

26) Gunpowder is made from sulphur, carbon and salt-petre in the ratio 1:1:6. How much sulphur is there in 40 lb of gunpowder?

27) A surveyor measures a distance as 125 metres, but his instruments may have an error of up to 2%. What is the maximum error? What is the greatest possible value of the distance?

Questions 28 to 31 are from early books of problems

28) How many apples are needed if 4 people out of 6 receive $\frac{1}{3}, \frac{1}{8}, \frac{1}{4}, \frac{1}{5}$ of the total number, while the fifth receives 10 apples, and 1 apple remains for the sixth?

   (The Greek Anthology, 500 AD)

29) Demochares has lived a fourth of his life as a boy, a fifth as a youth, a third as a man, and spent 13 years in his dotage. How old was he?

   (The Greek Anthology, 500 AD)

48

30) A dog chases a hare, which has a lead of 100 yards. After running 250 yards, the dog is 30 yards short of the hare. How much further is there to run?

(China, 200 AD)

31) One says: "Give me a hundred, friend, I shall then become twice as rich as you." The other replies: "If you give me ten, I shall be six times as rich as you." Tell me, what is the amount of their capitals?

(Bhaskara, India, 1150 AD)

Group C. Longer exercise

32) **Paper sizes**

The commonly used sizes of paper are A3, A4, A5 etc. Get hold of examples of each and find out the following.

a) What is the ratio of length to breadth for each size? Is it the same for each size?

b) What is the connection between the different sizes? How do we convert a sheet of A3 to A4 etc?

c) What are the length and breadth of A1 or A10 sheets?

Revision exercises

1) List the different ways you could make up a sum of £45 from £5, £10, and £20 notes.

2) The hero of a fairy story wins a pair of seven league boots, with which one stride takes him 7 leagues. (1 league = 3 miles). How many strides are necessary to cover a journey of 200 miles, and how many miles will be left after he has taken the boots off?

3) Which of the following are prime? Give factors for those which are not prime.

23, 39, 35, 67, 169

4) Find: a) 5^3 b) 2^5 c) $\left(\frac{1}{2}\right)^3$

5) Evaluate the following:

a) $3 \times 7 - 5$ b) $3 \times (7 - 5)$ c) $3 + 2 \times 3 + 8$

d) $(3 + 2) \times 3 + 8$ e) $3 + 2 \times (3 + 8)$ f) $(3 + 2) \times (3 + 8)$

6) Evaluate:

a) $-7 \times 4 \div -2$ b) $(-3)^3$ c) $(-2)^4$

7) Evaluate the following mentally:

a) $7 + 18 + 23$ b) 8×50 c) $1000 \div 8$

8) Evaluate the following using pencil and paper:

a) $43 + 94$ b) 73×8 c) $581 \div 7$

d) $2417 - 1852$ e) 739×51 f) $1288 \div 23$

9) Use a calculator to check your answers for Question 8.

10) For their holiday in Spain, Nigel has saved £163 and Fiona has saved £98. How many pesetas will they have in all, at a rate of 312 pesetas to the £?

11) a) Express $\frac{16}{36}$ in its simplest form.   b) Convert $\frac{22}{5}$ to a mixed number.

     c) Convert $5\frac{2}{3}$ to a vulgar fraction.

12) 5 cakes are shared between 25 people. What fraction of a cake does each person get?

13) Evaluate the following, giving your answers in the simplest possible form.

a) $\frac{1}{4} \times \frac{3}{7}$　　　　　　b) $\frac{8}{9} \times \frac{3}{4}$　　　　　　c) $\frac{2}{3} + \frac{1}{10}$

d) $\frac{2}{7} + \frac{3}{8}$　　　　　　e) $\frac{1}{4} + \frac{1}{3} + \frac{1}{2}$　　　　f) $\frac{9}{10} - \frac{3}{7}$

g) $2\frac{2}{3} + 1\frac{1}{9}$　　　　　h) $1\frac{3}{4} - \frac{7}{8}$

14) Bertram takes a third of a cake, and three other people share the rest equally. How much does each get?

15) A pastry mix contains flour and butter in the ratio 3:2. How much flour is there in 10 kg of the pastry?

16) Evaluate the following without a calculator:

a)　$3.997 + 1.004$　　　　b)　$1 - 0.0301$　　　　c)　1.43×0.7

17) What is the total cost of 6 gallons of petrol at £2.13 per gallon?

18) How much is left from 1.2 kg of sugar after 0.345 kg has been poured out?

19) A bookseller buys £400 worth of books, and sells at a profit of 35%. What is the selling price?

20) An investor buys £2,000 worth of Unit Trusts, but has to pay a commission of 5% to the bank. How much is the investment now worth?

21) Convert:

a)　35% to a fraction　　b)　$\frac{13}{20}$ to a percentage

c)　2% to a decimal　　d)　0.6 to a percentage

22) Out of 20 million votes, 8.5 million were for the Freedom Party. What was their percentage share of the vote?

23) An author gets royalties of 10% of each book sold. He obtains £9,000 for sales of 12,000. What was the price of the book?

24) A coat is reduced from £40 to £38. What is the percentage reduction?

25) Mrs Yates earns £20,000. Her allowance is £4,000. How much tax does she pay if the rate is 25%?

The rate changes, and her tax bill is £4,480. What is the new rate?

26) Round the following to the nearest whole number:　　a) $\frac{6}{7}$　　b) $-4\frac{3}{8}$　　c) -21.95

27) Round 12349 to the nearest:　　　a)　1000　　b)　100　　c)　10.

28) Hiring a tennis court costs £4.60 per hour. What is the cost per minute, to the nearest penny?

29) 43 people weigh an average of 63 kg each. What is their total weight, to the nearest 10 kg?

30) Round 0.0312784 to:　　a)　3 decimal places　　b)　5 significant figures.

31) Find $\sqrt{87}$, giving your answer to 3 decimal places.

32) Make rough estimates of:　　　a)　101×23　　b)　$42 \div 5.2$.

33) Convert the following:

a)　0.32 km to m　　　　b)　1,000,000 cm to km

c)　23 gallons to quarts　d)　8,000 ounces to pounds

e)　3 miles to yards　　f)　600 ounces to kg

g)　53 metres to yards　h)　50 gallons to litres

34) What is the weight in tonnes of 170 boxes weighing 27 kg each?

35) How many pints are left over after 17 pints have been taken from a 10 gallon keg?

Puzzles and paradoxes

1) We know that $\frac{1}{4}$ lb = 4 ounces. Square root both sides of this equation, and we get $\frac{1}{2}$ lb = 2 ounces. Is this right?

2) In the ratio –1:1, the left hand number is less than the right hand. In the ratio 1:-1, the left hand number is greater. But because –1 + 1 = 1+ –1 = –1, these two ratios are equal. Is this right?

3) A coach stopped at a cafe, and everyone on the coach bought the same drink. The total cost was £13.69. How many people were there on the coach?

4) a) You have an hourglass which lasts for 7 minutes and another which lasts 11 minutes. How can you use them to cook rice for exactly 15 minutes?

   b) With a 4 minute hourglass and a 7 minute hourglass, how can you cook spaghetti for exactly 9 minutes?

Chapter 8

Algebraic expressions

$(a+b)-1$

Natasha and Kevin and Sandra are on holiday in Holland. There are several things they need to get from a shop.

Sandra says; "Look at the prices – I've only got £35, we can't afford them –"

Kevin says: "You can't subtract Dutch money from British money. Convert each price to pounds by dividing by 3.95, and then add them up. But I haven't got a calculator with me –"

Natasha says: "It'll be easier to add up all the prices in Dutch money, and then convert that total to pounds."

Which is the best way to find the total cost of the items in pounds?

Fig 8.1

8.1 Adding and subtracting expressions

Algebraic expressions are expressions with letters that stand for unknown quantities. $3x + 2y$ is an algebraic expression. Until we know what x and y are we cannot find the value of the expression.

But often the expression can be simplified, to make it easier to evaluate when numbers are substituted for the letters.

Like and unlike terms

Suppose Gladys has 3 oranges and 2 bananas, and Wayne has 3 oranges and 1 banana. When they pool their food, they will have 6 oranges and 3 bananas. Note that we cannot combine together the oranges and the bananas.

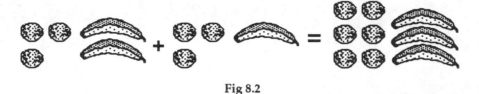

Fig 8.2

Algebraic terms are said to be like terms if they contain the same letters, raised to the same powers. So $3a^2$ and $2a^2$ are like terms. $7a^3$ and $3a$ are unlike terms.

Like terms can be added to make a single term.

$3a^2 + 2a^2 = 5a^2$

The order of the letters is not important. ab is the same as ba.

$2ab + 3ba = 2ab + 3ab = 5ab$

8.1.1 Example

Simplify $3ab + 5b - 2a + 4b - ba$.

Solution   The $3ab$ term and the ba term are like. The $5b$ and $4b$ terms are like. There is only one a term. Combine the appropriate terms to obtain:

$2ab + 9b - 2a$

8.1.2 Exercises

Simplify the following expressions:

1) $5x + 3x$

2) $7y - 2y$

3) $2z + 3z - z$

4) $a + 3b - 7a + b$

5) $5x + 7y - x + 3y$

6) $5p + 2q - 3p - q$

7) $5xy - 2xy$

8) $5ab + 3a + ab - a$

9) $2mn + m + n - mn$

10) $2x^2 + x^2 - 4x^2$

11) $5y^2 - 3y^2 + y^2$

12) $x^2 + 3x + 2x^2 - x$

13) $6 + 3z^2 + 5 - 2z$

14) $5x^2 + 3x + 2 - x^2 - 4x - 8$

15) $a^2 + 2b^2 + 7a + 3b + 2a^2 - b$

16) $2xy + 4yz - zx + 3zy$

17) $3pq^2 + 2qp^2 + 8p^2q - q^2p$

18) $2ab^3 + ba^3 - 3a^3b^3 + 2a^3b - b^3a$

8.2 Multiplying and dividing expressions

Basic arithmetical rules apply to algebraic expressions as well as to numbers. If you are in doubt whether an operation on an algebraic expression is valid or not, test it out on actual numbers.

Multiplying

When expressions with the same letter are multiplied, the powers of the letter are added.

$a^2 \times a^3 = a^5$

Dividing

When expressions with the same letter are divided, the powers are subtracted.

$b^6 \div b^2 = b^4$

More than one letter

If expressions involve several letters, then they are combined together individually.

$3ab \times 4abc = 12a^2b^2c; \qquad 6a^2b \div 2ab = 3a$

8. 2.1 Example

Simplify   a) $(-6x) \times (-4x^2)$ b) $8x^3y^2 \div 2xy$

Solution   a)   Multiply together the number terms, and add the powers of x. Recall that the product of two negative terms is positive:

$(-6x) \times (-4x^2) = 24x^3$

b)   Divide 8 by 2, and subtract the powers of x and y separately.

$8x^3y^2 \div 2xy = 4x^2y$

8.2.2 Exercises

Simplify the following expressions:

1) $2xy \times 3yx$

2) $4x \times 3yz$

3) $3ab^2 \times 2a^2b$

4) $2a \times 3a \times 2b$

5) $(-a) \times 2a$

6) $4b \times (-2ab)$

7) $(-x) \times (-y)$

8) $(-2x) \times (-3xy)$

9) $2mn \times 3mn \times 5mn$

10) $a \times a \times ab$

11) $(-x) \times (-x) \times (-x)$

12) $x \times (-xy) \times (-xyz)$

13) $4a \div 2a$

14) $7x^2 \div 2x$

15) $xy \div 2y$

16) $4a^2b^2 \div 2ab$

17) $9m^2n \div 3n^2$

18) $(-4ab) \div 2b$

19) $6x \div (-2y)$

20) $(-8a) \div (-2a)$

21) $4 \div 2x$

22) $5r \div 2r^2$

23) $12r^2st^2 \div 3rs^2t$

24) $3a \times 2a \div 4a^2b$

8.3 Expansion of brackets

Brackets

The order in which algebraic operations are done is important. Taking powers (i.e. squaring or cubing etc) is done first, then multiplying or dividing, then adding or subtracting. If the operations are to be done in a different order then they must be put in brackets.

For example, consider the expression $z \times x + y$. This means that z and x are multiplied, and y is added to the result. If we wish to add x and y first then put them in brackets, as $z \times (x + y)$.

Expansion

The process of eliminating brackets from an expression is called expansion. If a term z multiplies a pair of brackets, then when the brackets are removed all the terms inside must be multiplied by z. In the example above, when the brackets are removed we obtain $zx + zy$.

8.3.1 Examples

1) Expand and simplify $3(x + y)$

   Solution   Remove the brackets and multiply both terms by 3.

   $3x + 3y$

2) Expand and simplify $2(3x + 5) + 4(2x - 7)$.

   Solution   Multiply through to obtain:

   $6x + 10 + 8x - 28$

   The x terms can be collected, and the number terms can be collected:

   $14x - 18$

3) Expand and simplify $(x - 5)(x + 8)$.

Solution   Hold the first pair of brackets, and multiply out:

$(x - 5)x + (x - 5)8$

Multiplying out again,

$x^2 - 5x + 8x - 40$

$x^2 + 3x - 40$

4) Expand out $(a + b)(a - b)$

Solution   Hold the second pair of brackets, and multiply through:

$a(a - b) + b(a - b)$

Multiply through again:

$a^2 - ab + ba - b^2$

The two middle terms cancel, leaving:

$a^2 - b^2$

(Note: this formula is known as the difference of two squares)

5) Expand and simplify $(a + b)^2$.

Solution   This can be written as $(a + b)(a + b)$. This can be expanded as in the previous examples.

$a^2 + ab + ba + b^2$

$a^2 + 2ab + b^2$

8.3.2 Exercises

Expand the following and simplify as far as possible:

1) $5(x + 7)$

2) $4(a - b)$

3) $7(2x + y)$

4) $2(3x - 5y)$

5) $3(x - 4) + 5(x + 6)$

6) $7(y - 3) - 2(3 + y)$

7) $6(z - 3) - 8(z - 5)$

8) $5(2w + 3) + 9(3w - 4)$

9) $3(x + y) + 4(x - y)$

10) $2(a + b) + 3(2a + 3b)$

11) $4(x + y) - 2(x + y)$

12) $3(c - 2d) - 2(c + 4d)$

13) $3(5r - 2s) - 2(2r - 3s)$

14) $4(p + 2q) - 2(p - 3q)$

15) $(x + 1)(x + 5)$

16) $(y + 3)(y + 7)$

17) $(p + 3)(p - 4)$

18) $(z - 4)(z + 6)$

19) $(w - 7)(w - 11)$

20) $(q - 2)(q - 5)$

21) $(x + y)(x - y)$

22) $(2x + y)(2x - y)$

23) $(x + 3)^2$

24) $(y - 3)^2$

25) $(x + 2y)^2$

26) $(3z - 2w)^2$

27) $(x + 8)(3x - 5)$ 28) $(3y - 4)(2y + 7)$
29) $(a + b)(c + d)$ 30) $(x - y)(z + w)$

8.4 Factorisation

Factorization is the opposite operation to expansion. When an expression is factorized, it is written as the product of two or more simpler expressions.

If the same letter or number occurs more than once, then it can be taken out as a factor. Be sure to put in brackets.

8.4.1 Examples

1) Factorize $3xt - 6xs$.

   Solution   The letter x can be taken outside a pair of brackets.

   $x(3t - 6s)$

   Both the terms inside the brackets are divisible by 3. Take 3 outside the brackets:

   $3x(t - 2s)$

2) Factorize $x^2 + 3x$.

   Solution   Here both terms contain an x. The x can be taken outside a pair of brackets to obtain:

   $x(x + 3)$

8.4.2 Exercises

Factorize the following as far as possible

1) $xy + xz$ 2) $pq - 3q$ 3) $3s + rs$

4) $qt + rt$ 5) $rt - 5rs$ 6) $3xy - 4xz$

7) $2x + 4y$ 8) $3t - 9r$ 9) $2rs + 4rq$

10) $9xy - 3zy$ 11) $6fg + 9fh$ 12) $7t + 21tq$

13) $a^2 + ab$ 14) $z - z^2$ 15) $5x^2 - 15x$

16) $21y^2 - 14y$ 17) $8z^2 + 4cz$ 18) $3d + 9cd^2$

19) $ab + ac + ad$ 20) $3xy + 6xz + 15xw$ 21) $p^2 + pq + 4p$

22) Look again at the problem at the beginning of the chapter. Find the total of British money

   a)   by converting each Dutch price to a British price and then adding

   b)   by adding all the Dutch prices and then converting to a British price. Which method is easier?

8.5 Longer exercise

Algebra by geometry

The algebraic notation of letters for numbers and the symbols $+, -, \times, +, =$ are about 400 years old. But the operations themselves have been known for thousands of years.

Before modern algebraic symbols came into use a lot of algebra was done by geometry. Instead of a number, there would be a length. Instead of two numbers being added, two lengths would be laid end to end. Instead of two numbers being multiplied, the area of a rectangle would be found.

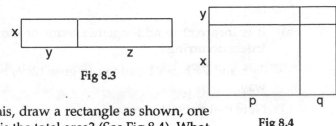

1) The expansion of $x(y + z)$. To find this geometrically, put two lengths of y and z end to end. Make a rectangle of height x. What is the total area? (See Fig 8.3). What are the individual areas? What can you say about the expansion?

Fig 8.3

Fig 8.4

2) The expansion of $(x + y)(p + q)$. To find this, draw a rectangle as shown, one side being $x + y$ and the other $p + q$. What is the total area? (See Fig 8.4). What are the areas of the four smaller rectangles? What can you say about the expansion?

3) The expansion of $(a + b)^2$ is $a^2 + 2ab + b^2$. This is a special case of the expansion of 2). See if you can draw the diagram which proves it geometrically.

4) Can you find geometrically the expansion of $(a + b + c)^2$?

5) If you are good at imagining solid shapes, try to find the expansion of $(x + y)^3$.

Multiple choice question *(Tick appropriate box)*

In its simplest form, the expansion of $(2 - x)(3 - x)$ is:

a) $6 + x^2$ ☐

b) $6 - 3x - 2x + x^2$ ☐

c) $6 - 4x^2$ ☐

d) $6 - 5x + x^2$ ☐

e) $6 - 5x - x^2$ ☐

Points to note

1) *Collecting*

   a) It is incorrect to add together terms unless they are of the same sort, with the same letters occurring.

   $5a^2b$ and $7a^2b$ can be added to give $12a^2b$, but $5a^2b + 7ab^2$ cannot be simplified in this way.

   b) Note that xy is the same as yx.

2) *Powers*

   In an expression like ab^2, only the b is squared. It is not the same as a^2b^2.

3) *Brackets*

   Do not ignore brackets: $a(b + c) \neq ab + c$

4) *Multiplying negative terms*

   Remember the basic rules of:

minus times minus is plus	$- \times - = +$
plus times plus is plus	$+ \times + = +$
minus times plus is minus	$- \times + = -$

   It is easy to get these wrong, when expanding out something like $(x - y)(p - q)$. The yq term is positive.

5) *Expansion*

   When multiplying out brackets, all the terms in the first pair must multiply all the terms in the second pair. Do not just multiply together the first two and the last two.

   $(a + b)(x + y) \neq ax + by$.

   The correct expansion is $ax + ay + bx + by$

   In particular, be careful when expanding $(a + b)^2$ or $(a - b)^2$

   $(a + b)^2 = a^2 + 2ab + b^2 \neq a^2 + b^2$

   $(a - b)^2 = a^2 - 2ab + b^2 \neq a^2 - b^2$

 **Chapter 9**

Formulas

Are you a healthy shape? The answer will depend on your height and sex as well as your weight.

One way to calculate the percentage of fat in your body is as follows:

Take your weight in pounds, divide by the square of your height in inches. Multiply by 850. Subtract 12 if you are male, and 1 if you are female.

What do you get? For a male, the result should be between 15% and 20%. For a female, it should be between 25% and 30%.

Fig 9.1

9.1 Constructing formulas

An algebraic expression contains letters which stand for numbers. An example of an algebraic expression is:

$$(F - 32) \times \frac{5}{9}$$

This expression converts the temperature from Fahrenheit to Celsius. Because the letter F can stand for any value, the formula will work for any possible temperature.

Another example is:

$$\sqrt{a^2 + b^2}$$

This formula gives the longest side of a right-angled triangle in terms of the other sides. As a and b can stand for any numbers, the formula will work for all right-angled triangles.

Construction

When an algebraic formula is constructed, arithmetic operations are applied to letters instead of to numbers.

9.1.1 Examples

1) Anne has y more pounds than Bill. Bill has x pounds.

   a) How much does Anne have?

   b) How much do they have in total?

   Solution   a)   Add y to Bill's money.

                  Anne has $x + y$ pounds

              b)   Add x and $x + y$.

                  Together they have $2x + y$ pounds

2) A car travels at x m.p.h. for 1 hour, then at y m.p.h. for 2 hours. How far has it travelled? What has been the average speed?

   Solution $x \times 1$ miles is travelled in the first stage, then $y \times 2$ in the second stage. The total distance is:

   $x + 2y$ miles

   The average speed is the total distance divided by the total time. This gives:

   The average speed is $\dfrac{x + 2y}{3}$ **m.p.h.**

3) An exam is taken by g girls and b boys. The boys score an average of p and the girls an average of q. Find the average for the whole exam.

   Solution   The total mark for the girls is gq, and for the boys bp. The total mark for all pupils is $(gq + bp)$. The number of pupils is $(g + b)$. The average is the total mark divided by the number of pupils:

   The average is $\dfrac{gq + bp}{g + b}$

9.1.2 Exercises

1) A plank 10 metres long has x metres sawn off. How much is left?

2) Two angles add up to $T°$. One is $d°$. What is the other?

3) A machine can produce x items in one hour. How many items can it produce in y hours?

4) A room is L metres long and B metres broad. What is the area and the perimeter?

5) A motorist drives for t hours at 68 m.p.h. If he covers x miles, find x in terms of t.

6) A dealer buys a car for £m and sells it for £n. What is the profit?

7) For an n-sided figure, to obtain the sum of the interior angles we multiply the number of sides by 180° and then subtract 360°. Write the sum of the angles in terms of n.

8) How many minutes are there between 12 o'clock and x minutes past 2 o'clock?

9) A child thinks of a number, doubles it, and then adds 5. If the original number was N, what is the final result?

10) In an innings a batsman hit x sixes, y fours and z singles. What was his total score?

11) A rectangle is twice as long as it is broad. If it is x cm broad find its length, area and perimeter.

12) In a test, C children scored an average of A. What was the total of marks?

13) The manageress of a clothing shop bought x black jackets at an average of £P each, and y blue jackets at an average of £Q each. Find the average cost of the jackets that she bought.

14) At the beginning of the chapter there was a formula for calculating the percentage of fat of a person's body. If the person is a woman, weight x pounds, height y inches, what does the formula give?

9.2 Substitution

Suppose we have an algebraic expression, and we want to evaluate it in some particular situation. Actual numbers are substituted for the letters in the expression and the numerical value of the expression is found. This process is called substitution.

9. 2.1 Examples

1) Find the value of $(F - 32) \times \frac{5}{9}$ when $F = 50$.

   Solution This formula converts the temperature from Fahrenheit to Celsius. So if the temperature is 50° Fahrenheit, then the formula finds the equivalent temperature in Celsius. Put $F = 50$ in the expression:

   $$(50 - 32) \times \frac{5}{9} = 18 \times \frac{5}{9} = 10$$

   The equivalent temperature is 10°

2) Find the value of $\sqrt{a^2 + b^2}$ when $a = 7$ and $b = 24$.

   Solution This formula will give the longest side of a right-angled triangle when the two shorter sides are 7 and 24. Put $a = 7$ and $b = 24$:

   $$\sqrt{7^2 + 24^2} = \sqrt{49 + 576} = \sqrt{625} = 25$$

   The value is 25

3) Find the value of $7xy + x$ when $x = -2$ and $y = -4$.

   Solution Put $x = -2$ and $y = -4$, being careful with the negative numbers.

   $$7(-2)(-4) + (-2) = 7 \times 8 - 2$$

   $$7xy + x = 54$$

4) Find the value of $\sqrt{1 + 2x}$ when $x = 3$, giving your answer to 3 decimal places.

   Solution Put $x = 3$, to obtain $\sqrt{1 + 2 \times 3} = \sqrt{7}$.

   $$\sqrt{1 + 2x} = 2.646$$

9.2.2 Exercises

1) If $M = 3N + 2$ find M when N is: a) 3 b) $\frac{1}{2}$ c) -1.

2) If $y = 2 + \frac{1}{2}x$, find y when x is: a) 4 b) 1 c) $\frac{1}{2}$ d) -2.

3) If $P = 7 - 4Q$, find P when Q is: a) 1 b) 3 c) $\frac{1}{2}$ d) -2.

4) If $w = 7z + 3$, find w when z is: a) 1 b) -1 c) $\frac{1}{2}$ d) $-\frac{1}{2}$.

5) In the formula $v = at + b$, find v when $a = 2$, $b = 30$, $t = 6$.

6) In the formula $s = ut + \frac{1}{2}at^2$, find s when $a = 2$, $u = 30$, $t = 6$.

7) If $z = 3x + 4y$, find z when: a) $x = 1$ and $y = 2$ b) $x = \frac{1}{2}$ and $y = \frac{1}{8}$ c) $x = -1$ and $y = -3$.

8) If $p = \frac{1}{4}q + \frac{1}{3}r$, find p when: a) $q = 8$ and $r = 6$ b) $q = 1$ and $r = 1$.

9) Find the value of $18xy$ when: a) $x = 2$ and $y = 3$ b) $x = \frac{1}{2}$ and $y = \frac{1}{3}$ c) $x = -2$ and $y = -1$.

10) Find the value of $x^2 + x$ when x is: a) 2 b) $\frac{1}{2}$ c) -1.

11) Find the value of $y(y - 1)$ when y is: a) 4 b) 1 c) $\frac{1}{2}$ d) –2.

12) Find the value of $\dfrac{12}{x}$ when x is: a) 3 b) 24 c) $\frac{1}{2}$ d) –2.

13) Find the value of $\dfrac{36}{y^2}$ when y is: a) 2 b) $\frac{1}{2}$ c) –3.

14) If $A = \sqrt{25 - h^2}$, find A when $h = 3$.

15) If $L = \sqrt{t^2 + 144}$, find L when $t = 5$.

16) Find $\sqrt{x + 2}$ when $x = 3$, giving your answer to 3 D.P.s.

17) Find $\sqrt{a^2 + b^2}$ when $a = 8$ and $b = 9$, giving your answer to 3 D.P.s.

18) At the beginning of this chapter there was a formula for finding the percentage fat in a person's body. Find this percentage for a man who is 150 pounds in weight and 70 inches high.

9.3 Changing the subject of a formula

Suppose we have an algebraic equation connecting together two or more letters which stand for unknowns. An example of such a formula is:

$$y = 3x + 5z$$

The subject of a formula is the letter which is expressed in terms of the other letters. In the example above y is the subject.

We might wish to re-arrange the formula above so that x is expressed in terms of y and z. The process of re-arranging the formula, so that a different letter is expressed in terms of the others, is called changing the subject.

The process of changing the subject of a formula is very similar to that of solving an equation. We must get the new subject by itself on one side of the equation.

As in the solution of equations, the basic rule which must be obeyed is:

> ***Do to the left what you do to the right.***

Provided that this rule is obeyed, then we can do any algebraic operation we please.

9.3.1 Examples

1) If $y = mx + c$, put x in terms of y, m and c.

   Solution   Subtract c from both sides, to obtain $y - c = mx$. Then divide both sides by m, to obtain:

   $$x = \frac{y - c}{m}$$

2) If $C = (F - 32) \times \dfrac{5}{9}$, express F in terms of C.

   Solution   Multiply both sides by 9, to get $9C = (F - 32) \times 5$.

   Divide both sides by 5, to get $\dfrac{9C}{5} = F - 32$.

   Add 32 to get:

   $$F = \frac{9C}{5} + 32$$

3) Make h the subject of the formula $V = \frac{1}{3}\pi r^2 h$.

   Solution   Multiply both sides by 3, to obtain $3V = \pi r^2 h$.

   Divide both sides by π and by r^2, to get:

$$h = \frac{3V}{\pi r^2}$$

4) Make r the subject of the formula $V = \frac{1}{3}\pi r^2 h$.

   Solution   Multiply by 3 and divide by πh, to get $\dfrac{3V}{\pi h} = r^2$

   Now square root both sides to get:

$$r = \sqrt{\frac{3V}{\pi h}}$$

9.3.2 Exercises

In each of these questions, change the subject to the letter in brackets.

1) $x = 3y + 2$ (y)

2) $a = b - c + d$ (d)

3) $F = \frac{9}{5}C + 32$ (C)

4) $rt = 3sp$ (s)

5) $y = 3ax^2$ (a)

6) $j = 59 - mn$ (m)

7) $b = \frac{1}{2}(c + a)$ (a)

8) $d + 3 = \dfrac{b}{2a}$ (b)

9) $V = \frac{4}{3}\pi r^3$ (π)

10) $\frac{1}{5}(X + 2Z) = 4Y$ (X)

11) $2(x + y) = 4z$ (x)

12) $p(q - r) = 7$ (p)

13) $y = \frac{1}{2}ax^2$ (x)

14) $A = 4\pi r^2$ (r)

15) $T + R = S^2 - 3$ (S)

16) $L = \sqrt{h^2 + 4r^2}$ (h)

17) $h + 3 = \sqrt{n}$ (n)

18) $t = 2\sqrt{\dfrac{L}{g}}$ (L)

19) $a = \dfrac{c + 1}{b - 3}$ (c)

20) $w = \dfrac{v}{u}$ (u)

9.4 Longer exercises

A. Other temperature scales

Absolute or Kelvin

For many scientific purposes temperature is measured in Absolute or Kelvin degrees. A Kelvin degree is the same size as a Celsius degree, but instead of starting from the freezing point of water it starts from absolute zero, the point so cold that all motion has stopped. This point is about $-273°C$. So $0°K$ is the same as $-273°C$.

1) What is $0°C$ in Kelvin? What is $100°C$ in Kelvin?

2) Suppose the Celsius temperature is C. What is the Kelvin temperature?

3) Suppose the Kelvin temperature is K. What is the Celsius temperature?

4) Convert $50°$ in Fahrenheit to Celsius and then to Kelvin.

5)   Convert 68°F to Kelvin.

6)   Convert 400°K to Fahrenheit.

7)   Suppose the Fahrenheit temperature is F. What is the Kelvin temperature?

8)   Suppose the Kelvin temperature is K. What is the Fahrenheit temperature?

Réaumur

Like Celsius, Réaumur starts with 0°R for the freezing point of water, but the boiling point of water is 80°R.

9)   What is 50°C in Réaumur? What is 120°R in Celsius?

10) Give a formula to convert Réaumur temperature R to Celsius temperature C.

11) Give a formula to convert Réaumur temperature R to Kelvin temperature K.

12) Give a formula to convert Réaumur temperature R to Fahrenheit temperature F.

What are the advantages of all these four scales? Which is easiest to use for practical purposes?

B. Think of a number

Children sometimes play the game of "Think of a Number". We can now put a game like this in terms of a formula.

1)   A simple such game is "Think of a number, double it, add three". If you start with 7, what number do you end with? If your partner ends with 21, what had he started with?

2)   With this game, if you start with N, what number do you end with?

3)   With this game, if your partner ends with E, what number did he begin with?

4)   Think up a more complicated version of this game.

5)   Find the formula connected with your game.

6)   This formula gives you the end from the start. Turn the formula round so that you can find the start from the end.

7)   Are there games in which you cannot find the start from the end?

Multiple choice question   *(Tick appropriate box)*

The value of $1 + y \div z$ when $y = -3$ and $z = -\frac{1}{4}$ is:

a)   13   ☐

b)   8   ☐

c) $1\frac{3}{4}$ ☐

d)   -11   ☐

e) $1\frac{1}{12}$ ☐

Points to note

1) *Order*

    Be careful with the order of arithmetical operations. Put brackets in where necessary. In the formula for converting Fahrenheit to Celsius, subtract 32 from F and then multiply the result by $\frac{5}{9}$. The term (F – 32) must be put in brackets.

2) *Algebra*

    a) Be careful that you do not make basic algebraic mistakes. In particular, be sure that you obey the rule of: *Do to the left what you do to the right.*

    b) Make sure that you do the correct operations when trying to get the new subject on its own. Suppose we wish to make x the subject:

    If a term has been added to x, we must subtract it away.

    If a term is multiplying x, then we must divide by it.

    If x is squared, then we must square root.

    In each case, to get x on its own, we do the opposite operation.

Chapter 10
Equations

You want to put down a concrete patio in your back garden. You have enough concrete for 25 m². You think that the shape should be a rectangle, with the length 1 metre greater than the width. What is the largest patio you can make?

If it is 5 by 4, then the area will be 20 m². If it is 6 by 5, then it will be 30 m². Try different sizes until you have got close to 25 m².

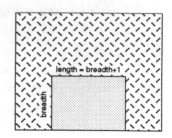

Fig 10.1

10.1 Solving equations

An equation states that one Mathematical expression is equal to another. Examples of equations are:

$$2x + 3 = 5 \qquad x^3 - 2x = 8 \qquad 2x + 3y = 14$$

There are unknowns in these equations. We solve the equation by finding the value or values of these unknowns.

Operations

When solving equations we should do operations which get the unknown on its own on one side of the equation.

There is one basic rule to obey when solving equations.

Do to the left what you do to the right

So if we add 3 to the left side, we must add 3 to the right side also. If the right side is divided by 2, then the left side must be divided by 2.

10.1.1 Examples

1) Solve the equation $2x - 3 = 21$

    Solution   Add 3 to both sides:

        $2x = 24$

        Divide both sides by 2:

        $x = 12$

2) Solve the equation $3x + 3 = 11 - x$

    Solution   Here the unknown occurs twice. Collect them together by adding x to both sides:

        $4x + 3 = 11$

        Subtract 3 and divide by 4:

        $x = 2$

3) Solve the equation $x^3 + 2 = 35$, giving your answer to 3 decimal places.

   Solution   Subtract 2 from both sides:

   $$x^3 = 33$$

   Here we have x cubed. To get rid of the cube we cube-root. Using the cube root button on a calculator:

   $$x = \sqrt[3]{33} = 3.208$$

10.1.2 Exercises

In Questions 1 to 14 solve the equations:

1) $2x + 8 = 20$ 2) $5x - 3 = 22$ 3) $4x + 1 = 101$

4) $7 - 2x = 3$ 5) $2 = 3 - x$ 6) $5 = 8 - 3x$

7) $x + 7 = 2x - 6$ 8) $2 + 3x = x - 4$ 9) $1 + 2x = 7 + 3x$

10) $x^2 + 1 = 10$ 11) $2 + x^2 = 4$ 12) $2x^2 - 3 = 5$

13) $x^3 - 3 = 24$ 14) $2x^3 + 1 = 13$

15) I think of a number x, double it and add 3. The result is 37. Write down an equation in x and solve it.

16) I think of a number x, square it and add 8. The result is 33. Write down an equation in x and solve it.

17) Jane has twice as much money as I do. I am given £30 and she is given £12, and we now have the same amount. If I originally had £x, find an equation in x and solve it.

18) You have twice as much money as I do, but if you give me £13 we will have the same. How much money do I have?

19) You have £40 more than I do, and if we both receive £10 you will have twice as much. How much do I have?

20) The area of a square table is 700 cm^2. What is the side of the square?

21) A rectangle is twice as long as it is broad. If the area is 200 cm^2, what is the breadth?

22) The height, breadth and length of a cuboid are in the ratio 1:3:5. If the volume is 120 cm^3 what is the height?

10.2 Solution by trial and improvement

Often we cannot solve an equation exactly. Then we have to find an approximation to the solution by trial and improvement. This involves trying different values and gradually getting closer to the true value.

Accuracy of solution

We might want to solve an equation to the nearest integer. Suppose that we have found that the solution lies between 5 and 6. Test the equation at 5.5, to see whether the solution is closer to 5 or to 6.

10. 2.1 Example

Find an approximate solution for the equation $x^3 + x = 40$, accurate to one decimal place.

Solution   First of all we find the whole number part of the solution. Try whole number values of x until $x^3 + x$ goes over 40.

$x = 1$	$x = 2$	$x = 3$	$x = 4$
$x^3 + x = 2$	$x^3 + x = 10$	$x^3 + x = 30$	$x^3 + x = 68.$
Under 40	*Under 40*	*Under 40*	*Over 40*

So we know the solution lies between 3 and 4. Now we find the first decimal place:

$x = 3.1$	$x = 3.2$	$x = 3.3$	$x = 3.4$
$x^3 + x = 32.9$	$x^3 + x = 36.0$	$x^3 + x = 39.2$	$x^3 + x = 42.7$
Under 40	*Under 40*	*Under 40*	*Over 40*

We can see that the solution lies between 3.3 and 3.4. To see whether it is closer to 3.3 or 3.4, try at 3.35.

For $x = 3.35$, $x^3 + x = 40.9$. This is over 40. So the solution must lie between 3.3 and 3.35.

To one decimal place, the solution is 3.3

10.2.2 Exercises

Solve the following equations by trial and improvement, giving your answers to 1 decimal place.

1) $x^2 + x = 13$ 2) $x^2 + 2x = 9$ 3) $x^2 = 2 - 3x$

4) $x^3 + x = 50$ 5) $x^3 - 2x = 100$ 6) $x^3 = 2 - 8x$

7) A rectangle is 2 m longer that it is broad. If the area is 60 m² what is the breadth?

8) The area of a square added to its perimeter is 20. What is the side of the square?

9) The volume of a cube added to the area of its base is 29. What is the side of the square?

10) Look again at the problem at the beginning of the chapter. If the breadth is x m, find an equation in x and solve it by trial and improvement.

10.3 Simultaneous equations

So far there has been only one unknown to find. However, if there are more, we need more equations.

Simultaneous equations consist of two equations with two unknowns.

Suppose we know that two buns and a cake cost 80 p, and that two buns and four cakes cost £1.70. In the diagrams below the bun and cake symbols represent their prices.

Elimination

The best method for solving such equations is by elimination. The process is to match up one of the two variables, and then subtract one equation from the other.

Subtracting the equations above, we see that the cost of three cakes is 90 p.

We are left with one equation in one unknown. Divide both sides by 3. The price of one cake is 30 p.

Substitution

Once one variable is found, it can be substituted in either of the original equations.

The price of one bun is 25 p.

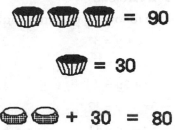

Checking

Say you have used the first equation to find the value of the other variable. Then the second equation can be used to check your answer. Substitute the values in and make sure that both sides are equal.

$$2 \times 25 \ + \ 4 \times 30 \ = \ 170$$

10.3.1 Examples

1) Solve the equations:

  [1] $3x - 5y = 1$

  [2] $2x + 7y = 11$

  Solution Here both equations must be multiplied by a number in order to match either the x terms or the y terms. If the y terms are matched:

  [3] $= 7 \times$ [1] $21x - 35y = 7$

  [4] $= 5 \times$ [2] $10x + 35y = 55$

  Eliminate y by adding.

  [5] $=$ [3] $+$ [4] $31x = 62$

  $x = 2$

  Substitute in either [1] or [2] to find that

  $y = 1$

2) 2 kg of apples and 3 kg of plums cost £3.40, while 4 kg of apples and 1 kg of plums cost £2.80. Find the cost of 1 kg of apples.

  Solution Here there are two unknown. Let x p be the price of 1 kg of apples, and y p be the price of 1 kg of plums. There are two bits of information, which lead to the two equations;

  $2x + 3y = 340$

  $4x + y = 280$

  These can be solved to give $x = 50$ and $y = 80$.

  1 kg of apples costs 50 pence

10.3.2 Exercises

Solve the following pairs of simultaneous equations.

1) $x + y = 3$

        $x - y = 7$

2) $2z + w = 3$

        $3z + w = 9$

3) $3x + 2y = 4$

        $5x - 2y = 12$

4) $3x + y = 7$

        $3x - 4y = -13$

5) $5q - 3p = 11$

        $q + p = 7$

6) $7x + 5y = 4$

        $3x + 2y = 7$

7) $3z - 5w = 8$

        $z + 3w = 12$

8) $4q - 3p = 5$

        $7q - 6p = 5$

9) $3x + 2y = 14$

        $x - 3y = 1$

10) $2x - 4y = 14$

        $3x + y = 7$

11) $3x + 2y = 20$

        $-5x + 3y = 11$

12) $4s + 5r = 1$

        $2s - 3r = 17$

13) $2x + 3y = 13$

        $7x - 5y = -1$

14) $6p - 7q = -1$

        $5p - 4q = 12$

15) $\dfrac{x}{6} + \dfrac{y}{3} = 8$

        $\dfrac{x}{4} - \dfrac{y}{9} = 1$

16) $\dfrac{m}{6} + \dfrac{2n}{3} = 6$

        $\dfrac{-m}{10} + \dfrac{2n}{5} = 2$

17) 3 pounds of butter at x p per pound and 4 pints of milk at y p per pint cost £3.84. 5 pounds of butter and 7 pints of milk cost £6.48. Form two equations in x and y and solve them.

18) In a certain factory, the basic rate of pay is £4.50 per hour, with overtime at £6.40. A man worked x hours at the basic rate, and did y hours of overtime. He worked 45 hours in all, and received £215.8. How many hours did he work at the basic rate?

19) At a concert 500 tickets were sold: the cheaper ones cost £5 and the more expensive ones £9. The total receipts were £3,220. Let x and y be the numbers of cheap and expensive tickets respectively. Form two equations in x and y, and hence find how many cheap tickets were sold.

20) In a pub, brandy is 10 p more expensive than whisky. A round of 3 brandies and 5 whiskies cost £7.10. Let x be the cost of a brandy, and y the cost of a whisky. Find the cost of a whisky.

21) Chuck saves money by putting every 50 p and every 20 p coin he receives in a box. After a while he find's that he has 54 coins, amounting to £17.10. How many 50 p coins does he have?

10.4 Longer exercise

Chinese algebra

The = sign which we use in equations first appears in *The Whetstone of Witte*, written in 1557 by an Englishman Robert Recorde. But equations had been known for many years before that. Over 2,000 years ago Chinese mathematicians were able to solve simultaneous equations, using counting rods on a counting board.

An equation like $3x + 2y = 4$ could be laid out with three rods representing the $3x$, two rods for the $2y$ and four rods for the 4.

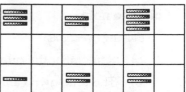

This is the top row of the diagram shown. What equation does the bottom row show?

The simultaneous equations $3x + 2y = 4$ and $x + 2y = 2$ can now be solved by moving the rods about the board.

Use a chessboard for the counting board, and matches for the rods. Show how to solve these simultaneous equations.

Fig 10.3

The counting rods for positive numbers were red, and rods for negative numbers were black. Use different coloured matches for negative numbers, to represent equations like $3x - 2y = 5$. Solve some simultaneous equations involving negative numbers.

Multiple choice question *(Tick appropriate box)*

A forger makes £3 and £5 notes. After printing 1000 notes, with a face value of £3560, it is pointed out to him that the £3 notes are worthless. How many £5 notes has he made?

a) 280 ☐

b) 720 ☐

c) 820 ☐

d) 1280 ☐

e) Not enough information ☐

Points to note

1) *Solving equations*

   a) Remember the rule: "Do to the left what you do to the right".

   b) The unknown cannot appear on both sides of the answer. If your solution is $x = 2 - 3x$, then you have not solved the equation at all. Collect together the x's on one side.

   c) Often the wrong operations are used when solving equations. The following examples show which operations should be used:

For $x + 3 = 7$,	subtract 3 from both sides.
For $x - 6 = 12$,	add 6 to both sides.
For $3x = 15$,	divide both sides by 3.
For $\frac{1}{2}x = 2$,	multiply both sides by 2.
For $x^2 = 13$,	square root both sides.

2) *Trial and improvement*

   Suppose you have found that the solution to an equation lies between 4.5 and 4.6. Then you do not yet know the answer to 1 decimal place. Test the value at 4.55, and then you will know whether the answer is closer to 4.5 or to 4.6.

3) *Simultaneous equations*

   a) Do not try to get by with one equation for two unknowns. Nearly always you must have two equations for two unknowns.

   b) Be careful when adding or subtracting equations. Remember the basic rule that two minuses make a plus. In the situation:

   [1] $3x + 4y = 20$

   [2] $3x - 5y = 2$

   When you subtract [2] from [1] you should obtain $9y = 18$

   c) State clearly what your letters stand for. It is not enough to say: *Let x be the apples.* We must make it clear whether x is the price, or the weight, or the number of the apples.

Chapter 11

Inequalities

In the United Kingdom one can vote after one's 18th birthday, and drive after one's 17th. Below, several people are talking about their ages: who can:

   a) vote   b) drive?

A: "I'm nearer 18 than 17."

B: "My next birthday will be my seventeenth."

C: "I'm not yet 18."

D: "I have seen eighteen summers."

E: "I have had more than 17 birthdays."

F: "I have had at least 17 birthdays."

11.1 The number line

An inequality tells us that one expression is different from another. There are various ways in which expressions could be different. The four signs which express inequality are:

$a < 3$ means that a is less than 3.

$a \leq 3$ means that a is less than or equal to 3. (Or at most 3.)

$a > 3$ means that a is greater than 3.

$a \geq 3$ means that a is greater or equal to 3. (Or at least 3.)

The number line

Inequalities can be illustrated on a number line.

The line can stretch as far as we like in both directions. Numbers, both positive and negative, are marked at regular intervals. A range of values of x can be shown by a bar above or below the number line.

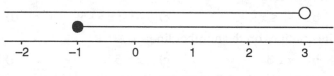

Fig 11.1

If the inequality involves $\leq$ or $\geq$, the endpoint is included in the range. The bar ends with a filled-in circle.

If the inequality involves $<$ or $>$, the endpoint is not included in the range. It ends with a hollow circle.

In the illustration of Fig 11.1, the top bar represents $x < 3$, and the lower bar represents $x \geq -1$.

Fig 11.2

Sometimes a range of values of x is bounded at both ends. The range shown in Fig 11.2 is $0 < x \leq 2$.

11.1.1 Examples

1) Describe the inequality shown on the number line below.

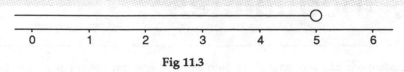

Fig 11.3

Solution   It starts at 5 with a hollow dot and goes to the left. So it includes numbers less than 5, not including 5 itself.

$x < 5$

2) Illustrate the inequality $6 \leq 3x < 12$ on the number line.

Solution   Divide through by 3, to obtain $2 \leq x < 4$. Draw a bar on the number line, with a solid dot on the left and a hollow dot on the right.

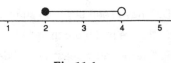

Fig 11.4

11.1.2 Exercises

1) Which of the following are true?

   a) $3 < 5$
   b) $5 < 3.6$
   c) $\frac{1}{3} \leq 0.3$
   d) $10^2 > 90$
   e) $\frac{1}{8} \leq 0.125$.

2) Arrange the following in increasing order, using the $<$ sign.

   $4.6, 4.45, \frac{19}{4}, \frac{14}{3}, \frac{9}{2}$.

3) Arrange the following in decreasing order, using the $>$ sign.

   $\frac{1}{8}, 0, 0.2, -\frac{1}{2}, -\frac{1}{8}, -\frac{3}{17}, -\frac{1}{4}$.

4) Find a whole number x for which $x > 3$ and $2x < 11$.

5) Find an integer y for which $y \leq -3$ and $y > -5$.

6) List the positive integers for which:

   a) $0 < x < 6$
   b) $2 \leq x \leq 7$
   c) $13 < x \leq 17$
   d) $7 \leq x < 10$

7) List the whole numbers for which:

   a) $-2 < x < 2$
   b) $-7 \leq x \leq -3$
   c) $-1 \geq x > -5$
   d) $4 > x \geq -2$

8) Illustrate the following inequalities on the number line:

   a) $x < 7$
   b) $x \geq 3$
   c) $x > 5$
   d) $x \leq 6$

9) Find the inequalities represented by the following number lines:

   a)

   b)

   c)

   d)

Fig 11.5

10) Illustrate the following inequalities on the number line:

a) $3 < x < 7$ b) $7 \leq x < 11$ c) $-4 \leq x \leq 20$

d) $4 \leq 2x \leq 12$ e) $-9 \leq 3x < 3$ f) $-15 < 5x \leq 20$

11) Policemen in a certain country must be at least 180 cm tall. Express this as an inequality in the height h.

12) Ordinary stamps are valid for letters up to 60 g in weight. Express this as an inequality in the weight w.

13) A calculator should be kept at a temperature between $-5°$ and $25°$. Express this as an inequality in the temperature T.

14) Tax is payable at 25% for incomes above £3,000 but less than £22,000. Express this as an inequality in income I.

15) In the example at the beginning of the chapter several people were talking about their ages. Express their statements as inequalities.

11.2 Solving inequalities

An inequality looks like an equation, with the = sign replaced by one of the four order signs.

The basic rules for equations apply also when solving inequalities.

> *Do to the left what you do to the right*

There is one additional rule for the solving of inequalities. When multiplying or dividing by a negative number, the inequality sign changes round.

$$\text{If } a < b, \text{ then } -2a > -2b$$

$$\text{If } c \leq d, \text{ then } -\tfrac{1}{2}c \geq -\tfrac{1}{2}d$$

This can be justified as follows. A temperature of 25° is hotter than one of 15°. But −25° is colder than −15°. We see that multiplying the temperature by −1 has the effect of changing round the words *hotter* and *colder*.

The solution to an inequality consists not of one single value, but of a whole range of values. The solution can either be written as a basic inequality, i.e. as $x < 3$, or as a bar on the number line.

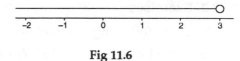

Fig 11.6

11.2.1 Examples

1) Find the solution of the inequality $3x - 2 < 4$, giving your answer in the form of an inequality.

Solution   Add 2 to both sides.

$3x < 6$

Divide both sides by 3. As 3 is a positive number, the inequality sign stays the same way round.

$x < 2$

2) Solve the inequality $2 - 3x \leq 2x + 17$.

   Solution   Subtract $2x$ from both sides, and subtract 2 from both sides.

   $-5x \leq 15$

   Divide by -5, being sure to reverse the inequality sign.

   $x \geq -3$

3) Solve the inequality $x^2 \leq 4$, illustrating your answer on the number line.

   Solution   Square root both sides, to obtain $x \leq 2$.
   We must be careful with negative values
   of x. If x were less than -2, its square
   would be greater than 4. So $x \geq -2$ also.
   This is illustrated on the number line in
   Fig 11.7.

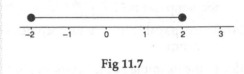

Fig 11.7

4) The hire of a car is £20 per day and 10 p per mile. A woman drives for x miles and her bill is less than £35. Form an inequality in x and solve it.

   Solution   The total bill, fixed charge plus mileage charge, comes to:

   $$20 + \frac{x}{10}$$

   This must be less than £35. The inequality which expresses this is:

   $$20 + \frac{x}{10} < 35$$

   Now solve this inequality:

   $$\frac{x}{10} < 15$$

   $x < 150$

11.2.2 Exercises

1) Solve the following inequalities:

   a) $3x + 1 < 10$ b) $7x - 4 \geq 10$ c) $7 - x \leq 2$

   d) $11 - 3x > 2$ e) $x + 2 < 2x - 10$ f) $4x + 5 < x + 14$

   g) $x + 1 < \frac{1}{2}x + 4$ h) $\frac{1}{2}(x - 3) \leq 5$

   i) $\frac{1}{3}(x + 10) \geq \frac{1}{2}(5 - x)$ j) $\frac{1}{2}(3x + 5) < 2(x - 7)$

2) Solve the following, illustrating your answers on the number line:

   a) $x^2 < 9$ b) $x^2 \leq 100$ c) $x^2 > 4$

   d) $x^2 \leq \frac{1}{4}$ e) $x^2 < 2$ f) $x^2 > 3$

3) A rectangle is 25 m long, and x m wide. If its area is less than 400 m^2, find an inequality in x and solve it.

4) A boy buys x apples at 10 p each. If he has at most £1 to spend, form an inequality in x and solve it.

5) Cakes cost 25 p each. Jane buys y of them, and spends less than £1.50. Form an inequality in y and solve it.

6) A car does 30 miles per gallon, and there are z gallons of petrol in the tank. If the car goes for 120 miles without re-fuelling, find an inequality in z and solve it.

7) I have hired a car for 5 hours, and the maximum speed is 50 m.p.h. If I drive for m miles, form an inequality in m and solve it.

8) A man buys x stamps at 21 p and $2x$ stamps at 25 p. He spends less than £9. Form an inequality in x and solve it.

9) The rental charge of a phone is £15 per quarter, and it costs 5 p per unit. A man uses x units, and his bill is less than £50. Form an inequality in x and solve it.

10) A room is 2 metres longer than it is wide. Its width is x metres, and the perimeter is less than 60 m. Form an inequality in x and solve it.

11) My car does 30 miles per gallon, and I must drive for 110 miles. Petrol costs £2 per gallon, and I have only £7. Can I afford to make the journey?

11.3 Two-dimensional inequalities

Some inequalities involve y as well as x. They can be illustrated by shading regions on a plane.

For the inequality $x \geq 1$, shade the region to the right of the vertical line through $x = 1$. See Fig 11.8.

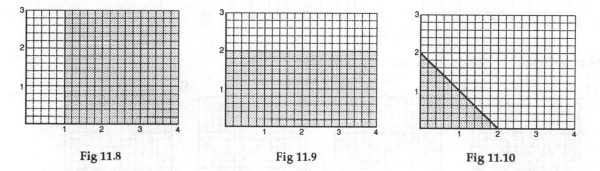

Fig 11.8   Fig 11.9   Fig 11.10

For the inequality $y \leq 2$, shade the region below the horizontal line through $y = 2$. See Fig 11.9.

To illustrate $x + y \leq 2$, first draw the line $x + y = 2$. Then shade the region below it. See Fig 11.10.

If the inequality involves $\leq$ or $\geq$, the boundary of the region is included. It is drawn with a filled-in line. If the inequality involves $<$ or $>$, the boundary is not included and it is drawn with a dotted line. See Fig 11.11.

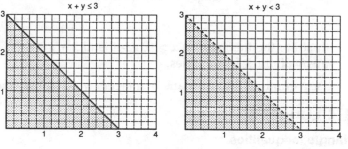

Fig 11.11

77

11.3.1 Example

Illustrate the inequalities $x \geq 1, y \geq 2, x + y < 5$.

Solution   Draw the vertical line $x = 1$, the horizontal line $y = 2$, and the slanting line $x + y = 5$. The first two are filled-in lines, and the third is a dotted line.

We want the region to the right of the first line, above the second line and below the third line. It is shown shaded on the diagram.

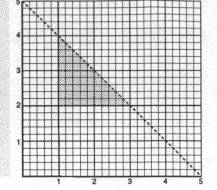

Fig 11.12

11.3.2 Exercises

1) Illustrate the following inequalities on the grids shown:

   a) $x > 1, y > 0, x + y \leq 6$ b) $x \geq 1, y \leq 5, y \geq x$

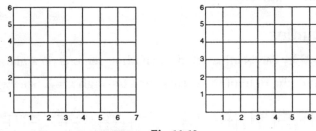

Fig 11.13

2) Describe in terms of inequalities the regions shown.

   a)   b)   c)   d)

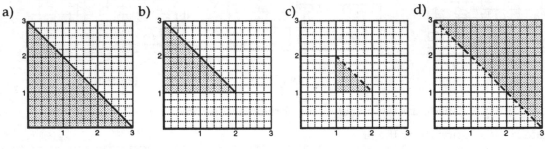

Fig 11.14

3) Illustrate the inequalities $x > 0, y > 0$ and $x + y < 4$ on a graph. List all the pairs of integers which satisfy all three inequalities.

4) Use a graph to find the pairs of integers which satisfy the inequalities $x \geq 1, y \geq 1$ and $x + y \leq 3$.

11.4 Longer exercise

Triangle inequalities

If a, b and c are the three sides of a triangle, then $a + b > c$. This is called the triangle inequality (Fig 11.15).

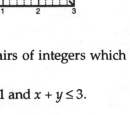

Fig 11.15

1) If you had sticks of length 7, 9 and 14, could they form a triangle? What about sticks of length 4, 10, 6?

2) Suppose a, b, c and d are the four sides of a quadrilateral. Is it true that $a + b + c > d$?

3) a, b, c, d and e are the five sides of a pentagon. Is it always true that $a + b + c > d + e$?

4) On the right is a tetrahedron. Suppose the areas of the four faces are A, B, C and D. Is it true that $A + B + C > D$?

5) Suppose you have sticks of length 1, 1, 2, 3, 5, 8, 13, 21. Can you make a triangle out of them?

6) Can you find a group of ten different lengths, so that a triangle could be formed out of any three of them?

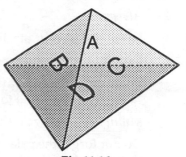

Fig 11.16

Multiple choice question *(Tick appropriate box)*

Which of the following number lines corresponds to the solution of the inequality $10 - 3x > 2 + x$?

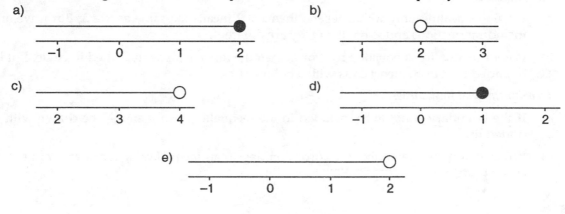

Fig 11.17

a) ☐

b) ☐

c) ☐

d) ☐

e) ☐

Points to note

1) *Algebra*

   Be careful of your algebra when solving inequalities.

2) *Expressing inequalities*

   There are different ways of expressing the same inequality. "*x* is at least 3" means the same as "*x* is greater or equal to 3". "*y* is at most 7" means the same as "*y* is less than or equal to 7".

3) *Multiplying by negative numbers*

   Do not forget the rule that when multiplying or dividing by a negative number the inequality sign must be reversed. If you ignore this rule you will get exactly the wrong answer, i.e. you will get $x < 3$ instead of $x > 3$.

4) *The number line*

   a) If we are dealing only with integers, then $x > 2$ means the same as $x \geq 3$. But if we are including fractions and so on, then they are different.

   b) If your inequality is bounded by $\leq$ or $\geq$, then the range ends with a filled in circle. If it is bounded by $<$ or $>$, then it ends with a hollow circle.

5) *Two dimensional inequalities*

   a) If the boundary is not to be included in the inequality, then it should be drawn with a dotted line.

   b) When you have drawn the line corresponding to an inequality, make sure you get the correct side of it.

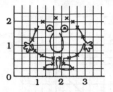

Chapter 12

Graphs

The Highway Code gives values for the distance D feet it takes for a car to stop when it is travelling at speed s m.p.h.

When learning to drive it is wise to get a feeling for these figures. On the right is a graph of D against s. If a car is travelling at 55 m.p.h., how long does it take to stop? If during fog visibility is down to 100 feet, what is the greatest safe speed?

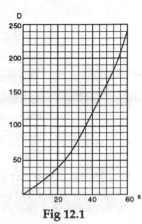

Fig 12.1

12.1 Drawing graphs

Suppose y is given in terms of x. For each value of x there is a value of y. If these pairs (x, y) are plotted on graph paper, then the line they form is the graph of the function.

It is often best to write out a table giving the x and y values.

12.1.1 Examples

1) Complete the table for the function $y = (x - 1)^2$. Draw a graph of the function using a scale of 1 cm per unit.

x	-1	0	0.5	1	1.5	2	3
$x - 1$	-2		-0.5				
y	4		0.25				

Solution For $x = 0$, $x - 1 = -1$. So $y = (-1)^2 = 1$. Complete the rest of the table similarly. The final result is:

x	-1	0	0.5	1	1.5	2	3
$x - 1$	-2	-1	-0.5	0	0.5	1	2
y	4	1	0.25	0	0.25	1	4

The graph is shown in Fig 12.2.

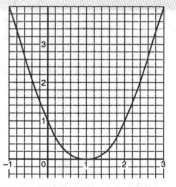

Fig 12.2

2) Let $y = 2x + 3$. Find the values of y corresponding to $x = 0, 1, 2$. Plot these points on a graph. Describe the graph.

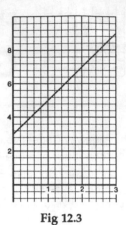

Fig 12.3

Solution   For $x = 0, y = 2 \times 0 + 3 = 3$.

For $x = 1, y = 2 \times 1 + 3 = 5$.

For $x = 2, y = 2 \times 2 + 3 = 7$.

The points are shown plotted on Fig 12.3.

Notice that it is not necessary to find other points, as all the points lie on a straight line which can be drawn with a ruler.

The graph is a straight line

(3) On the same paper plot the graphs of $y = 2x + 3$ and $y = 6 - x$. Write down the coordinates of the crossing point. Check that these coordinates obey the simultaneous equations $y = 2x + 3$ and $y = 6 - x$.

Solution   The graph of $y = 2x + 3$ was drawn in Example 2. The graph of $y = 6 - x$ goes through the points (0,6) and (2,4). Draw this line also (Fig 12.4).

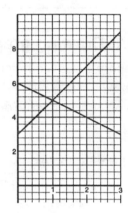

Fig 12.4

Read off the crossing point:

The crossing point is (1,5)

Check these values.

$5 = 2 \times 1 + 3$. **Hence $y = 2x + 3$ is true at (1,5)**

$5 = 6 - 1$. **Hence $y = 6 - x$ is true at (1,5)**

12.1.2 Exercises

1) Complete the following table for the function $y = (x - 2)^2$.

x	0	1	1.5	2	2.5	3	4
$x-2$			-1				2
y			1				4

Draw a graph of the function, using a scale of 1 cm per unit.

2) Complete the table for the function $y = x^2 - 1$.

x	-2	-1	-0.5	0	0.5	1	2
x^2	4			0			
y	3			-1			

Draw a graph of the function.

3) Complete the following table for the function $y = 2x - 1$.

x	-3	-2	-1.5	-1	-0.5	0	1
y							

Draw the graph of your function.

4) Complete the following table for the function $y = 3x + 1$.

x	0	1	2	3
y				

Draw a graph of the function.

5) Set up a table of values for the function $y = 2 - x$, using the x-values 1, 2, 3, 4. Draw a graph for the function, using a scale of 1 cm per unit.

6) Let $y = 2 - 3x$. Find values of y corresponding to $x = 0, 1, 2$. Plot the graph of this function.

7) On the same paper draw the graphs of $y = 3x - 1$ and $y = \frac{1}{2}x + 4$. Read off the crossing point. Check that the coordinates obey the equations $y = 3x - 1$ and $2y - x = 8$.

8) By the method of Question 7 solve the equations $y = x + 3$ and $y = 5 - x$.

9) Plot the graph of $D = s + 0.05s^2$, taking values of s between 0 and 60. Is your graph like the one at the beginning of the chapter? Use the formula to check the answers obtained from the graph.

12.2 Applications of straight line graphs

Straight line graphs have many applications. If a quantity is changing at a constant rate, its graph will be a straight line.

12.2.1 Example

The cooking instructions for beef tell one to roast it for 30 minutes plus 20 minutes per pound. Find the cooking time for joints of 2 lb, 3 lb, 4lb. Plot the time T against the weight W. If a joint takes 120 minutes, how much does it weigh?

Solution   Putting $W = 2, 3, 4$ lb, we obtain values of $T = 70, 90, 110$ minutes. Plotting the points we get the straight line graph shown.

From the graph, we see that when $T = 120$ then $W = 4.5$.

A 4.5 lb joint would take 120 minutes

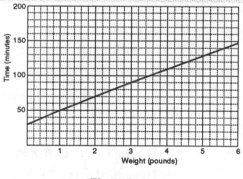

Fig 12.5

12.2.2 Exercises

1) The oven times for chicken are 20 minutes plus 15 minutes per pound. Draw a graph of the time T for roasting against the weight W. If a chicken is to be cooked for 80 minutes, how heavy is it?

2) A money changer will exchange Pounds into French Francs, at a rate of 9 FF per £ plus a £5 commission. Let x be the number of Pounds, and y the number of FF. Plot y against x. How many pounds must I change to obtain 900 FF?

3) A telephone company charges £15 down payment plus 10 p per unit used. Let x be the number of units, and y the payment in £. Plot a graph of y against x. If I pay £43, how many units did I use?

4) A taxi firm charges £2 for journeys up to 2 miles, then 50 p for each mile on top of 2 miles. Draw a graph of the charge C against the mileage m. How far can I go for £5?

5) A plumber charges a £15 call-out fee, then £12 for each hour spent working. Draw a graph of the charge *C* against the time *T*.

6) An income tax scheme is as follows: no tax is paid for the first £4,000 of income, then tax is levied at 30% on any amount above that. Plot a graph of tax *T* against income *I*. If £6,000 is paid in tax how much was earned?

7) A more complicated income tax scheme is as follows: no tax is paid on the first £3,000 earned, then tax is paid at 25% on the next £17,000 up to £20,000, then tax is paid at 40% on all money earned above £20,000.

   Find the tax paid on: a) £4,000   b) £10,000   c) £15,000   d) £25,000   e) £30,000.

   Plot a graph of tax *T* against income *I*. If I pay £5,450 in tax, how much did I earn?

8) The charges of two vehicle hire firms are as follows. Firm A charges £10, then 20 p for each mile. Firm B charges £15, then 15 p for each mile. On the same paper draw the graphs showing the charges of the two firms against distance. For what distances is it cheaper to use Firm B?

9) In its election manifesto, the Purple Party says it will levy income tax at a rate of 20% on all income. The Crimson Party says it will allow the first £8,000 of income to be tax-free, then raise tax at 30% on income above that. On the same paper draw graphs showing tax against income. For what income would you be better off under the Crimson Party?

12.3 Travel graphs

A journey can be shown by drawing a graph of distance against time. This is a travel graph.

12.3.1 Example

Allen cycles to see his grandmother. On the way his bike gets a puncture. He repairs it and cycles on. The picture shows a graph of the distance travelled against time.

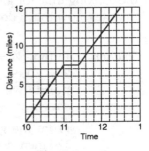

   a)   How long did it take to mend the puncture?

   b)   How fast was he cycling for the first part of the journey?

Solution   a)   He was stationary between 11.00 and 11.24.

   He took 24 minutes to mend the puncture

Fig 12.6

   b)   For the first stretch of the journey, he travelled 7.5 miles in one hour.

   His speed was 7.5 m.p.h.

12.3.2 Exercises

1) Every morning Karen walks to the bus-stop and waits for the bus which will take her to the gate of her school. The graph of her distance from home against time is shown in Fig 12.7.

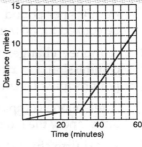

   a)   How far is the bus-stop from her home? How long does it take to walk there?

   b)   How far is it from the bus-stop to school? How long does the bus take?

Fig 12.7

   c)   What speed did she walk at? What speed was the bus?

84

2) George sets off for school one morning, but on his way he realises that he has forgotten his books. He returns home to collect them and sets off for school again. The graph of his distance from home against time is shown in Fig 12.8.

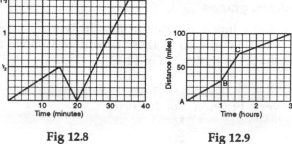

a) How far had he gone when he turned back?

b) How long did the total journey take?

c) What were his speeds in the three parts of the journey?

Fig 12.8

Fig 12.9

3) The Jameson family sets off for their holiday by car. They drive from their home A to the motorway at B. Then they travel along the motorway to C, where they turn off and drive to the hotel at D. The graph of Fig 12.9 shows the distance travelled against time.

a) Find the times taken for the three stages of the journey, AB, BC, CD.

b) Find the distances of the three stages.

c) Find the speeds of the three stages.

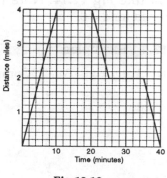

4) Dr Forster drives from her surgery to see a patient. On her way back she stops to visit another patient. The graph of her distance from the surgery against time is shown in Fig 12.10.

a) How long did she spend with each patient?

b) How far was the first patient from the surgery?

c) What was her speed when she drove to the first patient?

Fig 12.10

5) Karen walks three miles to the shops, taking 1 hour. She spends 15 minutes shopping, then walks back in 45 minutes. Draw a travel graph (Fig 12.11) showing her distance away from home.

6) Nigel walks 100 metres in 30 seconds. He rests for 10 seconds, and then walks a further 100 metres in 50 seconds. Draw a travel graph showing the distance he has walked.

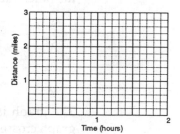

7) A salesman drives 120 miles at 60 m.p.h to meet a customer. He spends 1 hour with the customer, then drives home at 40 m.p.h. Draw a travel graph showing his journey.

Fig 12.11

8) Jane lives 14 miles North of John. At the same time they set off to each other's house, Jane walking South at 3 m.p.h. and John walking North at 4 m.p.h.

On the diagram shown draw graphs showing Jane's and John's distances from John's house in terms of time. When do they meet? How far are they from John's house when they meet?

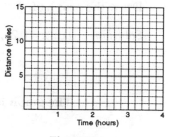

Fig 12.12

12.4 Quadratic and inverse graphs

Quadratic graphs

A quadratic function is one which involves x^2, but not x^3, x^4 etc. The graphs of these functions all have the same shape, as shown in Fig 12.13.

Inverse graphs

An inverse function is of the form

$$y = \frac{k}{x}$$

for some constant k. The graph of such a function will look like Fig 12.14. Note that the function is not defined for $x = 0$.

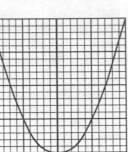

Fig 12.13

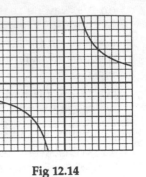

Fig 12.14

12.4.1 Examples

1) Let $y = x^2 - 3x - 1$. Complete the following table:

x	-1	0	1	1.5	2	3	4
x^2							
$3x$							
y							

Plot the graph of this function. When is $x^2 - 3x - 1 = 0$?

Solution   For $x = 2$, $x^2 = 4$ and $3x = 6$. So $y = 4 - 6 - 1 = -3$. Find the other values similarly.

x	-1	0	1	1.5	2	3	4
x^2	1	0	1	2.25	4	9	16
$3x$	-3	0	3	4.5	6	9	12
y	3	-1	-3	-3.25	-3	-1	3

The graph is shown. The function is zero when the graph crosses the x-axis.

$x^2 - 3x - 1 = 0$ for $x = 3.3$ or -0.3

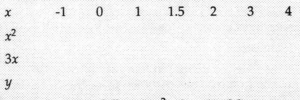

2) Draw the graph of $y = \dfrac{2}{x}$, with values 0.25, 0.5, 1, 1.5, 2, 3, 4.

Solution   For $x = 0.25$, $y = 2 + 0.25 = 8$. Fill up the table as below.

x	0.25	0.5	1	1.5	2	3	4
y	8	4	2	1.3	1	0.67	0.5

The graph is shown plotted.

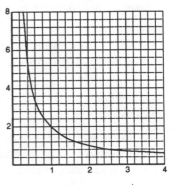

Fig 12.15

Fig 12.16

12.4.2 Exercises

1) Fill in the following table for the function $y = x^2 + x - 3$. Plot the graph. When is this function zero?

x	-3	-2	-1.5	-1	-0.5	0	1	2
x^2								
y								

2) Let $y = \dfrac{1}{x}$. Fill in the following table and plot the graph.

x	-2	-1	-0.5	0.25	0.5	1	2
y							

3) Plot the graphs of the following functions, taking values of x as suggested:

a) $y = x^2 + 2x + 1$. $x = -3, -2, -1.5, -1, -0.5, 0, 1$

b) $y = x^2 + 4x - 3$. $x = -4, -3, -2.5, -2, -1.5, -1, 0, 1$

c) $y = \dfrac{3}{x}$ $x = -1, -0.5, -0.25, 0.25, 0.5, 1, 1.5, 2$

d) $y = \dfrac{1}{x} + 1$ $x = 0.2, 0.4, 0.5, 0.6, 0.8, 1, 1.5, 2.$

e) $y = \dfrac{1}{x + 1}$ $x = -0.5, 0, 1, 1.5, 2$

4) A stone is thrown vertically upwards. Its height h above the ground t seconds later is given by:

$$h = 2 + 20t - 5t^2.$$

Plot the graph of this function, taking t values 0, 1, 1.5, 2, 2.5, 3, 4. When does the stone hit the ground again?

12.5 Longer exercises

A. Use of computer/calculator

In this chapter many graphs have been considered. Plotting by hand takes up a long time and is very liable to error. Use of a calculator or computer can make the whole business quicker and more reliable.

There are many graph-plotting calculators on the market, or you may have access to a graph-plotting program for a computer.

In every case, you type in the form of the function, then the limits within which you want it plotted. The rest is done by machine.

1) Try some of the functions of the chapter. Were your hand-drawn graphs accurate?

Cubic and quartic graphs

Every quadratic (with x^2) graph is the same shape. There is more variety to cubic (with x^3) graphs.

2) Try plotting $x^3 - 1$, $x^3 + 1$, $x^3 + 3x^2 + 3x + 1$, $x^3 - x^2$. Describe the differences between them. How many solutions could a cubic equation have?

3) Try various quartic (with x^4) graphs. How many different shapes are there? How many solutions could a quartic equation have?

B. Picture stories

In section 12.3 the situation behind each travel graph was given. Below are some travel graphs – see if you can describe journeys which might give rise to the graphs.

a)   b)   c)

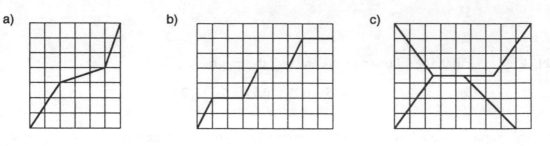

Fig 12.17

Multiple choice question *(Tick appropriate box)*

Which of the graphs below could be of $y = x^2 - 1$?

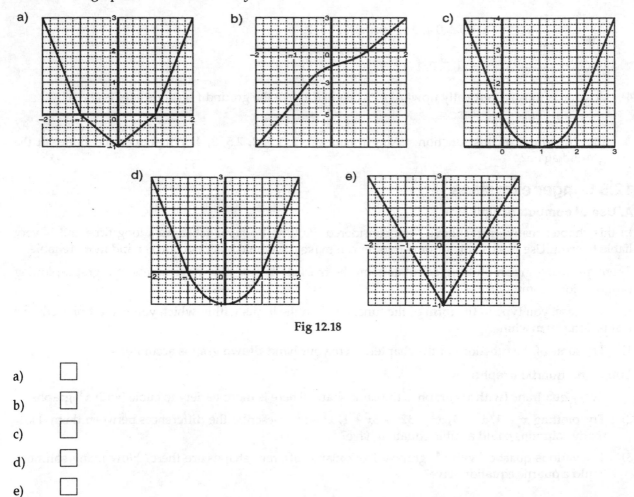

Fig 12.18

a) ☐

b) ☐

c) ☐

d) ☐

e) ☐

Points to note

1) *Graphs of functions*

   a) Be careful when working out tables of values, especially with negative or fractional numbers. For example, it is easy to get the wrong sign when working out $1 - 2x^2$ for $x = -1$.

   b) Once you have plotted the points of a graph, do not join them up by straight lines. Make as smooth a curve as you can to connect them.

   c) If your scale is not simple, then be very careful when plotting points. It is easy to make mistakes when the scale is, for example, 1 cm per 2 metres.

2) *Applications of graphs*

   In most schemes of income tax, tax is only charged above the tax-free allowance. So if the allowance is £4,000, a person earning £10,000 will be taxed on £6,000, not on the full £10,000.

3) *Inverse graphs*

   Be careful also when dividing by fractions. When $x = \frac{1}{2}$, $\frac{1}{x}$ is equal to 2, not $\frac{1}{2}$.

   Do not divide by 0. $1 + \frac{1}{x}$ has no meaning when $x = 0$.

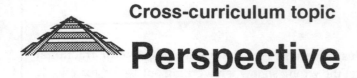

Cross-curriculum topic

Perspective

If an object is far away, it looks smaller. Lines which are parallel may seem to come together at a distance. An artist who wants to paint a realistic picture has to take account of these difficulties. The technique which has been developed is called perspective.

The apparent size of an object depends on the angle it subtends at the eye. If an object is twice as far away, it will seem half the size. The Sun is about 400 times as wide as the Moon. But the Sun is 400 times as far away from the Earth. So they appear to be roughly the same size. In the diagram below (not to scale) the triangles formed by Sun and Moon are similar to each other.

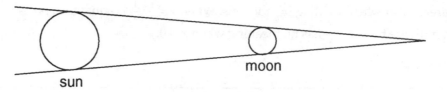

The pictures of children often show no regard for depth. People are drawn without any attempt to show how they would actually look. The paintings of primitive people also do not take account of any apparent shrinking due to distance. Sometimes the relative size of figures is meant to reflect their social importance, so a king will be drawn much larger than a servant.

The picture plane

Why do we not just paint things as they seem? This is a very hard thing to do, and as we shall see there are many objectives which conflict with each other.

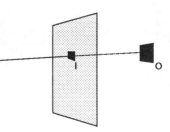

A realistic painting is often described in terms of a picture plane. The plane is between the observer and the scene which is being painted. In the diagram E stands for Eye, where the observer is meant to be standing. O stands for object, which the artist draws on the picture. Draw a line between O and E, then this line crosses the plane at I (for Image). This is where the artist should paint the object.

This seems very reasonable. It describes more or less what a camera does when a photograph is taken. But there are complications. Only one point is labelled E for Eye. What if more than one person wants to look at a painting? Or what if we want to look at it from different angles, or are not of the correct height? After all, paintings are meant to be displayed in rooms, so that they can be enjoyed by the people in the room. It would destroy the enjoyment of a painting if we had to enter a special viewing gallery to see it, and place our eye in exactly the correct position!

A realistic painting should give a correct picture of the sizes of things as they seem to us. Strict adherence to the picture-plane method does not do this. Suppose we want to paint a picture of a wall with several equal windows. For convenience let the picture plane be exactly halfway between the wall and the eye.

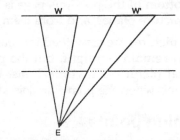

In the illustration we are looking down on the picture plane from above. The window W directly in front of the eye is exactly halved on the picture plane, by similar triangles. But the window W' is also exactly halved. So the painting will show the two windows as equal in size, even though W' is further away.

This distortion is worse in the case of round objects. Suppose that in the windows there are spheres S and S'. The image of the sphere S' will be stretched out on the picture plane. So even though it is farther away than S, it will appear larger!

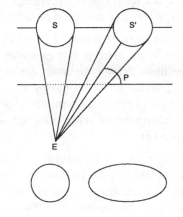

The factor by which it is stretched is $1/\sin P$, where P is the angle which the line to the sphere makes with the picture plane. So if this angle is 30°, the picture of S' will be twice as wide as that of S.

The shape of S' will also be distorted. The stretching effect described above will stretch the image from side to side. The top to bottom image is unaltered. So the image of the whole sphere will be an ellipse instead of a circle, as shown on the right.

It is very difficult to avoid the distortions caused by the phenomena above. If a scene is painted from a single viewpoint, then objects to the side will be distorted in size and shape. The solution usually adopted is to have a narrow angle of vision, maybe 45°, so that no object is far to one side.

Plan and elevation

The other thing a realistic picture must do is to give an impression of depth. Architects often depict buildings by their plan and elevation. The plan is the view directly from above, and the elevation is the view from one side. In about 1420 an Italian artist called Brunelleschi devised a way to go from the plan and elevation of an object to a three-dimensional view of it.

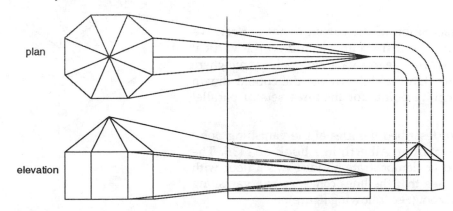

plan

elevation

At the bottom of the previous page is the plan and elevation of a eight-sided tower with a turret. There are two picture planes, and from them there are two pictures, one of the plan and one of the elevation.

The two pictures are combined into one by extending them by the dotted lines shown. The picture of the elevation remains straight, but the picture of the plan is curved through 90°, to convert it from a horizontal picture to a vertical one. Where the dotted lines meet is where we are to draw the final picture, and when the points are joined up we have a reasonable three-dimensional picture.

Vanishing points

The method above works very well for diagrams of buildings. It would not do for a landscape. One way to deal with distant scenes is by considering what happens to the sets of parallel lines in them.

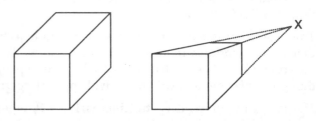

One definition of parallel lines is that they are straight lines which never meet. But straight railway lines appear to meet far away. The point in the distance where they seem to meet is called the vanishing point. In a painting of railway lines, the vanishing point will be an actual point on the surface of the picture.

Above right are two pictures of a cuboid. The front face is parallel to the paper. The one on the left has the other lines parallel to each other, and we see that the cube seems to expand as we go deeper into the picture. The cuboid on the right has been drawn in perspective, and the lines are all converging to a vanishing point marked with an X.

The right-hand cuboid above has one vanishing point. This sort of perspective is very suitable for drawing a long thin room, as seen from one end.

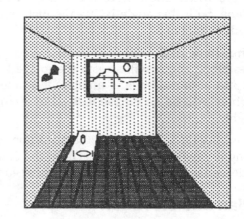

One-point perspective is not quite correct. We must be viewing the cuboid from a point on its right, and so the horizontals of the front face should converge to a vanishing point. A drawing which takes account of this is shown on the right below. This is called angular or two-point perspective.

Even this representation of the cuboid is not perfect. We are viewing the cuboid from above, and so the vertical lines should also converge to a vanishing point somewhere below the picture. On the right we see the cuboid drawn with three vanishing points for the three sets of parallel lines.

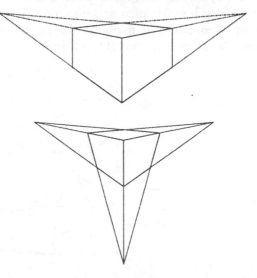

The person who described the idea of the vanishing point was the Italian painter Alberti, in a book of 1436. The example he used to demonstrate his idea was a floor with square tiles. We see that the lines converge to a vanishing point on the horizon. (See following figure).

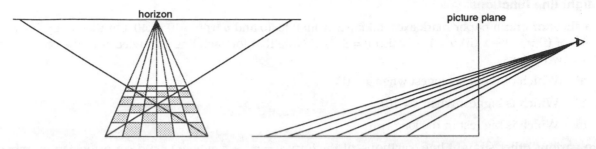

He was also careful to ensure that the distances between the rows of tiles decreased in the correct way. To ensure this he looked at the picture plane from the side. The light rays leave the rows and cut the picture plane as shown, and he was able to find where they should be on the picture. To check that the final picture was correct, he joined up the diagonals of the checker pattern and found that they were in straight lines.

Photography

When photography was invented in the last century the role of the artist changed. There was no longer such a need to paint realistic pictures of buildings or scenes, and the study of perspective was no longer as important. In this century artists have moved away from realism, sometimes to complete abstraction, sometimes to pictures which seem to be completely unlike what they are meant to show. Modern artists are often criticized for not painting realistically, though we have seen that there is no such thing as a completely realistic picture.

There is a story about the Spanish painter Pablo Picasso, whose later paintings of men and women were very unrealistic. An American visitor asked him why he did not paint people as they actually seemed. Picasso pretended not to understand, and asked his visitor what he meant. The visitor claimed that a photograph would give a realistic picture, and took from his wallet a snapshot of his wife. Picasso stared at it. "Is she really so small?" he asked.

The mathematics of perspective

A lot of Mathematics is involved in perspective drawing. Here material from Chapters 13, 17 and 19 has been touched upon.

Extended task. Which function is faster?

Introduction

If two numbers are given, it is easier to determine which is the greater. But if we have two functions the answer may not be so simple. Let y_1 and y_2 be two functions. Suppose they are defined by $y_1 = x^2 - 3$ and $y_2 = 5x + 3$. When x is 0 y_2 is greater than y_1. But for x bigger than 6, y_1 is greater than y_2. In this case we say that y_1 is greater than y_2 *in the long run*.

In this investigation we look at various functions, and decide which is bigger "in the long run". The functions we shall consider will be straight line functions, quadratic functions, cubic functions and exponential functions.

93

Straight line functions

On a sheet of graph paper mark axes, taking x from 0 to 10 and y from -10 to 40. On the paper draw the graphs of (i) $y = 3 + x$ (ii) $y = 1 + 2x$ (iii) $y = 3x - 2$. Note that for each line you need find the coordinates of only two points.

    a)   Which of these is biggest when $x = 0$?

    b)   Which is biggest when $x = 10$?

    c)   Which is biggest in the long run?

Take various other straight line equations, of the form $y = mx + c$, where m and c are constant numbers. Draw their graphs on the same paper. Continue until you can answer the question: With two straight line graphs, $y = mx + c$ and $y = kx + d$, which is bigger in the long run?

Quadratic functions

If we have functions whose graphs are curved, it is more difficult to see which is bigger.

Mark axes on graph paper, taking x from 0 to 5 and y from -10 to 50. Plot the graphs of $y_1 = 2x^2 - 4$ and $y_2 = x^2 + 5$. Which function is bigger in the long run?

It will save time if a computer or calculator is used. There are two ways they could help us decide which of two functions, y_1 and y_2, is bigger in the long run.

    1)   Plot the graphs of y_1 and y_2 simultaneously. (Make sure that the x and y scales are big enough). See which graph is higher than the other.

    2)   Make a new function y_3 by dividing y_1 by y_2.

$$y_3 = \frac{y_1}{y_2}$$

Then see what happens to y_3 as x gets very large. If y_3 becomes small, i.e. less than 1, then y_2 must be bigger than y_1 in the long run.

Take various other quadratic functions, and by either (1) or (2) decide which is greatest in the long run.

Cubic functions

Consider now cubic functions, i.e. ones in which there is an x^3 term. Compare the graphs of $y_1 = x^3 - 4$ and $y_2 = 2x^2 + 7$. Which is bigger in the long run?

Investigate with other cubic and quadratic functions, until you find out whether a cubic or a quadratic function is bigger in the long run.

Exponential functions

An exponential function is something like $y = 2^x$, in which successive powers of 2 are taken. Compare this function with some of the previous ones, using the methods (1) and (2) indicated above. Which is bigger in the long run?

Further investigation

Can you find a function which is bigger in the long run than all the exponential, quadratic, cubic functions we have discussed so far?

If you have any two functions y_1 and y_2, is one of them always bigger in the long run than the other?

Miscellaneous exercises

Group A

1) Simplify the following:

   a) $3p + 4q - q - 2p$ b) $4mn + 2m + 3n - 3mn$

   c) $6r^2 + 2s^2 + 2r^2 - s^2$ d) $a^2 + 2ab - 3ba - 2b^2$

2) Simplify the following:

   a) $8a^2b \times 2b^2a$ b) $(4b)^3$ c) $12x^2y^3 \div 3xy^2$

3) Expand the following and simplify:

   a) $3 \times (x + 2)$ b) $4 \times (y - 3) - 3 \times (y + 4)$

   c) $(z + 5)(z - 3)$ d) $(w + 5)^2$

4) Factorize the following:

   a) $5x + 10y$ b) $x^2 + 8xy$

   c) $7 + 14x$ d) $r^2 + rs + r^2s$

5) The volume of a pyramid is found by multiplying the base area by the height, and then dividing by 3. Find the volume of a pyramid whose height is 12 cm and with base area 10 cm^2.

6) If $H = n(n + 1) + \frac{1}{4}$, find H when n is

   a) 2   b) -3 c) $\frac{1}{2}$.

7) If $z = 5x - 3y$, find z when

   a) $x = 2$ and $y = 1$ b) $x = -3$ and $y = 4$ c) $x = \frac{1}{10}$ and $y = \frac{1}{2}$.

8) The cost of a table is £T, with a £D discount for cash. What is the final cost?

9) In darts, a total of 301 must be reached. How much is left after scoring p points?

10) In the following formulas, change the subject to the letter in brackets.

   a) $y = 4x - 3$ (x) b) $z + 7 = 3 + 2y$ (y) c) $8zy = 4$ (z)

   d) $\frac{6}{p} = q$ (p) e) $x^2 = y + 3$ (x) f) $a^2 + b^2 = 3$ (a)

11) Solve the following equations:

   a) $3x - 1 = 20$ b) $21 - 4x = 5$

   c) $1 + 3x = 5 + x$ d) $x^2 + 3 = 28$

12) Smith has three times as much money as Brown. If Smith gives £12 to Brown they will have the same amount. How much does Smith have?

13) Jones has £50 less than McTavish. If they both receive £20, McTavish will be three times as rich. How much does Jones have?

14) Use Trial and Improvement to solve the following to 1 decimal place:

   a) $2x^3 + 4x = 3$ b) $x^2 + x = 1$ c) $5x^3 = x^2 + 18$

15) The height of a triangle is 1 m less than the base. If the area is 7 m^2, what is the height? Use Trial and Improvement to find the answer to 1 decimal place.

16) Solve the following:

    a) $3x + 2y = 7$ b) $7x - y = 15$

        $5x + 4y = 13$ $3x + 4y = 2$

17) Adult tickets to a cinema cost £4, and children's tickets cost £2.50. 20 people went, and paid a total of £71. How many adults were there?

18) Illustrate on the number line:

    a) $x \le 5$ b) $x < 2$ c) $x > -1$ d) $x \ge 0$

19) Describe the inequalities illustrated below:

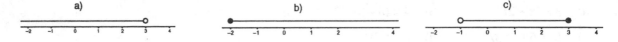

20) List the whole numbers for which:

    a) $1 < x < 5$ b) $-3 < x \le 1$ c) $x^2 < 3$

21) Solve the following inequalities:

    a) $2x + 1 < 13$ b) $7 - 3x \le x - 1$ c) $2x^2 < 7$

22) After buying x cakes at 40 p each I have less than £2 change from a £10 note. Form an inequality in x and solve it.

23) Illustrate the following inequalities on graph paper. List the integer value points inside the region.

    $x > \frac{1}{2}, y < 2\frac{1}{2}, y > x.$

24) Identify with inequalities the region shown unshaded on the right.

25) Plot the graphs of the following functions:

    a) $y = x^2 + 1$ b) $y = x^2 + x - 3$ c) $y = \dfrac{4}{x}$

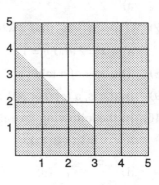

26) On the same paper plot the graphs of $y = 2x + 1$ and $y = \dfrac{x}{3} + 6$.

    Read off the coordinates of the crossing point, and check that they obey the original equations.

Group B. Challenge questions

27) Expand $(x - 1)(x^2 + x + 1)$. What is the expansion of $(x - 1)(x^3 + x^2 + x + 1)$? What is the factorization of $x^5 - 1$?

28) Use the fact that $x^2 - 1 = (x + 1)(x - 1)$ to evaluate 1001×999 without a calculator.

29) A cricketer scores r runs in m completed innings. What is his average? If he is out for 20 in the next match, what is his new average?

30) In the formula $\dfrac{1}{f} = \dfrac{1}{v} + \dfrac{1}{u}$, change the subject to v.

31) Solve the equation $x + \sqrt{1 + x} = 3$ by trial and improvement.

32) The area and perimeter of several circles were measured and plotted against the radius. Which of the graphs below could be correct for the area and which for the perimeter?

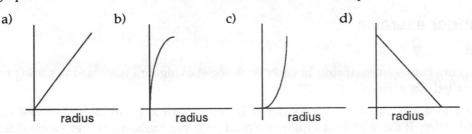

33) Below are graphs of quadratic functions $y = ax^2 + bx + c$. In each case, what can you say about a and c?

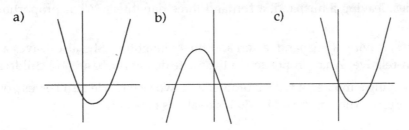

34) If the bearing of A from B is $x°$, what is the bearing of B from A?

35) a) The quadrilateral on the right is a parallelogram. Find x and y.

b) The triangle on the right is equilateral. Find p and q.

Questions 36 to 40 are from early books of problems

36) A lion can eat a sheep in 2 hours, a wolf can eat it in 3 hours, and a dog in 5 hours. How long would they take if they were all eating it together?

(Cataneo, Italy, 1546)

37) A man can drink a cask of wine in 20 days. If his wife joins him they will drink it in 14 days. How long would the wife take to drink the cask on her own?

(Frisius, Germany, 1540 AD)

38) Make me a crown of gold, copper, tin and iron weighing 60 minae: gold and copper shall be $\frac{2}{3}$ of it; gold and tin $\frac{3}{4}$ of it; gold and iron $\frac{3}{5}$ of it. Find the weights of gold, copper, tin and iron.

(The Greek Anthology, 500 AD)

39) Five merchants buy a jewel for 377 pieces of gold. This price is $\frac{1}{2}$ the money of the first merchant and all the money of the others; or it is $\frac{1}{3}$ the money of the second and the money of the others; or $\frac{1}{4}$ the money of the third and the money of the others; or it is $\frac{1}{5}$ the money of the fourth and the money of the others; or it is $\frac{1}{6}$ the money of the fifth and the money of the others. How much did each merchant have?

(India, 400 AD)

40) Three brothers are silk merchants. The eldest brother's bales and half the other brothers' bales come to 79 bales. The middle brother's and half the other brothers' come to 68 bales. The youngest brother's and half the other brothers' come to 57 bales. How much does each brother have?

(China, 200 AD)

Group C. Longer exercise

41) 'ilm al faraid

The word algebra comes from Arabic. In early Arab societies algebra was used to settle problems of inheritance, called *'ilm al faraid*.

The law was that if a husband died a quarter of his estate would go to his wife and a sixth to his mother, if still living. If the wife died a quarter would go to her husband. If there were children sons would receive twice as much as daughters. If there were no children brothers of the deceased would receive twice as much as sisters.

a) A woman dies, leaving a husband, a son and three daughters. What proportion of her estate does each receive?

b) A woman dies, leaving a husband, a son and three daughters. She also leaves a legacy of $\frac{1}{8}$ of the estate to a non-relative. What proportion of the estate do her husband and children receive?

c) A man dies leaving a mother, a wife, a brother and two sisters. He also leaves $\frac{1}{9}$ of the estate to a non-relative. What proportion of the estate do his relations receive?

Revision exercises

1) It costs £8 to enter an amusement park, and the first 6 rides are free. After the first 6 rides they cost 50 p. How much will it cost to go on 12 rides?

2) Another amusement park costs £4 to get in, and each ride costs £1. How much does it cost for m rides?

3) How much do m rides cost in the amusement park of Question 1? (m is at least 6.)

4) a) Find $4x + 7$ when $x = 2$.

   b) Find $3a - 7b$ when $a = 8$ and $b = 2$.

5) Continue the sequences below for two more terms:

   a) 2, 9, 16, 23, ...   b) 1, 8, 27, 64, ...

6) Find rules for the sequences of Question 5.

7) Continue the shape sequence on the right for one more term.

8) Find the number of dots in the shape sequence of Question 7. Continue the number sequence for 2 more terms.

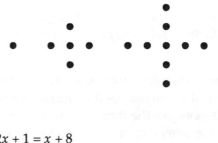

9) Solve the following equations:

   a) $x + 7 = 16$ b) $3x - 4 = 20$ c) $2x + 1 = x + 8$

10) Read off the coordinates of the points A, B, C, D on the graph shown.

11) A sofa is bought for £200 deposit plus £50 per month for 10 months. Find how much has been paid after

   a)   2 months   b)   5 months   c)   10 months.

   Plot a graph of the amount paid against time.

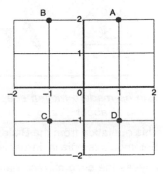

Puzzles and paradoxes

1)   Here are two problems about "Truth-tellers and Liars".

   a)   You land on a strange island in which people either always tell the truth or always lie. You meet three people, X, Y, Z. X mumbles something which you cannot hear.

   Y says: "He said he's a truth-teller"

   Z says: "He said he's a liar."

   What can Y and Z be?

   b)   You meet two people, and from their costume you can tell that either they are both truth-tellers or both liars, but you don't know which. What question could you ask to find which of two roads leads back to your ship?

2)   Here are two paradoxes in algebra.

   a)   Suppose $a = b$. Then $a^2 = ab$, and $a^2 - b^2 = ab - b^2$.

   Factorizing the last equation, $(a + b)(a - b) = b(a - b)$.

   Dividing by $(a - b)$, we obtain $a + b = b$. This is only true when $a = 0$. What has gone wrong?

   b)   Suppose $a > b$, with a and b positive. Then $ab > b^2$, and so $ab - a^2 > b^2 - a^2$.

   Factorizing, $a(b - a) > (a + b)(b - a)$.

   Dividing by $(b - a)$, $a > a + b$. How can this be, if b is a positive number?

3)   Some words in the English Language describe themselves: *short* is a short word, and *English* is an English word. Some words do not describe themselves: *big* is not a big word, *monosyllabic* is not a monosyllabic word.

   If a word describes itself, it is called homological. If it doesn't describe itself, it is heterological.

   Now, what about the word heterological itself? Work out the consequences if it is heterological and if it isn't.

4)   If you are right-handed, when you look in the mirror you see a left-handed person. Why does the mirror switch round left and right but not top and bottom?

Chapter 13

Area and volume

And he made a molten sea, ten cubits from the one brim to the other: it was round all about ... and a line of thirty cubits did compass it round about.

This quotation from the Bible, I Kings 7, describes a great bowl in front of King Solomon's temple in Jerusalem.

It gives the circumference and diameter of a circle. What is the ratio between these? Are the figures correct? Or can you show, by measurement or calculation, that they are not correct?

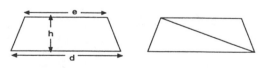

Fig 13.1

13.1 Straight line shapes

Rectangles

The area of a rectangle is the product of the length and the breadth.

$$A = L \times b$$

This can be shown by dividing the rectangle into little squares; L along the base and b up the side. (Fig 13.2).

The perimeter of a rectangle is the sum of twice the length and twice the breadth.

$$P = 2L + 2b$$

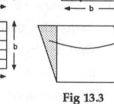

Fig 13.2   **Fig 13.3**

Parallelograms

The area of a parallelogram is the product of the base and the height.

$$A = b \times h$$

This can be shown by shifting the shaded triangle to the other side, making a rectangle which is b by h. (Fig 13.3)

Triangles

The area of a triangle is half the product of the base and the height.

$$A = \frac{1}{2} b \times h$$

This can be shown by considering the triangle as half a parallelogram.

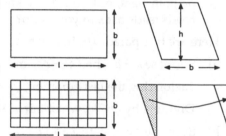

Fig 13.4

Trapezia

The area of a trapezium is the product of the height and the average of the parallel sides.

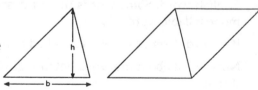

Fig 13.5

$$A = h \times \frac{d + e}{2}$$

This can be shown by considering the trapezium as two triangles, both with height h and with bases d and e.

13.1.1 Examples

1) A rectangular lawn measures 5 metres by 16 metres. What is its area and its perimeter?

   Solution   For the area multiply the length by the breadth.

   Area = $5 \times 16 = 80$ m^2

   For the perimeter add twice the length to twice the breadth.

   Perimeter = $2 \times 5 + 2 \times 16 = 42$ m

2) The dots of Fig 13.6 are 1 unit apart. Find the area of the triangle shown.

   Solution   The base of the triangle is 3. Its height is 2.

   $A = \frac{1}{2} \times 3 \times 2 = 3$ square units

3) Find the area of the parallelogram shown on Fig 13.6

   Solution   The base AB is 3 long, and the height is 2.

   The area is $3 \times 2 = 6$ square units

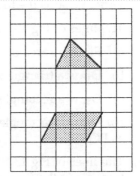

Fig 13.6

4) A garden shed is 2 m from back to front: the back wall is 1.5 m high and the roof slopes up uniformly to the front wall which is 2.5 metres high. Find the area of a side wall.

   Solution   Fig 13.7 shows a diagram of the shed. The side wall is a trapezium, in which the parallel sides are of length 1.5 and 2.5. The height is 2.

   The area is $2 \times (1.5 + 2.5) \times \frac{1}{2} = 4$ m^2

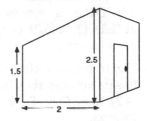

Fig 13.7

13.1.2 Exercises

1) A lawn measures 30 feet by 63 feet.

   a) What is its area and its perimeter?

   b) What would it cost to spread it with fertiliser at 0.4 p. per square foot?

   c) What would it cost to surround it with a fence costing 35 p per foot?

2) One side of a rectangle is 20 cm, and its area is 600 cm^2. What is the length of the other side?

3) The perimeter of a square is 100 m. What is its side? What is its area?

4) The base of a triangle is 3 ft, and its area is 18 ft^2. What is its height?

5) The height of a triangle is 5 cm, and its area is 25 cm^2. What is its base?

6) A rectangle on graph paper has its vertices at (1,1), (3,1), (3,4), (1,4). What is its area and its perimeter?

7) A triangle on graph paper has its vertices at (1,1), (5,1), (2,4). What is its area?

8) A square carpet of side 2 metres is on the floor of a room 3 metres by 4 metres. What is the area of the uncarpeted floor?

9) A garden is 40 ft by 20 ft. The flower beds are 2 ft wide on all sides. (Fig 13.8). What area of the garden is covered by lawn?

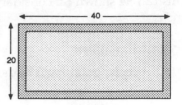

Fig 13.8

10) A picture which is 25 cm by 15 cm is framed within a border 4 cm wide. What is the total area of picture and border?

11) The lines of Fig 13.9 are 1 unit apart.

   a) Find the area of PQRS.

   b) Draw a triangle with equal area to PQRS.

   c) Draw a rectangle with twice the area of PQRS.

   d) Draw a rectangle, with one side of length 1 unit, with the same perimeter as PQRS.

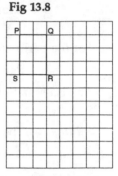

Fig 13.9

12) The lines of Fig 13.10 are 1 cm apart. Find the areas of the parallelograms and trapezia in the figure.

13) The parallelogram ABCD has its vertices at (1,1), (2,2), (5,2), (4,1). Find its area.

14) The trapezium ABCD has its vertices at (4,2), (4,7), (3,6), (3,4). Find its area.

a) b) c) d)

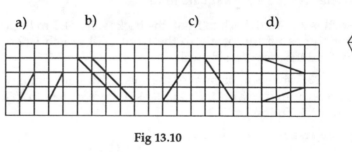

Fig 13.10

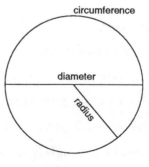

Fig 13.11

15) The kite of Fig 13.11 has diagonals of length 4 cm and 7 cm. Find its area.

13.2 Circles

The distance from the centre of a circle to its rim is the radius. The distance across the circle is the diameter. The diameter is twice the radius.

The length round the circle is the circumference. The ratio of the circumference to the diameter is the same for every circle. The ratio is called π (pronounced *pie*). π can never be written down exactly. It is sometimes approximated by $\frac{22}{7}$ or by 3.14.

The area of a circle is π times the square of the radius.

Fig 13.12

$$\text{Area} = \pi r^2$$

13.2.1 Examples

1) Find the area of a circle with radius 7 cm. Take π to be $\frac{22}{7}$.

    Solution   Put $r = 7$ into the formula above.

    The area is $\frac{22}{7} \times 7^2 = 154$ cm^2

2) The radius of a big-wheel at a fair is 3 m. How far does a point on the rim travel during one revolution? (Take π to be 3.14).

    Solution   The diameter of the wheel is twice the radius, i.e. 6 m.

    The distance travelled is the circumference of the wheel, which is π times the diameter.

    Distance travelled is $3.14 \times 6 = 18.8$ m

13.2.2 Exercises

Throughout these exercises either use the π button on your calculator or take π to be 3.14.

1) A circular running track has radius 50 m. What is the diameter? If an athlete runs round once, how far has she gone?

2) The minute hand of a clock is 4 cm long. How far does the tip of the hand travel during one hour?

3) The hour hand of a clock is 2.5 cm long. How far does the tip travel in 6 hours?

4) A coin of diameter 3 cm rolls along the ground. How far has the coin travelled when it has made a complete revolution?

5) The driving wheel of a car is 6 inches in radius. How far does a point on the rim move when the wheel goes through a quarter turn?

6) A running track is to be made in the form of a circle with circumference 400 metres. What should the diameter be? What should the radius be?

7) The circumference of a circle is 20 cm. What is the radius?

8) A cotton reel is 2.6 cm in diameter. Cotton is wound round it 200 times. What is the length of cotton?

9) Find the areas of the circles with:

    a) Radius 30 cm   b) Diameter 4 ft   c) Radius 12 m   d) Diameter 0.5 in.

10) Find the radii of the circles with:

    a) Diameter 6 cm   b) Circumference 12 in c) Area 9 m^2 d) Area 5 ft^2.

11) Look at the problem at the beginning of the chapter. If the diameter is 10 cubits what is the circumference?

13.3 Solids

Cuboids

The volume of a cuboid is the product of its length, breadth and height.

Volume = $L \times b \times h$

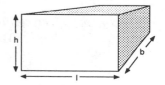

Fig 13.13

103

Prisms

A prism is a solid with constant cross-section.

If the cross-section is a triangle, then it is a triangular prism.

The volume of a prism is the product of the height and the area of the cross-section.

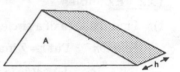

$$\text{Volume} = A \times h$$

Fig 13.14

Cylinders

If the cross-section of a prism is a circle, then it is a cylinder. The volume of a cylinder is found by the same formula as for a prism:

$$\text{Volume} = A \times h = \pi r^2 h$$

Density

The density of a solid is its mass divided by its volume.

Fig 13.15

13.3.1 Examples

1) The surface of a pond is a rectangle 50 cm by 30 cm. During a cold spell it froze to a depth of 2 cm. Find the mass of ice, given that the density of ice is 0.9 g/cm^3.

   Solution   The ice may be thought of as a cuboid, 50 cm long, 30 cm wide and 2 cm deep. Its volume in cm^3 is:

   $$50 \times 30 \times 2 = 3{,}000 \text{ cm}^3.$$

   Its mass is:

   $$0.9 \times 3{,}000 = 2{,}700 \text{ g} = 2.7 \text{ kg}$$

2) Fig 13.16 shows a wedge of cheese, with the dimensions as shown. Find its price, given that the density of the cheese is 1.5 g/cm^3 and that it costs £4.50 per kilogram.

   Solution   The wedge is a triangular prism. The cross-sectional area is a right-angled triangle, with area $\frac{1}{2} \times 2 \times 10 = 10 \text{ cm}^2$.

   $$\text{Volume} = 8 \times 10 = 80 \text{ cm}^3$$

   $$\text{Weight} = 1.5 \times 80 = 120 \text{ grams} = 0.12 \text{ kg}$$

   $$\text{Price} = 0.12 \times 4.50 = £0.54 = 54 \text{ p}$$

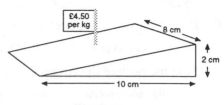

Fig 13.16

3) A room is 2 m high, 4 m long and 3 m wide. Find the surface area of the walls and ceiling.

   Solution   The ceiling is 4 by 3. There are two walls which are 2 by 4, and two walls which are 2 by 3. The total area is therefore:

   $$3 \times 4 + 2 \times 2 \times 4 + 2 \times 2 \times 3 = 40 \text{ m}^2$$

4) A shoe-polish tin has height 1.3 cm and radius 3 cm. What is its volume?

Solution   The tin is a cylinder, with $h = 1.3$ and $r = 3$. Apply the formula:

$$\textbf{Volume} = \pi 3^2 \times 1.3 = 37 \textbf{ cm}^3$$

13.3.2 Exercises

1) Squash balls are sold in cubes of side 4 cm. How many of these cubes can be packed in a carton which is 20 cm by 24 cm by 16 cm?

2) A field is in the shape of a rectangle 50 m by 40 m. Snow falls on the field to a depth of 1.2 m. What is the weight of snow when it melts, given that the density of snow is 50 kg/m³?

3) A cuboid has a square base of side 3 cm. What is its height, given that its volume is 36 cm³?

4) A water tank is a cuboid, with a base of 1.2 m by 0.8 m. How deep is the water when the tank contains 0.384 m³ of water?

5) Sugar cubes are cubes of side $1\frac{1}{2}$ cm. How many fit in a box which is 24 cm by 6 cm by 12 cm? If the density of sugar is 1.5 g/cm³, what is the mass of one sugar cube?

6) Find the volumes of the prisms of Fig 13.17.

    a)

    b)

Fig 13.17

7) What is the area of the walls and ceiling of a room which is 2.5 m high, 4 m long and 3.2 m wide?

8) What is the surface area of a cube of side 3 cm?

9) An open-topped tank is 1 m high and its base is a rectangle which is 0.8 by 0.6 m. What is the surface area of the sides and base of the tank?

10) Fig 13.18 shows a shed which is 3 m long, 1.5 m deep, 2 m high at the back and 1.5 m high at the front.

    a) Find the area of a side wall.

    b) Find the volume of the shed.

11) Wire is made with a cross-sectional area of 0.1 cm². What length of this wire can be made from 100 cm³ of metal? How many times will the wire wrap round a square post of side 2 cm?

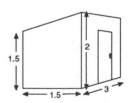

Fig 13.18

12) Find the volumes of the cylinders shown in Fig 13.19.

13) A cylinder has radius 12 cm and volume 523 cm³. What is its height?

14) A cylinder has height 3.7 cm and volume 12.9 cm³. What is its radius?

a) b) c)

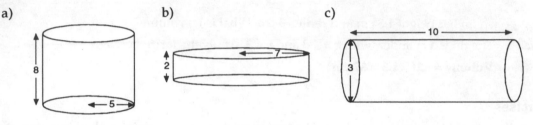

Fig 13.19

13.4 Longer exercise

Volume of pyramids

Suppose a cube has side x. Then its volume is x^3. You could fit a pyramid inside this cube (Fig 13.20), with the same square base and also with height x.

Fig 13.21 shows the the net of a pyramid. It is not regular, when you assemble it you will find that the

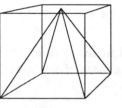

Fig 13.20

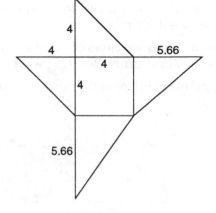

vertex is over one corner of the base, not over the centre. Cut out this net three times and assemble to make three pyramids.

Fit together the three pyramids to make a cube. What can you conclude about the volume of the pyramid?

What is the significance of the 5.66?

Fig 13.21

Multiple choice question *(Tick appropriate box)*

The cross-section of the prism shown is a right-angled triangle with sides 3 cm, 4 cm, 5 cm. Its length is 1 m. The volume is:

a) 1,200 cm^3 ☐

b) 6 cm^3 ☐

c) 750 cm^3 ☐

d) 600 cm^3 ☐

e) 1,000 cm^3 ☐

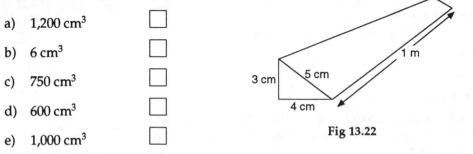

Fig 13.22

Points to note

1) *Triangles and parallelograms*

   The area of a triangle or a parallelogram is found by the product of the base and the height. It is not found by the product of adjacent sides, unless the triangle or parallelogram happens to be right-angled.

2) *Units*

   Mistakes are common with questions in which the units are mixed. It is safest to express all the measurements in the same units.

3) *Circumference and radius*

   a) The value of π is only approximately 3.14 or $\frac{22}{7}$. If you calculate using these values for π, it is misleading to give your answer to more than 3 significant figures.

   b) The circumference of circle is π times the diameter. So if you know the circumference, in order to find the diameter you must divide by π. Do not multiply.

   c) Be careful not to confuse the radius and the diameter. Read the question carefully, to see which you are given or which you are required to find.

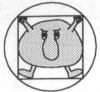

Chapter 14

Circles and constructions

Three towns A, B, C are to be supplied with electricity. The power station should be placed as close as possible to the towns: where should it be put?

A •
B •
C •

Fig 14.1

14.1 Circles

Definitions

In ordinary speech we use many of the words associated with circles, such as centre, arc, sector, tangent etc. Here are the formal definitions:

Centre and radius

All the points of a circle are a fixed distance (the radius) from a fixed point (the centre).

Diameter

The greatest distance across the circle is the diameter. The diameter is twice the radius.

Sector

The region between two radii is a sector.

Chord and arc

The straight line between two points on a circle is a chord. The part of the circle between two points is an arc.

Segment and semicircle

The regions on either side of a chord are segments. In particular, if the chord is a diameter the segments are semicircles.

Tangent

A tangent is a line which touches a circle at one point.

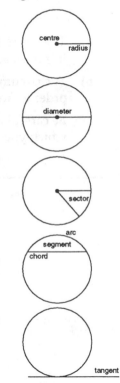

Fig 14.2

14.1.1 Example

Two circles with centres X and Y cross at A and B (Fig 14.3). Give the names for the line XA, the two curves AB, the straight line AB.

Solution   XA goes from the centre to the rim of the circle. The curves AB go round part of the circles, and the line AB joins two points of the circle.

XA is a radius

The curves AB are arcs. The line AB is a chord

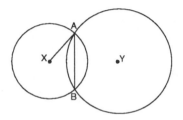

Fig 14.3

108

14.1.2 Exercises

1) Give the names for the lines below.

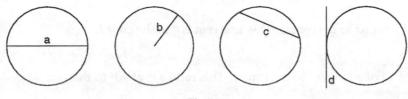

Fig 14.4

2) Give the names for the regions dotted below.

a)   b)   c)

Fig 14.5

3) On the right are four copies of a circle with centre X. Mark on them:

   a)   The arc AB   b)   The chord AB

   c)   The sector AXB

   d)   The smaller segment enclosed by AB.

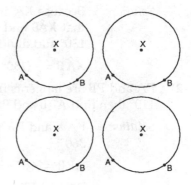

4) Two circles have radii of length x and y. The distance apart of the centres is z. How many times do the circle cross in the following cases? Sketch the circles in each case.

   a) $x = 3, y = 4, z = 5$ b) $x = 6, y = 8, z = 15$

   c) $x = 6, y = 5, z = 11$ d) $x = 10, y = 4, z = 6$

Fig 14.6

5) a) A conker is swung round on the end of a string. What path does it follow?

   b) The string is let go. What path does the conker follow now?

   How are (a) and (b) connected?

6) Below are five pairs of circles. For each pair draw the lines which are tangents to both circles. How many are there in each case?

a)   b)   c)   d)   e)

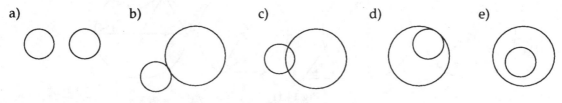

Fig 14.7

14.2 Angles and lengths

There are several facts about the angles and lengths connected with a circle.

Chord and radius

Join the midpoint of a chord to the centre. This line is at 90° to the chord.

Tangent and radius

Join the point of contact of a tangent to the centre. This radius is at 90° to the tangent.

Equal radii

All the radii of a circle are equal in length.

Equal tangents

If a point is outside a circle, then two tangents can be drawn from it to the circle. These tangents are equal in length.

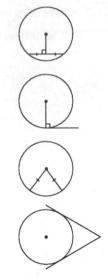

Fig 14.8

14.2.1 Examples

1) AB is a chord of a circle whose centre is X. If $A\hat{X}B = 40°$ find $X\hat{A}B$.

   Solution Because XA and XB are radii they are equal. It follows that $X\hat{A}B$ and $X\hat{B}A$ are also equal. Subtract $A\hat{X}B$ from 180° and divide by 2:

   $$X\hat{A}B = \tfrac{1}{2}(180° - 40°) = 70°$$

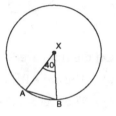

Fig 14.9

2) PA and PB are tangents from P to a circle with centre X. If $A\hat{X}B = 110°$ then find $A\hat{P}B$ and $P\hat{A}B$.

   Solution $P\hat{A}X$ and $P\hat{B}X$ are both equal to 90°. Subtracting from 360°:

   $$A\hat{P}B = 360° - 90° - 90° - 110° = 70°$$

   PA and PB are equal. It follows that $P\hat{A}B$ and $P\hat{B}A$ are equal.

   $$P\hat{A}B = \tfrac{1}{2}(180° - 70°) = 55°$$

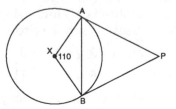

Fig 14.10

14.2.2 Exercises

1) Find the angles in the diagrams below. Throughout X denotes the centre of the circle.

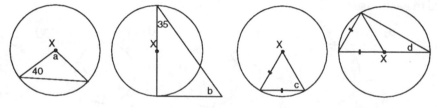

Fig 14.11

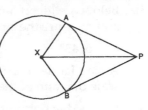

2) AB is a chord of a circle with centre X, and M is the midpoint of AB. What can you say about AM̂X? What is the relationship between the triangles AMX and BMX?

3) AB is the chord of a circle with centre X, and M is the midpoint of AB. If AX̂M = 30° find XÂM and XB̂M.

4) In the diagram on the right (Fig 14.12) X is the centre of the circle, and PA and PB are tangents. Mark in pairs of equal angles.

Fig 14.12

14.3 Constructing triangles

Triangles can be constructed as follows.

Three sides

Suppose we know the lengths of the three sides of a triangle. Measure out one length. Stretch compasses to the second length, and draw an arc. Repeat with the third length. The arcs will cross at the third point of the triangle. (Fig 14.13).

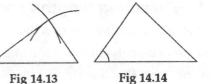

Fig 14.13   **Fig 14.14**

Two sides and an angle

Suppose we know two sides of a triangle and the angle between them. Measure out one of the sides. Use a protractor to form the angle, and measure out the other side. (Fig 14.14).

One side and two angles

Suppose we know one side of a triangle and the angles at each end. Measure out the line, and form the angles at each end. (Fig 14.15).

Fig 14.15

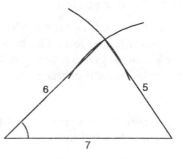

14.3.1 Example

Construct a triangle with sides 5 cm, 6 cm, 7 cm. Measure the smallest angle.

Solution   Follow the procedure above. Measure out 7 cm, then draw arcs of radius 6 cm and 5 cm. The smallest angle is opposite the 5 cm line. Use a protractor to measure this angle.

The smallest angle is 44.5°

Fig 14.16

14.3.2 Exercises

1) Construct triangles with the following sides. In each case measure the largest angle. Lengths are in cm.

   a) 5, 7, 8   b) 10, 11, 13   c) 8, 15, 17

2) Below are given two sides of a triangle and the angle between them. In each case construct the triangle and measure the third side.

   a) 8, 9, 45°   b) 4, 7, 63°   c) 5, 6, 120°

3) Below are given one side of a triangle and the angles at its ends. In each case construct the triangle and measure the smallest side.

  a) 5, 43°, 65°   b) 8, 25°, 30°   c) 7, 25°, 110°

4) A step ladder has sides of length 2 m and 1.8 m. The feet of the sides are 1.3 m apart. Construct a scale diagram of the ladder, and find the angle between the sides.

5) Joan is due north of a tree, and Jane is due south. They are 90 m apart. The angles of elevation of the top of the tree are 15° and 20°. Construct a scale diagram, and find the height of the tree.

6) Ayville is 10 miles from Beetown, and 12 miles from Ceebury. Ceebury is 15 miles from Beetown. Construct a map of the three towns.

14.4 Bisecting lengths and angles

Perpendicular bisector of a line

The perpendicular bisector of a line AB cuts it in half at right angles.

To construct this line draw a circle with centre A. Without altering the compasses, draw a circle centre B. The dotted line joining the intersection points of the circles is the perpendicular bisector.

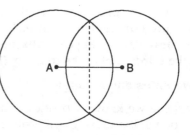

Fig 14.17

Bisector of angle

The bisector of the angle between two lines cuts the angle in half.

To construct this line put the point of a compass at the meet X of L and M. Draw arcs cutting L at A and M at B. Draw arcs with centres A and B, meeting at Y. Then XY will be the bisector of the angle between L and M. (See Fig 14.18).

Circles and triangles

Given a circle, it is easy to draw a triangle round it or a triangle inside it. But how do we go the other way? That is, given a triangle, how do we construct the circle inside it or the circle round it?

Fig 14.18   **Fig 14.19**

Incentre

The Incentre of a triangle is the centre of the circle which touches the sides of the triangle. It is constructed as follows.

Construct the bisectors of the angles BÂC and AĈB. Where these lines cross is the centre of the circle. (See Fig 14.19).

Circumcentre

The circumcentre of a triangle is the centre of the circle which goes through all the corners. It is constructed as follows.

Construct the perpendicular bisectors of AB and AC. Where these lines cross is the circumcentre of the circle.

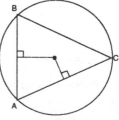

Fig 14.20

14.4.1 Example

Find the circumcentre of the triangle of 14.3.1. Draw the circle going through the points of the triangle, and measure its radius.

Solution   Construct perpendicular bisectors of AB and AC, meeting at X. The circumcentre is X. Draw the circle with centre X going through A, B, C. Measure its radius.

The radius is 3.6 cm

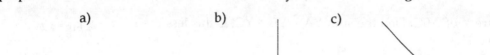

Fig 14.21

14.4.2 Exercises

1) Make copies of the lines below, and construct their perpendicular bisectors. Check with a ruler that you have cut the lengths in half.

    a)   b)   c)

Fig 14.22

2) Make copies of the angles below, and construct their bisectors. Check with a protractor that you have cut the angles in half.

    a)   b)   c)

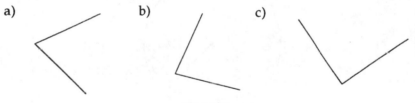

Fig 14.23

3) Find the circumcentres of the triangles constructed in Question 1 of 14.3.2. In each case find the radius of the circle which goes through all the points.

4) Find the incentres of the triangles constructed in Question 1 of 14.3.2. In each case find the radius of the circle which touches all the sides.

5) Three towns are shown in Fig 14.24. AB = 50 miles, BC = 56 miles, CA = 43 miles. Make a scale diagram of ABC. A radio transmitter is to be sited so that it is an equal distance from the three towns. Where should it be put?

6) Three roads are shown in Fig 14.25. Make a copy of the diagram. A helicopter rescue service is to be sited

Fig 14.24   Fig 14.25

at an equal distance from the three roads. Mark on your diagram where the service should be put.

14.5 Longer exercise

A. Circle words

Many circle words or phrases have become part of the language. See if you can explain how the words and phrases below are connected with circles.

Archer   arch   diametrically opposed   private sector

fly off at a tangent   centrifuge   touch the right chord   radiate

B. Least distance

In the example at the beginning of the chapter you were asked to find where a power station should be put to minimize the distances to three towns.

Mark three points A, B, C on a sheet of paper. $\triangle$ABC should not be equilateral.

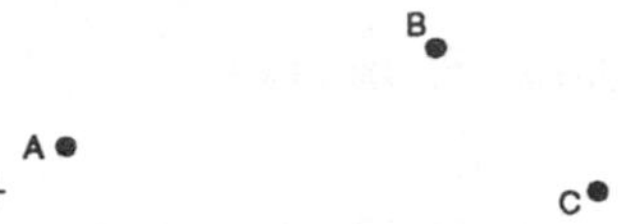

1) Find the circumcentre X of ABC. Find the sum of the distances XA + XB + XC.

2) Find the incentre Y of ABC. Find the sum YA + YB + YC. Is this less than your answer to (1)?

3) See if you can find a point Z such that ZA + ZB + ZC is less than your answers to (1) and (2).

4) It can be shown that the point Z for which ZA + ZB + ZC is least is such that $A\hat{Z}B = B\hat{Z}C = C\hat{Z}A = 120°$. See if you can find this point for your triangle, and check that it does have the right property.

Fig 14.26

Multiple choice question *(Tick appropriate box)*

In the diagram below , X is the centre of the circle and AT is a tangent. $T\hat{A}B = 40°$. The angle $A\hat{X}B$ is:

a)   100°   ☐

b)   130°   ☐

c)   260°   ☐

d)   50°   ☐

e)   80°   ☐

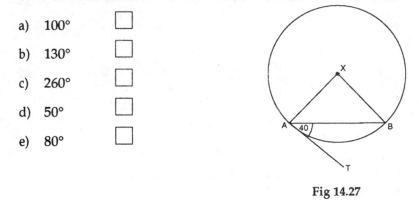

Fig 14.27

Points to Note

1) *Circles*

   a) Read a question carefully, so that you do not give the radius when asked for the diameter or vice-versa.

   b) If two chords cross inside a circle, then don't assume that the crossing point is the centre unless you are told so. Don't assume that a chord is a diameter unless you are told so.

2) *Constructions*

   a) When constructing a triangle with two sides and an angle, the angle must be between the sides.

   b) When constructing a triangle with a side and two angles, the side must be between the angles. But if you know two angles of a triangle the third can be found by subtraction from 180°.

Chapter 15

Loci and machines

A field is 10 m by 15 m. A sheep is tethered in the middle, on a 5 m rope. A fierce dog is on a 4 m leash, which is fastened at one corner of the field. Is the sheep ever in danger from the dog?

Fig 15.1

15.1 Loci

If the motion of a point obeys a certain rule, then the path of the point is called its locus.

Circles. Suppose a point P moves so that it is a fixed distance from a fixed point A. The locus of P is a circle with centre A.

Lines. Suppose a point P moves so that it is a fixed distance above a fixed line L. The locus of P is another line parallel to L.

Bisectors. Suppose a point P moves so that it is an equal distance from two fixed points A and B. The locus of P is the perpendicular bisector of AB.

Suppose P moves so that it is an equal distance from two lines L and M. The locus of P is the bisector of the angle between L and M.

These bisectors can be constructed by the methods of 14.4.

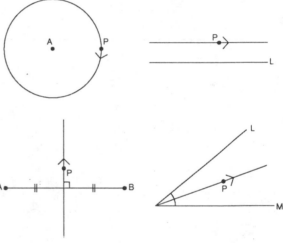

Fig 15.2

15.1.1 Examples

1) A point P on graph paper is 2 units from the origin (0,0) and 1 unit above the *x*-axis. Show where P could be, and give its coordinates.

   Solution   P must lie on the circle with centre (0,0) and radius 2. It must also lie on the line $y = 1$.

   These loci cross at two points, shown circled.

   P is at (1.7, 1) or (–1.7, 1)

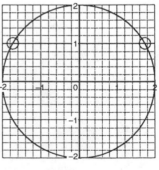

Fig 15.3

2) A man holds one end of a thin string. The other end is nailed to a round post. The man walks round the post, keeping the string taut. Draw a sketch of his locus.

Solution   As he walks round, the free length of string gets shorter and shorter, until he is actually at the post.

The locus is shown sketched. It is a spiral.

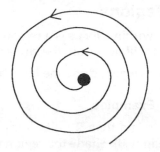

Fig 15.4

15.1.2 Exercises

In Questions 1 to 6 draw the locus of P on graph paper.

1) P is 3 units from the origin (0,0).

2) P is 5 units to the right of the y-axis.

3) P is the same distance from (0,0) as from (2,0).

4) P is the same distance from (1,2) as from (5,6).

5) P is the same distance from the x-axis as from the y-axis.

6) P is the same distance from the line $y = x$ as from the x-axis.

7) Mark down two points A and B which are 10 cm apart. P moves 6 cm from A, and Q moves 7 cm from B. Draw the loci of P and Q. Where do they cross?

8) Draw a line XY. Find the points which are 3 cm from X and 2 cm from the line XY.

9) Mark two points X and Y 8 cm apart. P moves so that it is 5 cm from X. Draw the locus of P. Q moves so that it is k cm from Y.

   a)   Draw the locus of Q when $k = 4$. How many intersection points are there?

   b)   Draw the locus of Q when $k = 2$. How many intersection points are there?

   c)   For what values of k will there be exactly one intersection point?

10) P is 3 units from (0,0) and 2 units to the right of the y-axis. Where could P be?

11) P is 4 units from (0,0) and the same distance from (0,0) as from (6,0). Where could P be?

12) P is the same distance from the x and y axes, and is 4 units above the x-axis. Where could P be?

13) Fig 15.5 shows a map, to a scale of 1 inch per 10 yards. A treasure is buried 15 yards from the wall, 10 yards from the tree. Mark on the map the two places where the treasure might be.

Fig 15.5

14) In the three diagrams of Fig 15.6, the wheel rolls without slipping on the rail. In each case sketch the locus of the point X.

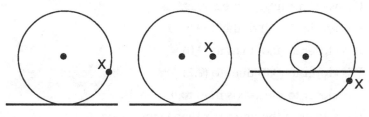

Fig 15.6

15.2 Regions

The area within a locus is a region. If a point P is always within 3 cm of A, then it will lie within the circle of radius 3 cm and centre A.

To show a region, draw the locus and then shade one side of it.

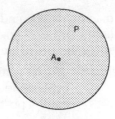

Fig 15.7

15.2.1 Examples

1) P is less than 2 units from the origin (0,0), and is nearer (0,2) than (0,0). Shade the region within which P must lie.

     Solution   The locus of points 2 units from (0,0) is a circle. The locus of points at the same distance from (0,2) as from (0,0) is the perpendicular bisector of these points, which is the line $y = 1$.

                       P must lie within the circle and above the line $y = 1$. It is shown shaded.

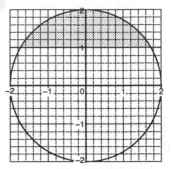

Fig 15.8

2) A straight waterway of width 120 miles separates two countries A and B. X is a port in A, and its fishing ships can reach up to 100 miles from X. They must not fish within 40 miles of the coastline of the country B. Draw a map, to a scale of 1 cm per 20 miles. Shade the region within which the ships may fish.

     Solution   First draw two lines 6 cm apart. Draw a line 2 cm from B, to represent its exclusion zone.

                       Draw a circle of radius 5 cm, with centre X. This represents the region which the ships can reach.

                       The shaded region is inside the circle, but outside the exclusion zone.

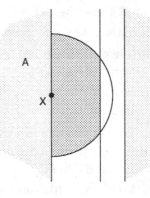

15.2.2 Exercises

Fig 15.9

In Questions 1 to 8 shade the region on graph paper.

1) P is within 2 units of the origin (0,0).

2) P is more than 3 units from (1,2).

3) P is within 1 unit of the x-axis.

4) P is within 1 unit of the line $y = x$.

5) P is closer to (0,0) than to (2,0).

6) P is closer to (0,0) than to (2,2).

7) P is closer to the x-axis than to the y-axis.

8) P is nearer to the line $y = x$ than to the x-axis.

9) Construct a square ABCD of side 2 cm. Shade the region of those points which are within 1 cm of A and within $\frac{1}{2}$ cm of AB.

10) A field is a rectangle ABCD, with AB = 20 m and AC = 15 m. Draw a scale diagram of the field, using a scale of 1 cm per 5 m.

   A donkey is tethered at A, on a 10 m rope. Shade the region within which the donkey can graze.

   The ground within 5 m of CD becomes flooded. Shade the flooded region on your map.

11) Mark two points X and Y 5 cm apart. Shade the region of points which are within 3 cm of X, and closer to Y than to X.

12) A ship is sailing due East at 10 m.p.h. An enemy gun site with a range of 3 miles is 5 miles East and 2 miles South. Draw a scale diagram, using 1 cm to represent 1 mile, of the ships course and the region which is in range of the gun. For how long is the ship in danger?

13) Look at the problem at the beginning of the chapter. Make a scale diagram of the field, and shade the regions which can be reached by sheep and dog. Do these regions overlap?

15.3 Machines

A machine enables force to be modified in one way or another. A car-jack is an example of a machine. It enables a person of ordinary strength to lift a car which may weigh a ton.

The movement of machine parts can be described in terms of loci. The parts are connected in various ways.

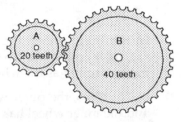

Fig 15.10

Gears

Gear wheels are used to convert one sort of circular motion to another. In Fig 15.10, if the wheel A rotates clockwise, then the wheel B rotates anticlockwise at half the speed.

Piston

The piston in a steam engine or petrol engine moves in a straight line. This is converted to the circular motion of the crankshaft. See Fig 15.11.

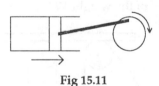

Fig 15.11

Pulleys

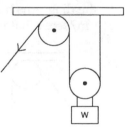

Fig 15.12

The weight W is on a pulley wheel supported by two ropes. When the rope on the left is pulled at 1 m/sec, W will rise at $\frac{1}{2}$ m/sec. See Fig 15.12

15.3.1 Example

The gear wheels A and B have 20 and 60 teeth respectively. A is made to rotate anti-clockwise at 30 revolutions per minute. Describe the motion of B.

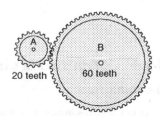

Fig 15.13

15.3.2 Exercises

1) In each of the diagrams below the wheel A rotates clockwise at 120 revolutions per minute. Predict the motion of the wheel B. See Fig 15.14.

a)   b)   c)

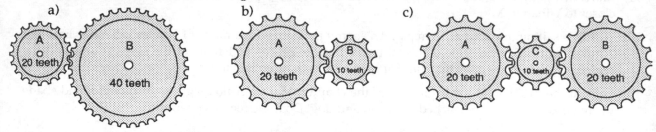

Fig 15.14

2) In the diagram on the right, the wheel has radius 5 cm. What distance does the piston move through as the wheel rotates?

3) In Fig 15.16, the outer wheel has radius 20 cm and the inner wheel has radius 5 cm. Both have ropes wound round them. The outer rope is pulled at 1 m per second. What is the direction and speed of the weight attached to the inner rope.

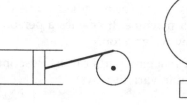
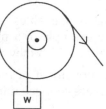

Fig 15.15   **Fig 15.16**

4) In the diagrams below, the top pulleys are fixed but free to rotate. The free length of rope is pulled at 1 m/sec. What is the speed of the weight W?

a)   b)   c)

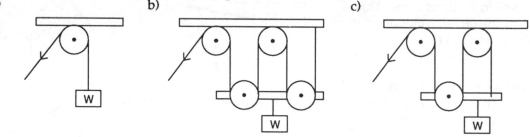

Fig 15.17

15.4 Longer exercise

Bicycle gears

Many bicycles have several gears in order to cope with different gradients. If you have such a bicycle, count the numbers of teeth on each gear wheel and find how many times the back wheel rotates for each turn of the pedals.

Multiple choice question *(Tick appropriate box)*

In the diagram on the right, A has 20 teeth and B has 30 teeth. A rotates clockwise at 12 revolutions per minute. B rotates:

a)   Clockwise at 8 r.p.m.

b)   Anticlockwise at 18 r.p.m.

c)   Clockwise at 18 r.p.m.

d)   Anticlockwise at 8 r.p.m.

e)   None of these

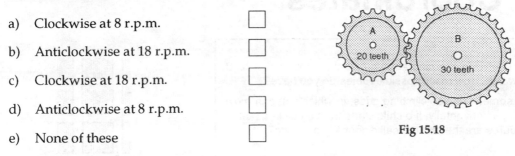

Fig 15.18

Points to note

1)   *Loci*

Don't confuse the distance from a point with the distance from a line.

2)   *Gears*

a)   Think carefully before you decide whether a gear wheel will move clockwise or anticlockwise.

b)   Be careful about ratios. If A has more teeth than B, then A will rotate more slowly than B will.

Chapter 16

Coordinates

On the street map shown in the diagram, you want to get from A to B. Without going backwards, how many possible routes do you have?

In playgrounds you sometimes see climbing grids, in which you can move up and down as well as horizontally. If a child starts from a cell in a bottom corner, how many routes are there to the cell diagonally opposite?

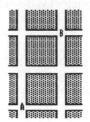

16.1 Three-dimensional coordinates

Two-dimensional coordinates are used to describe points in a plane. If we want to describe points in space, then we need three coordinates.

The x-axis and y-axis are horizontal, the z-axis is vertical. The position of a point is given by coordinates (x,y,z) relative to these axes.

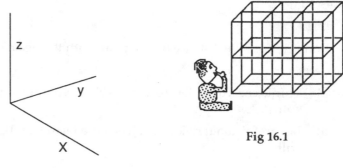

Fig 16.2

Fig 16.1

16.1.1 Examples

1) An aircraft is 10 km North, 5 km East and 2 km high. Regarding these as x, y, z coordinates respectively, give its position in terms of coordinates. If it is flying North at 8 km per minute, give its coordinates 3 minutes later.

   Solution   Write down its position in (x,y,z) form:

   The position is (10,5,2)

   3 minutes later it will have travelled 24 km North. Add 24 to the x coordinate:

   3 minutes later it is at (34,5,2)

2) A regular pyramid has a square base with corners at (0,0,0), (2,0,0), (2,2,0), (0,2,0). If the pyramid has height 3 units, give possible coordinates for the vertex.

Solution   The centre of the square base is at (1,1,0), halfway between (0,0,0) and (2,2,0).

Because the pyramid is regular, the vertex must be either above or below the centre of the square base. The vertex is 3 units away along the z-axis.

The vertex is at (1,1,3) or (1,1,-3)

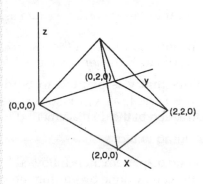

Fig 16.3

16.1.2 Exercises

1) A box is 20 cm high, 30 cm wide, 40 cm long. Taking the origin at one of the bottom corners, find the coordinates of the top corners. (See Fig 16.4).

2) A room is 5 m long, 4 m wide, 3 m high. Taking the origin at a corner of the floor, give the coordinates of the opposite corner on the ceiling. Give the coordinates of the centre of the ceiling.

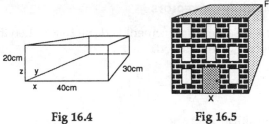

Fig 16.4   Fig 16.5

3) Positions in an office block are given as 3-dimensional coordinates, with the origin at the front door X. The far corner F has coordinates (20,30,40). See Fig 16.5. What is the height of the block? What is its width and depth?

4) Coordinates of the box of Fig 16.6 are given from the centre of the base. Find the coordinates of the top corners.

5) One face of a cube has corners at (0,0,0), (1,0,0), (1,1,0), (0,1,0). Find the possible coordinates of the corners of the opposite face.

6) The vertices of a solid are at (0,0,0), (2,0,0), (2,3,0), (0,3,0), (0,0,1), (2,0,1), (2,3,1), (0,3,1). What is this solid? What is its volume?

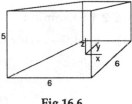

Fig 16.6

7) The vertices of a solid are at (0,0,0), (3,0,0), (0,4,0), (0,0,5), (3,0,5),(0,4,5). What is the name for this solid? What is its volume?

8) A pyramid has a square base of side 2 and height 3. It is placed with the centre of the base at the origin. Find possible coordinates for the vertices.

9) A prism has triangular cross-section. One end triangle has vertices at (0,0,2), (1,0,2), (0,1,2). If the prism is 3 long find possible coordinates of the other end triangle.

10) Look at the climbing grid illustrated at the beginning of the chapter. If the origin is at a cell at a bottom corner, what are the coordinates of the cell diagonally opposite on the top?

16.2 Vectors

A displacement or translation is a movement in a particular direction. For example, the translation might be 3 units to the right and 2 up as in Fig 16.7.

Fig 16.7

This translation can be written as a vector $\mathbf{v} = \begin{pmatrix} 3 \\ 2 \end{pmatrix}$

The top coordinate of the vector is the x-movement, and the bottom coordinate is the y-movement.

Note that $\mathbf{v}$ is printed in bold type. Handwritten vectors are underlined, as $\underline{v}$, or "overlined" as $\bar{v}$. The arrow shows the direction of the displacement (Fig 16.8).

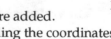

Fig 16.8

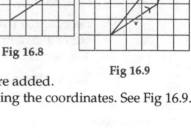

Fig 16.9

Adding vectors

If one displacement is followed by another, the corresponding vectors are added.
This can by done by putting the vectors head to tail as shown, or by adding the coordinates. See Fig 16.9.

$$\text{If } \mathbf{v} = \begin{pmatrix} 3 \\ 2 \end{pmatrix} \text{ and } \mathbf{u} = \begin{pmatrix} 1 \\ 3 \end{pmatrix}, \text{ then } \mathbf{v} + \mathbf{u} = \begin{pmatrix} 3 \\ 2 \end{pmatrix} + \begin{pmatrix} 1 \\ 3 \end{pmatrix} = \begin{pmatrix} 4 \\ 5 \end{pmatrix}.$$

Multiplying vectors

If the same displacement is done twice, then the coordinates of the corresponding vectors are doubled.

$$2 \times \begin{pmatrix} 3 \\ 2 \end{pmatrix} = \begin{pmatrix} 6 \\ 4 \end{pmatrix}$$

Position vectors

Vectors can also be used to describe positions of points in the plane. The position vector of a point is the vector which goes from the origin to the point.

So if the point is (3,2), its position vector is $\mathbf{v} = \begin{pmatrix} 3 \\ 2 \end{pmatrix}$. See Fig 16.10.

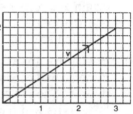

Fig 16.10

16.2.1 Examples

1) Find the vector which represents the translation shown on the right.

   Solution   Counting squares, we see that the triangle has moved 4 to the right and 3 down.

   The vector is $\begin{pmatrix} 4 \\ -3 \end{pmatrix}$

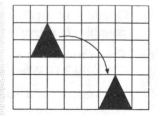

Fig 16.11

2) If $\mathbf{a} = \begin{pmatrix} 1 \\ 3 \end{pmatrix}$ and $\mathbf{b} = \begin{pmatrix} 5 \\ 2 \end{pmatrix}$, find   (a) $\mathbf{a} + \mathbf{b}$ (b) $3\mathbf{a}$

   Solution   a)   Add the coordinates of $\mathbf{a}$ and $\mathbf{b}$:

   $$\mathbf{a} + \mathbf{b} = \begin{pmatrix} 6 \\ 5 \end{pmatrix}$$

   b)   Multiply the coordinates of $\mathbf{a}$ by 3:

   $$3\mathbf{a} = \begin{pmatrix} 3 \\ 9 \end{pmatrix}$$

3) Illustrate on a graph the vectors **a**, **b** and **a** + **b**, where **a** and **b** are as in Example 2.

Solution For **a**, start at the origin and move 1 unit to the right and 3 up. Draw **b** similarly.

For **a** + **b**, start at the end of **a** and move 5 units to the right and 2 up. Join the origin to the end of this line to show **a** + **b**.

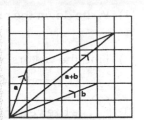

Fig 16.12

16.2.2 Exercises

1) Find the vectors which correspond to the translations shown.

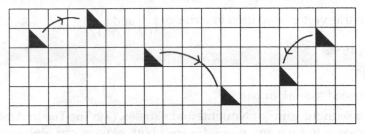

Fig 16.13

2) On Fig 16.14 show where the following vector translations would take the triangle T.

(a) $\begin{pmatrix} 2 \\ 3 \end{pmatrix}$ (b) $\begin{pmatrix} -1 \\ 4 \end{pmatrix}$ (c) $\begin{pmatrix} 0 \\ 4 \end{pmatrix}$

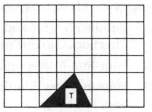

Fig 16.14

3) For $\mathbf{a} = \begin{pmatrix} 2 \\ 7 \end{pmatrix}$ and $\mathbf{b} = \begin{pmatrix} -3 \\ 3 \end{pmatrix}$, find **a** + **b** and 4**b**.

4) Illustrate on a graph **a**, **b**, **a** + **b**, 4**b**, where **a** and **b** are as in Question 3.

5) Write down in terms of coordinates the vectors shown in Fig 16.15.

6) Let $\mathbf{c} = \begin{pmatrix} 3 \\ -2 \end{pmatrix}$ and $\mathbf{d} = \begin{pmatrix} -1 \\ 1 \end{pmatrix}$

Find: a) **c** + **d**   b) 3**c**   c) **c** + 3**d**

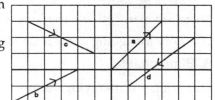

Fig 16.15

7) With **c** and **d** as in Question 6, illustrate **c** + **d** and 2**c**.

8) Find **e** such that $\mathbf{e} + \begin{pmatrix} 4 \\ 7 \end{pmatrix} = \begin{pmatrix} 8 \\ 3 \end{pmatrix}$.

9) Find **f** such that $2\mathbf{f} - \begin{pmatrix} 3 \\ 7 \end{pmatrix} = \begin{pmatrix} 1 \\ 3 \end{pmatrix}$.

10) If $\begin{pmatrix} 5 \\ x \end{pmatrix} + \begin{pmatrix} y \\ 3 \end{pmatrix} = \begin{pmatrix} 2 \\ 7 \end{pmatrix}$, find x and y.

11) Write down the position vectors of:

a) (4,5) b) (0,4) c) (3,-2)

12) Find the vectors between the following pairs of points:

a) (1,1) and (3,4) b) (2,1) and (5,1) c) (4,7) and (8,2) d) (2,-1) and (-3,6)

13) $\begin{pmatrix} 3 \\ 2 \end{pmatrix}$ is the vector of a translation.

Where would this translation take:

a) (2,7) b) (0,3) c) (-4,-3) ?

14) Look at the street map at the beginning of the chapter. What vector will go from A to B?

How many ways can this vector be written in terms of $\begin{pmatrix} 1 \\ 0 \end{pmatrix}$ and $\begin{pmatrix} 0 \\ 1 \end{pmatrix}$?

16.3 Longer exercises

A. Noughts and crosses

For this exercise you will need to work in pairs.

You are probably familiar with the game of Noughts and Crosses. (Tic Tac Toe in America). After you've played it for a while, it ceases to have any point, because both players can always ensure a draw. Try some variants of the game! Here are some suggestions.

1) Infinite noughts and crosses. You still have to get 3 in a row, but you can go as far as you like in any direction. Can one player always win? Can both players force a draw?

2) Four-in-a-row noughts and crosses. Use a 4 by 4 grid, and try to get four in a row.

3) Four-in-a-row infinite noughts and crosses. Combine the previous two: you have to get four in a row, but the grid can stretch as far as you like.

4) 3-Dimensional noughts and crosses. You have to get three in a row, using a 3-Dimensional grid. How do you draw the board? The rows can go up through the grid and diagonally across it.

There are many other variations which you could invent.

One very intriguing game is *Go Manchu*, in which you have to get five in a row on an infinite board.

B. Blind chess

This is a game involving vectors; it needs two players and a scorer.

Use an ordinary chess board for this. (Or mark out an 8 by 8 grid). The players both have Queens, which can move any number of spaces, straight or diagonally. They start on opposite sides of the board, not in line with each other. So they cannot immediately take each other.

After the initial position, neither player can see the board. Alternately they call out their moves, in the form of a vector. You win if either your opponent goes off the board or your Queen manages to strike the other.

A harder version of this game involves Knights, which can make any of the following moves:

$$\begin{pmatrix} 1 \\ 2 \end{pmatrix} \begin{pmatrix} 2 \\ 1 \end{pmatrix} \begin{pmatrix} -1 \\ -2 \end{pmatrix} \begin{pmatrix} -2 \\ -1 \end{pmatrix} \begin{pmatrix} -1 \\ 2 \end{pmatrix} \begin{pmatrix} -2 \\ 1 \end{pmatrix} \begin{pmatrix} 1 \\ -2 \end{pmatrix} \begin{pmatrix} 2 \\ -1 \end{pmatrix}$$

Multiple choice question *(Tick appropriate box)*

The vector which will go from (2,7) to (3,-2) is:

a) $\begin{pmatrix} 1 \\ -5 \end{pmatrix}$ ☐

b) $\begin{pmatrix} 3 \\ -2 \end{pmatrix}$ ☐

c) $\begin{pmatrix} 1 \\ 9 \end{pmatrix}$ ☐

d) $\begin{pmatrix} -1 \\ 9 \end{pmatrix}$ ☐

e) $\begin{pmatrix} 1 \\ -9 \end{pmatrix}$ ☐

Points to note

1) *Coordinates*

    a) When going from one point to another be careful with signs. If going from (3,1) to (1,4) the change in x is –2, not 2.

    b) Be careful with negative numbers. When subtracting –3 from 4, the answer is 7 not 1.

2) *Vectors*

    a) The top term of a vector is the x bit. Do not get this the wrong way round.

    b) The position vector of a point goes from the origin to the point. If the starting place is different then the vector will be different.

Chapter 17

Enlargement and similarity

The earliest cameras did not have lenses. Instead they had a small pin-hole in the front. Light would enter through the hole, and give an upside-down image on the rear.

Suppose such a camera is used to take a picture of a man, height 6 ft, standing 20 ft from the camera, and a house 30 ft high 50 ft from the camera. The distance from front to back of the camera is 2 inches. Draw a picture of what the photo might look like.

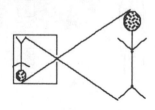

Fig 17.1

17.1 Enlargement with positive scale factor

An enlargement is a transformation which increases the size of shapes by a constant k. This number is the scale factor of the enlargement.

When a balloon is being blown up, its size is constantly increasing. The letters on the right are twice those on the left, so the scale factor is 2.

The scale factor does not have to be a whole number. It could even be a number less than 1, causing the object to grow smaller. The transformation can be called either an enlargement or a reduction.

Fig 17.2

Whenever an enlargement is done, one point remains fixed. This point is the centre of enlargement. In Fig 17.2 the mouth is the centre of enlargement.

Suppose we wish to enlarge a line AB, with scale factor 2 and centre of enlargement X. Join X to A, and double the length XA. This will give us A'. Construct B' similarly.

In every case, if X is the centre and point A is enlarged to A',

then XA'/XA = k, where k is the scale factor.

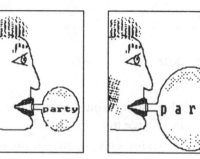

Fig 17.3

17.1.1 Examples

1) Make an enlargement of the triangle ABC shown, with centre X and factor $1\frac{1}{2}$.

   Solution   Join X to A, and multiply the length of XA by $1\frac{1}{2}$. This gives us XA'. B' and C' are found similarly.

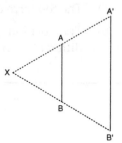

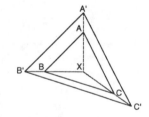

Fig 17.4

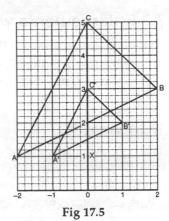

2) Plot the triangle ABC with vertices at A(-2,1), B(2,3), C(0,5). This triangle is enlarged from the point (0,1) by a scale factor of $\frac{1}{2}$. Draw the enlarged triangle and write down the new coordinates A′, B′, C′.

Solution The triangle is shown plotted. A is 2 units to the left of X. So A′ will be $\frac{1}{2} \times 2 = 1$ units to the left of X. Plot A′.

Find the positions of C′ and B′ similarly. Plot the enlarged triangle, and read off the coordinates:

A′(-1,1), B′(1,2), C′(0,3)

Fig 17.5

17.1.2 Exercises

1) Enlarge the triangle ABC on Fig 17.6, with a scale factor of $1\frac{1}{2}$ and centre of enlargement X.

2) Repeat Question 1 with a scale factor of $\frac{1}{2}$.

3) Enlarge the shapes in Fig 17.7 about the points labelled X, with scale factors

   a) 2   b) $1\frac{1}{2}$ c) $\frac{1}{2}$.

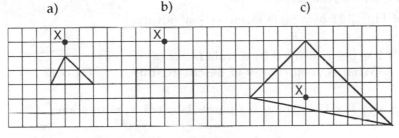

4) Triangle ABC has vertices at A(1,2), B(3,2), C(5,0). The triangle is enlarged by a factor of $2\frac{1}{2}$ about the point (1,4). Draw the transformed triangle and write down the coordinates of its vertices.

Fig 17.6

a)   b)   c)

Fig 17.7

5) The rectangle PQRS has corners at P(1,1), Q(4,1), R(4,-5), S(1,-5). The rectangle is enlarged by a factor of $1\frac{1}{3}$ about the point (4,-2). Plot the enlarged rectangle and write down the coordinates of its vertices.

6) Triangle ABC of Question 4 is reduced by a factor of $\frac{1}{2}$ about the point (1,0). Draw the reduced triangle and write down the coordinates of its vertices.

7) Rectangle PQRS of Question 5 is reduced by a factor of $\frac{2}{3}$ about the point (4,-2). Draw the reduced rectangle and write down the coordinates of its vertices.

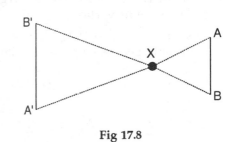

Fig 17.8

17.2 Enlargements with negative scale factor

An enlargement with a negative scale factor turns a shape upside down as well as changing its size.

Suppose the line AB (Fig 17.8) is enlarged by a scale factor of –2 about X. Join A to X. When this length is multiplied by –2, it is doubled and its direction is reversed. Notice that A' is on the opposite side of X from A.

17.2.1 Example

Triangle ABC has coordinates at A(-2,1), B(2,3), C(0,5). It is enlarged about the point (1,1) by a scale factor of –2. Plot the new triangle and write down its coordinates A', B', C'.

Solution   Plot ABC. B is 2 above and 1 to the right of the centre of enlargement. Multiply by –2, to find B' 4 below and 2 to the left of the centre of enlargement. Plot B'.

Find the positions of A' and C' similarly. The enlarged triangle is shown plotted. Read off the coordinates:

A'(7,1), B'(-1,-3), C'(3,-7)

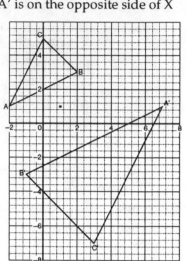

Fig 17.9

17.2.2 Exercises

1) Enlarge triangle ABC of Fig 17.10 about point X with a scale factor of –2.

2) Repeat Question 1, with a scale factor of $-\frac{1}{2}$.

3) Enlarge PQRS of Fig 17.11 by a scale factor $-1\frac{1}{2}$ about the point X.

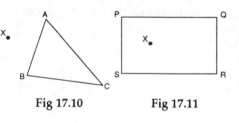

Fig 17.10   Fig 17.11

4) In Fig 17.12 LMN has been enlarged by a scale factor of –1 about the point X. What is another way of describing this transformation?

5) Enlarge the shapes in Fig 17.13 about the points labelled X, with scale factors

     a)   –1   b)   –2   c) $-\frac{1}{2}$.

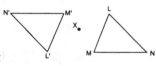

Fig 17.12

6) ABC has vertices at (1,2), (3,2), (5,0). It is enlarged by a factor of –3 about the point (2,1). Draw the enlarged triangle and write down the coordinates of its vertices.

7) PQRS has vertices at (1,1), (4,1), (4,-5), (1,-5). It is enlarged by a factor of –2 about the point (0,-2). Plot the enlarged rectangle and write down the coordinates of its vertices.

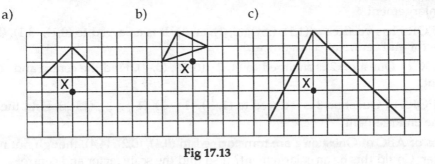

Fig 17.13

8) Triangle ABC of Question 6 is enlarged by a factor of −1 about (0,0). Plot the new triangle and write down its vertices.

9) Rectangle PQRS of Question 7 is reduced by a factor of $-\frac{1}{3}$ about the point (1,1). Plot the new rectangle and write down its vertices.

17.3 Describing an enlargement

Scale factor

The scale factor of an enlargement can be found be measuring lengths before and after the enlargement.

Centre of enlargement

Suppose an enlargement takes a triangle ABC to A′B′C′. Then if X is the centre of enlargement, X, A and A′ must lie on a straight line. Similarly X, B and B′ are also on a straight line. So X lies on the intersection of AA′, BB′ and CC′.

17.3.1 Example

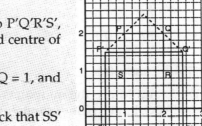

The square PQRS is at P(1,2), Q(2,2), R(2,1), S(1,1). It is enlarged to P′Q′R′S′, at P′($\frac{1}{2}$,1$\frac{1}{2}$), Q′(2$\frac{1}{2}$,1$\frac{1}{2}$), R′(2$\frac{1}{2}$,$\frac{1}{2}$), S′($\frac{1}{2}$,$\frac{1}{2}$). Find the scale factor and centre of enlargement

Solution   The squares before and after enlargement are shown. PQ = 1, and P′Q′ = 2, Hence the scale factor is 2.

Join up PP′ and QQ′. They cross at (1$\frac{1}{2}$,2$\frac{1}{2}$). We can check that SS′ and RR′ also pass through this point.

The scale factor is 2, and the centre is (1$\frac{1}{2}$, 2$\frac{1}{2}$)

Fig 17.14

17.3.2 Exercises

1) In the enlargements below, find the scale factors and centres of enlargement.

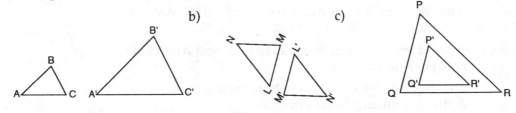

Fig 17.15

2) Triangle ABC is at A(1,1), B(3,1), C(3,2). It is enlarged to (1,0), (5,0), (5,2). Find the scale factor and

131

centre of enlargement.

3) Rectangle PQRS has vertices at (1,1), (2,1), (2,-1), (1,-1). It is enlarged to (0,1), (3,1), (3,-5), (0,-5). Find the scale factor and centre of enlargement.

4) Triangle ABC of Question 2 is enlarged to (4,-2), (0,-2), (0,-4). Find the centre and scale factor of the enlargement.

5) Rectangle PQRS of Question 3 is reduced to $(1,\frac{1}{2})$, $(1\frac{1}{2},\frac{1}{2})$, $(1\frac{1}{2},-\frac{1}{2})$, $(1,-\frac{1}{2})$. Find the scale factor and centre of the enlargement.

6) The vertices of ABC of Question 2 are transformed to (0,4), (0,2), (4,4), though not necessarily in the correct order. Could this be an enlargement? If so find the scale factor and centre.

7) Look at the pinhole camera illustrated in Fig 17.1. Suppose the camera is 2 inches deep, and the object is 8 inches in front of the camera. What is the centre of enlargement? What is the scale factor?

17.4 Similarity

If one figure is an enlargement of another, then they have the same shape, but not necessarily the same size. In this case they are said to be similar.

If two figures are similar then they have the same angles. There is also a fixed ratio between the sides of the figures. This would be the scale factor k of the enlargement.

In particular, suppose two triangles ABC and DEF are similar. There is
a fixed ratio between the sides of $\triangle$ ABC and the sides of $\triangle$ DEF.

$$\frac{AB}{DE} = \frac{BC}{EF} = \frac{AC}{DF}$$

The ratio of sides is the same for both triangles.

$$\frac{AB}{BC} = \frac{DE}{EF} \; : \; \frac{AB}{AC} = \frac{DE}{DF} \; : \; \frac{AC}{BC} = \frac{DF}{EF}$$

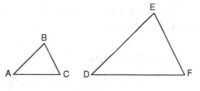

Fig 17.16

17.4.1 Examples

1) L and M are the midpoints of the sides AB and AC of the triangle ABC. Find a pair of similar triangles. If BC = 8 find LM.

   Solution   Triangle ALM is a reduction of ABC, with scale factor $\frac{1}{2}$ and centre A.

   Hence $\triangle$ ABC is similar to $\triangle$ ALM.

   It follows that LM:BC is equal to $\frac{1}{2}$.

   $$LM = 8 \times \frac{1}{2} = 4$$

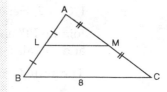

Fig 17.17

2) L and M are on the sides AB and AC of the triangle ABC. AM = 4, MC = 5, AL = 3, LB = 9. Find the ratio LM:BC.

   Solution   AB = 12 and AC = 9. So the ratios AL:AC and AM:AB are both equal to 1:3.

   The angle A is the same in both triangles. So ABC and AML are similar. It follows that:

   LM:BC = AM:AB = 1:3

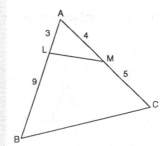

Fig 17.18

17.4.2 Exercises

1) Which of the pairs of triangles below are similar to each other?

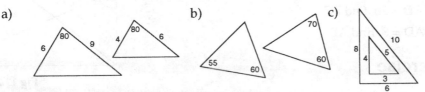

a)   b)   c)

Fig 17.19

2) L and M lie on the sides AB, AC of the triangle ABC, so that LM is parallel to BC (Fig 17.20). Write down a pair of similar triangles.

3) L, M and N lie on the sides AB, BC, CA of △ ABC. LM, MN, NL are parallel to CA, AB, BC respectively (Fig 17.21). Find as many similar triangles as you can.

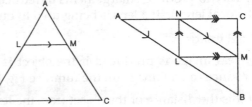

Fig 17.20   **Fig 17.21**

4) Fig 17.22 shows a 3 barred gate in which AB, EF, DC are horizontal and AD, BC are vertical. AGC is a straight line. Write down as many similar triangles as you can.

5) The triangles ABC and DEF of Fig 17.23 are similar. They are not drawn to scale.

   a) If AB = 4, DE = 2 and AC = 6, find DF.

   b) If AB = 3, AC = 2 and DE = 6, find DF.

   c) If BC = 9, EF = 12 and DE = 8, find AB.

   d) If AB = $\frac{3}{4}$, DE = $\frac{1}{2}$ and BC = $1\frac{1}{2}$, find EF.

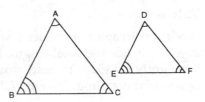

Fig 17.22

Fig 17.23

6) In Fig 17.24 a ladder AB is laid against two walls as shown. The higher wall is 3 m high, and the lower wall is 1 m high. If the foot of the ladder is 0.5 m from the lower wall, how far is it from the higher wall? How far apart are the walls?

7) X and Y are on the sides AB and AC of △ ABC, such that AX:XB and AY:YC are both equal to 1:3. (See Fig 17.25). Find the ratio XY:BC.

8) P and Q lie on the sides AB and AC of △ ABC. AP = 12, PB = 3, AQ = 10, QC = 8.

   Write down a pair of similar triangles. What is the ratio PQ:BC?

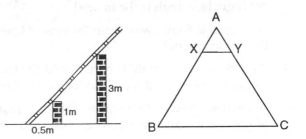

Fig 17.24   **Fig 17.25**

9)   In Fig 17.26 BÂD = AB̂C = 90°, and BĈA = AB̂D. Write down a pair of
     similar triangles.

     a) If AB = 10 and AD = 20, find BC.

     b) If BC = 2 and AD = 8, find AB.

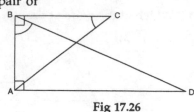

Fig 17.26

17.5 Longer exercise

Magnifying glasses

A way to produce enlargements or reductions is by a magnifying lens. Each lens has a constant f called
its focal length. If a lens is being used to burn paper, this is the distance from the lens to the focus.

Real image

A real image is produced if the object is outside the focal length. For example, the lens of a camera
produces a real image on the film. See Fig 17.27.

If u is the distance of the object from the lens, and
v the distance of the image, then

$$\frac{1}{v} + \frac{1}{u} = \frac{1}{f}$$

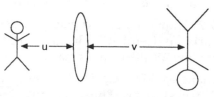

Fig 17.27

Virtual image

A virtual image is produced when the original
object is inside the focal length. When a long-sighted person uses
a magnifying glass to read small writing, he looks at a virtual
image of the writing. See Fig 17.28.

The rule is: $\dfrac{1}{u} - \dfrac{1}{v} = \dfrac{1}{f}$

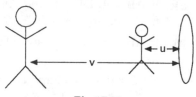

Fig 17.28

In both cases the scale factor of the enlargement is $\frac{v}{u}$.

1)   Suppose a lens has focal length 10 cm. An object is 30 cm away. Where is the image? If the object is 5
     cm high, how high is the image?

2)   An object is 8 cm away from the lens of Question 1. Where is the image? What is the scale factor of
     the enlargement?

3)   An object is 1 cm high. Where should the lens of Question 1 be held to ensure a real image of height
     3 cm? Where should it be held for a virtual image of height 3 cm?

4)   A microscope uses two lenses. The first creates a real image, and the second creates a virtual image
     of the real image. See if you can draw a diagram showing how a microscope works.

Multiple choice question *(Tick appropriate box)*

An enlargement of scale factor –2 takes place about (0,1). The point A(2,2) is taken to:

a)   (4,3)   ☐

b)   (-4,-1)   ☐

c)   (-6, -2)   ☐

d)   (-4, 3).   ☐

e)   (-4, -4)   ☐

Points to note

1)   *Enlargement*

   a)   When a figure is enlarged by a factor of 2, the distances from the centre are doubled. Measure this new distance from the centre, not from the figure itself.

   b)   Be careful when the scale factor is fractional or negative. If it is negative then the lines must be reversed in direction.

2)   *Similarity*

   a)   If △ ABC is similar to △ DEF, then the triangles are similar in that order. So Â = D̂ etc.

   b)   If you are told that L is on AB, with AL:LB = 1:3, then the ratio AL:AB is 1:4. Do not think that AL:AB is also 1:3.

Chapter 18

Pythagoras's theorem

It is possible that this most famous of theorems was discovered by accident, when people took a closer look at the patterns made by floor tiles.

On the sides of the shaded triangle, there are three squares. How many triangles are there:

a) in the squares on the shorter sides

b) in the square on the longer side.

What can you conclude?

Fig 18.1

18.1 Pythagoras's theorem

Pythagoras's Theorem gives a formula connecting the sides of a right-angled triangle.

> *The square on the hypoteneuse is equal to the sum of the squares on the other two sides.*

In Fig 18.2, the side farthest from the right-angle is the hypoteneuse. The theorem says:

$$c^2 = a^2 + b^2.$$

(A proof of the result is outlined in 18.4 of this chapter.)

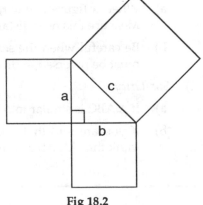

Fig 18.2

18.1.1 Examples

1) In the triangle of Fig 18.3, C = 90°, CB = 3 and AC = 5. Find BA to 3 decimal places.

Fig 18.3

Solution   Comparing with Fig 18.2, BA is the longest side, so BA is the hypoteneuse. BA = c, AC = b, BC = a. The theorem gives:

$$c^2 = 3^2 + 5^2$$

$$c^2 = 9 + 25 = 34$$

$$c = \sqrt{34} = 5.831$$

2) A ladder of length 2.5 metres leans against a wall, so that the foot of the ladder is 1 metre from the base of the wall. How far up the wall does the ladder reach?

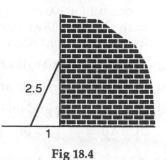

Fig 18.4

Solution   Here the length of the ladder is c, and a is the distance to the base of the wall. The height up the wall is b. The theorem gives:

$2.5^2 = b^2 + 1^2$

$b^2 = 6.25 - 1 = 5.25$

It reaches $\sqrt{5.25} = 2.29$ m

18.1.2 Exercises

In these exercises give your answers to 3 significant figures.

1) For the following triangles, find the unknown sides.

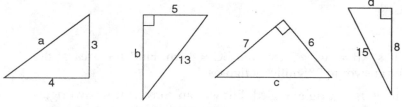

Fig 18.5

2) In Δ ABC, B = 90°, AB = 7 cm and CB = 8 cm. What is AC?

3) Δ PQR has a right-angle at P. QR = 12 m and PQ = 9 m. Find PR.

4) I travel 3 miles North and 5 miles East. How far am I from my starting point?

5) A rectangle is 8 cm by 11 cm. How long are the diagonals?

6) A kite is flying so that it is 55 feet high, and is above a point 75 ft from the flyer. How long is the string of the kite?

7) The diagonals of a rhombus are 10 cm and 13 cm. What is the length of the side of the rhombus?

8)· P is a point 6 cm from the centre C of a circle of radius 2 cm. A tangent is drawn from P, touching the circle at T. How long is the tangent PT?

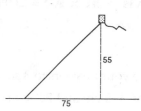

Fig 18.6

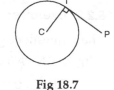

Fig 18.7

9) A road has a gradient of 1 in 20. (Which means that it rises 1 metre for every 20 metres horizontally.) If I walk so that I have risen 2 metres, how far have I travelled horizontally? How far have I walked along the road? (Give your answer to 2 D.P.)

10) A stick of length 5 feet is held at an angle, so that when the sun is vertically above the stick the shadow is 3 feet long. How high is the end of the stick above the ground?

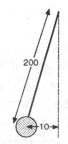

Fig 18.8

11) A pendulum 200 cm long is pulled aside so that the bob has moved 10 cm to the left (Fig 18.8). How far is the bob below the support? By how much has the bob risen? (Give your answer to 2 D.P.)

12) The sides of a triangle are 8, 9 and 12. Is this a right-angled triangle?

13) The sides of a triangle are 15, 8 and 17. Is this a right-angled triangle?

14) The lines of the grid on the right are 1 unit apart. Find the lengths of:

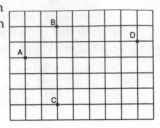

   a) AB   b) AC   c) CD.

Fig 18.9

18.2 Isosceles triangles

Pythagoras's Theorem holds only for right-angled triangles. But we can extend it to some cases where there is not a right-angle.

Suppose $\triangle$ ABC is isosceles, with AB = AC. Then when we drop a perpendicular from A to BC, it divides $\triangle$ ABC into two equal right-angled triangles.

Fig 18.10

18.2.1 Example

The triangle ABC has AB = AC = 7 cm, and BC = 8 cm. Find the area of the triangle, giving your answer to 3 significant figures.

Solution   The triangle is not right angled. But we can convert it to two right-angled triangles by dropping a perpendicular from A to BC as shown.

Now the triangles ABD and ACD are right angled. Use Pythagoras:

$$AD = \sqrt{7^2 - 4^2} = \sqrt{33} = 5.7446$$

Use the formula for the area of the triangle;

The area is $\frac{1}{2} \times BC \times AD = 23.0 \text{ cm}^2$

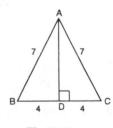

Fig 18.11

18.2.2 Exercises

In these questions give your answers to 3 significant figures

1) In $\triangle$ ABC, AB = AC = 5 cm and BC = 4 cm. Find the height of the triangle and its area.

2) $\triangle$ PQR is a triangle with PQ = QR and PR = 6 m. If the height of the triangle is 7 m find PQ.

3) $\triangle$ LMN has LM = LN, MN = 12 cm, and area 300 cm². Find the height of the triangle and hence find LM.

4) PQR is an equilateral triangle of side 4 cm. Find the length of the perpendicular from P to QR. Find the area of the triangle.

5) A chord of length 5 is drawn in a circle of radius 20. What is the shortest distance from the centre of the circle to the chord?

6) A cylindrical horizontal drain has radius 4 inches. There is water in it to a depth of 1 inch. How far below the centre of the drain is the water? How wide is the water in the drain?

7) A step-ladder consists of two sides of length 2 m. The feet of the sides are 1.5 m apart. How high is the top of the step-ladder?

18.3 Coordinates

Suppose we are given the coordinates of two points, and we want to find the distance between them. We can find the vertical and horizontal distances between them. We now have a right-angled triangle as shown in Fig 18.12. Pythagoras's Theorem can be applied.

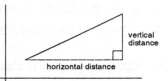

Fig 18.12

18.3.1 Example

Find the distance between the points (1,1) and (4,3), giving your answer to 3 significant figures.

Solution   The vertical distance between the points is the difference between the y-coordinates. The horizontal distance is the difference between the x-coordinates.

Vertical distance = $3 - 1 = 2$

Horizontal distance = $4 - 1 = 3$

Now Pythagoras's Theorem can be used:

Distance = $\sqrt{2^2 + 3^2} = \sqrt{13} = 3.61$

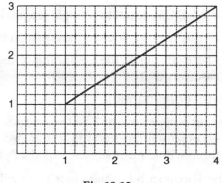

Fig 18.13

18.3.2 Exercises

1) A graph is drawn to a scale of 1 cm per unit. Find the following distances:

a) (0,0) to (1,2)   b) (0,0) to (5,-3)   c) (1,1) to (5,7)

d) (1,3) to (6,1)   e) (2,3) to (3,-3)   f) (-2,-3) to (5,7)

2) The three points of a triangle are at A(1,1), B(4,5), C(1,6). By finding the lengths of the sides show that △ ABC is isosceles.

3) A quadrilateral has its vertices at A(0,0), B(7,24), C(22,44), D(15,20). Find the lengths of the sides. What sort of quadrilateral is ABCD?

4) The three points of a triangle are at A(1,1), B(4,5), C(5,-2). Find the lengths of the side of the triangle, and show that it is isosceles. What else can you say about the triangle?

5) A quadrilateral has its vertices at P(2,1), Q(6,3), R(5,5), S(1,3). Show that PQRS is a parallelogram. Find the lengths of the diagonals PR and QS. What more can you say about PQRS?

6) X is at (2,3), Y at (3,5), Z at (5,9). Find the lengths of XY, YZ, XZ. What can you say about the three points X, Y, Z?

18.4 Longer exercises

A. Proof of Pythagoras

There are well over 100 different proofs of Pythagoras's Theorem. This one involves similar triangles.

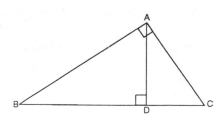

Fig 18.14

In the original triangle ABC, drop a perpendicular to D as shown in Fig 18.14.

1) Show that $\hat{BAD} = \hat{C}$ and $\hat{CAD} = \hat{B}$.

2) Show that triangles ABC, DBA and DAC are similar to each other.

3) Complete the formulas: $\dfrac{BD}{AB} = \dfrac{AB}{**}$ and $\dfrac{DC}{AC} = \dfrac{**}{BC}$.

4) Multiply the first equation by AB and the second by AC.

5) Add these equations. You should have: $BD + DC = \dfrac{AB^2}{BC} + \dfrac{AC^2}{BC}$

6) BD + DC is equal to a single length. Put it in the equation above.

7) Multiply both sides of the equation by BC. What do you have now?

8) The example at the beginning of the chapter was a proof of Pythagoras in one special case. What case was that?

B. Pythagorean triads

Pythagoras lived about 2,500 years ago. He was born in Greece and lived mainly in Southern Italy. He was especially interested in right-angled triangles for which the lengths of the sides are whole numbers. The three whole numbers are called a Pythagorean Triad.

By the Theorem, a Pythagorean Triad will be three whole numbers a, b, c for which $a^2 + b^2 = c^2$.

1) The simplest Pythagorean Triad has $a = 3$ and $b = 4$. What is c?

2) The next one up has $a = 5$ and $c = 13$. What is b?

3) Complete the table:

a	b	c
3	4	
5		13
7	24	
9		41

4) Note that a is taking successive odd number values. How are the values of b and c obtained? (Find the relationship between a^2 and b and c.) Once you have found the rule for the series find the Pythagorean Triads for which $a = 11$ and $a = 13$.

5) a does not have to be an odd number. Try doubling the values of a, b, c. Is the result still a Pythagorean Triad?

6) Not all the Pythagorean Triads are obtained by this method. If $a = 8$ and $b = 15$ then find c.

7) It can be shown that all Pythagorean Triads can be found by taking whole numbers r and s, with $r > s$, and writing down $2rs$, $r^2 - s^2$, $r^2 + s^2$. The result is always a Pythagorean Triad. Check this by taking various values of r and s. Can you show why it always works?

Multiple choice question *(Tick appropriate box)*

A triangle has sides 17 cm, 17 cm, 16 cm. The area of the triangle is:

a)   46 cm^2 ☐

b)   120 cm^2 ☐

c)   150.3 cm^2 ☐

d)   72 cm^2 ☐

e)   60 cm^2 ☐

Points to note

1) *Right-angled triangles*

   a)   Do not use Pythagoras for a triangle which is not right-angled. The theorem only holds if the triangle does have a right-angle. If your triangle is isosceles then drop a perpendicular before you apply the theorem.

   b)   Do not use the wrong sides for the theorem. The longest side is always the hypoteneuse. Make sure that you have labelled the sides correctly before using the equation $c^2 = a^2 + b^2$.

2) *Errors in algebra*

   When using the theorem, the a^2 and b^2 terms must be added before the square root is taken. Do not take the square root first. $\sqrt{a^2 + b^2} \neq a + b$

3) *Coordinates*

   Be careful with negative numbers when dealing with coordinates. The horizontal distance between (-2,3) and (3,8) is 5, not 1.

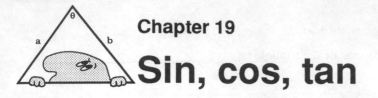

Chapter 19

Sin, cos, tan

Suppose there is a tree whose height you wish to find. It is not safe to climb to the top, so you must use measurement from the ground.

Pace out 50 m from the base of the tree. Point a stick at the top of the tree, and measure the angle that the stick makes with the horizontal. Say the angle is 35°.

Now you can go home and make a scale diagram of the situation. Draw a triangle, with base side 5 cm and base angles 90° and 35°. What do you get for the height of the tree?

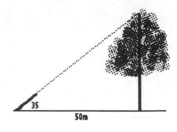

Fig 19.1

19.1 Finding unknown sides

If two triangles have the same angles, then they are the same shape.

Suppose two right-angled triangles ABC and DEF are similar, with an angle as well as the right-angle in common. Their sides may be different, but the ratios between the sides are the same.

These ratios are determined by the angles. They are known as trigonometric ratios.

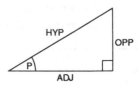

Fig 19.2

Definitions

A right-angled triangle is labelled as follows. The side farthest from the right-angle is the Hypoteneuse. (HYP). The side opposite to the angle $P°$ is the Opposite. (OPP). The side next to the angle $P°$ is the Adjacent. (ADJ). The three trigonometric ratios are defined by:

$$\sin P° = \frac{OPP}{HYP}; \quad \cos P° = \frac{ADJ}{HYP}; \quad \tan P° = \frac{OPP}{ADJ}$$

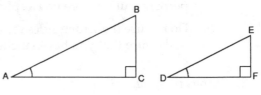

Fig 19.3

These functions are called respectively: the sine of $P°$, the cosine of $P°$, the tangent of $P°$.

A way of remembering them is by the word SOHCAHTOA.

Sine = Opp/Hyp,   Cosine = Adj/Hyp,   Tangent = Opp/Adj.

The ratios can be found from tables or from a calculator. When using a calculator, press the angle first and then the sin, cos or tan button. There is no need to press the ☐= button. To find sin 27°, the sequence is:

☐2 ☐7 ☐sin

The value 0.4539905 will appear.

142

Suppose we are given a right-angle triangle, in which we know the other angles and one side. Then the trigonometric ratios can be used to find the other sides.

19.1.1 Examples

1) In the triangle ABC shown, $\hat{B} = 90°$, $\hat{A} = 43°$, and AC = 12 cm. Find BC and AB. Give your answers to 3 sig. figs.

   Solution   Compare the triangle with that of Fig 19.3. AC is the hypoteneuse and BC is the opposite side. The ratio which involves HYP and OPP is the sine ratio. Write down the sine formula for this triangle.

   $$\text{Sin } 43° = \frac{\text{OPP}}{\text{HYP}} = \frac{\text{BC}}{\text{AC}} = \frac{\text{BC}}{12}$$

   Multiply both sides by 12:

   $$12 \times \sin 43° = \text{BC}$$

   Use a calculator to find that sin 43° = 0.681998.

   BC = 12 × 0.681998 = 8.18 cm

   The procedure for finding AB is similar. AB is the adjacent side. The ratio which connects ADJ and HYP is cosine.

   $$\cos 43° = \frac{\text{ADJ}}{\text{HYP}} = \frac{\text{AB}}{\text{AC}} = \frac{\text{AB}}{12}$$

   AB = 12 × cos 43° = 8.78 cm

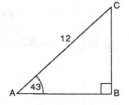

Fig 19.4

2) In the triangle DEF, $\hat{E} = 90°$, $\hat{F} = 50°$ and EF = 5 cm. Find ED, to 3 sig. figs.

   Solution   The triangle is in a different position, but its sides can still be labelled. FD is the hypoteneuse (because it is farthest from the right-angle), ED is the opposite (because it is opposite the angle of 50°), EF is the adjacent (because it is next to the angle of 50°). The ratio which connects together OPP and ADJ is the tangent ratio.

   $$\tan 50° = \frac{\text{OPP}}{\text{ADJ}} = \frac{\text{ED}}{\text{EF}} = \frac{\text{ED}}{5}$$

   ED = 5 × tan 50° = 5.96 cm

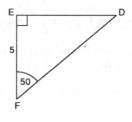

Fig 19.5

19.1.2 Exercises

Throughout give your answers to 3 significant figures.

1) Use your calculator to find the following:

   a)   sin 31°   b)   cos 43°   c)   tan 87°

2) Find the unknown side in each of the following triangles:

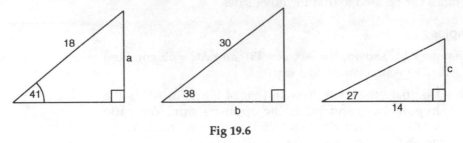

Fig 19.6

3) Find the unknown side in each of the following triangles:

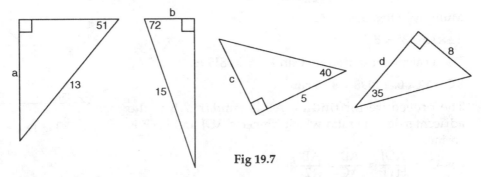

Fig 19.7

4) In the triangle ABC, $\hat{B} = 90°$, $\hat{A} = 59°$ and AC = 20 cm. Find AB and BC.

5) In the triangle ABC, $\hat{B} = 90°$, $\hat{A} = 37°$ and AC = 45 cm. Find AB and BC.

6) In the triangle PQR, $\hat{Q} = 90°$, $\hat{P} = 32°$ and PR = 40 cm. Find QR and PQ.

7) In the triangle ABC, $\hat{B} = 90°$, $\hat{A} = 73°$ and AB = 10 cm. Find BC.

8) In the triangle PQR, $\hat{Q} = 90°$, $\hat{P} = 17°$ and PQ = 120 cm. Find QR.

19.2 Finding unknown angles

So far we have been given the angles of a triangle, and have used trigonometry to find its sides. If we are given the sides of a right-angled triangle, then we can use trigonometry to find its angles.

The sine function goes from the angle to the ratio. The $\sin^{-1}$ or arcsin function goes from the ratio to the angle.

If $\sin P° = x$, then $\sin^{-1} x = P°$.

$\cos^{-1}$ and $\tan^{-1}$ are defined similarly.

To find $\sin^{-1}$ of a ratio, enter the ratio, then press the inverse button, then the sin button. To find $\sin^{-1} 0.4$:

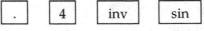

The answer 23.578178 will appear.

19.2.1 Example

In the triangle ABC, $\hat{B} = 90°$, AC = 8 cm, AB = 5 cm. Find the angle $\hat{A}$, giving your answer to the nearest degree.

Solution　Compare with the triangle of Fig 19.3. AC is the Hypoteneuse, AB is the Adjacent. The ratio which connects HYP and ADJ is cosine.

$$\cos A = \frac{ADJ}{HYP} = \frac{AB}{AC} = \frac{5}{8}$$

Use the $\cos^{-1}$ buttons to find $\cos^{-1}\frac{5}{8} = 51.317813°$.

To the nearest degree, $\hat{A} = 51°$

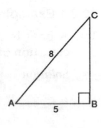

Fig 19.8

19.2.2 Exercises

Throughout give your answers to the nearest degree.

1) Use a calculator to find the following:

 a) $\sin^{-1}0.8$ b) $\cos^{-1}0.4$ c) $\tan^{-1}2.4$

2) Find the unknown angles in the triangles below:

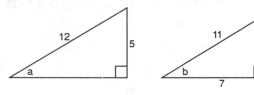

Fig 19.9

3) Find the unknown angles in the triangles below:

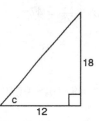

Fig 19.10

4) ABC is a triangle in which $\hat{B} = 90°$, AC = 12 cm and AB = 4 cm. Find $\hat{A}$

5) In triangle XYZ, $\hat{Y} = 90°$, XZ = 20 cm and YZ = 17 cm. Find $\hat{X}$

6) In triangle ABC, $\hat{B} = 90°$, AB = 7 cm and BC = 8 cm. Find $\hat{C}$

7) PQR is a triangle in which $\hat{Q} = 90°$, PR = 0.3 cm and PQ = 0.2 cm. Find $\hat{R}$

8) In triangle LMN, $\hat{M} = 90°$, MN = 14 cm and LM = 24 cm. Find $\hat{N}$

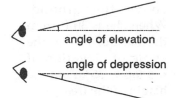

angle of elevation

angle of depression

19.3　Angles of elevation and depression

When we look up at something, the angle which our line of vision makes with the horizontal is the angle of elevation. See Fig 19.11.

Fig 19.11

145

When we look down at something, the angle which our line of vision makes with the horizontal is the angle of depression.

19.3.1 Examples

1) A boat is 2000 m out to sea. From the boat, the angle of elevation of the top of a cliff is 5°. How high is the cliff?

   Solution Let *d* be the height of the cliff. From the picture:

   $$\tan 5° = \frac{d}{2000}$$

   $$d = 2000 \times \tan 5° = 175 \text{ m}$$

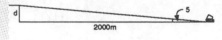
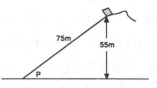

Fig 19.12

2) A kite on 75 m of string is 55 m high. What angle does it make with the horizontal?

   Solution Let *P°* be the angle. From the picture:

   $$\sin P° = \frac{55}{75}$$

   $$P° = \sin^{-1} \frac{55}{75} = 47°$$

Fig 19.13

19.3.2 Exercises

Give your answers to 3 sig. figs. or to the nearest degree.

1) 200 metres from the base of a tower the angle of elevation of the top is 24° (Fig 19.14). Find the height of the tower.

2) A cliff is 75 m high, and a boat is 3000 m out to sea (Fig 19.15). Find the angle of depression of the boat from the cliff.

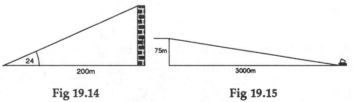

Fig 19.14   **Fig 19.15**

3) A ladder of length 2 m leans against a wall at an angle of 35° to the vertical (Fig 19.16). Find how far up the wall it reaches.

4) A flagpole 12 feet high throws a shadow of length 20 ft. What is the angle of elevation of the sun?

5) A girl's eyes are 5 feet above the ground. When she is 30 ft from the base of a tree, the angle of elevation of the top is 35°. Find the height of the tree.

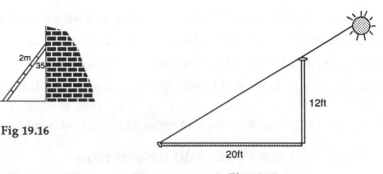

Fig 19.16

Fig 19.17

6) Two minarets of a mosque are 40 m and 55 m in height. Their bases are 30 m from each other. What is the angle of elevation of the higher minaret from the lower?

7)   A terrace of seats at a football ground is 30 m long and rises 4 m from top to bottom. Find the angle of slope of the terrace.

8)   A rocket is fired at an elevation of 50°. It continues in a straight line at 40 metres per second. How high is it after 5 seconds?

9)   I stand on the bank of a river, and see a tree directly opposite me on the other side. I now walk 20 m upstream, and the line from me to the tree makes 83° with the bank. How wide is the river?

10) 100 m from a church the base of the spire has angle of elevation 12°, and the top of the spire has elevation 23°. What is the height of the spire?

11) The gradient of a hill is 1 in 10. (Which means that we go 1 unit vertically for every 10 units horizontally.) Find

   a)   the angle of slope

   b)   how far we have climbed after walking 100 m.

12) A plane flies at 6000 m above the ground. I spot it directly above me, and 10 seconds later its angle of elevation is 72°. How fast is the plane flying?

13) A line is drawn from the origin to the point (5,2). What angle does this line make with the *x*-axis?

14) In the problem at the beginning of the chapter, use trigonometry to find the height of the tree.

19.4 Longer exercises

A. Surveying

The angle of elevation of a tree can be measured roughly by looking along a stick, and measuring the angle the stick makes with the horizontal. A more accurate instrument to measure angles of elevation is a clinometer. You can make a simple clinometer as follows:

1)   Glue a thin tube, such as a drinking-straw, to the straight edge of a protractor. Make a hole in the protractor, thread a bit of cotton through it, with a weight at the other end.

When you look through the tube at a high object, the cotton will measure the angle with the vertical. Subtract from 90° to obtain the angle of elevation.

2)   Pace out the distance from the base of a tree or a high building. Measure its angle of elevation. Use trigonometry to calculate its height. Measure the heights of some other objects.

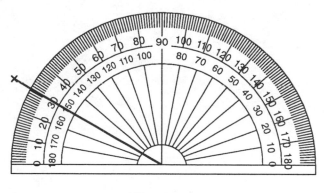

Fig 19.18

3)   Another use of surveying is as follows. Suppose that you cannot reach a certain object. (Because it is out to sea, or because there is a river in between.) How, by measuring angles and distances, and by using trigonometry, could you find out how far away it is?

B. Finding sine

Your calculator uses a complicated formula to work out trig. functions. Before the days of calculators tables had to be used. You can make a simple sine table using graph paper.

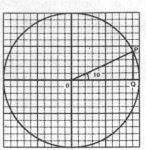

Draw a circle on the paper, with centre at the origin. Draw a radius from the centre making 10° with the x-axis, meeting the circle at P. The y-coordinate of P will be the opposite side of OPQ. Find sin 10° from the values of the radius and the y-coordinate.

Repeat, for 20°, 30° and so on. Write down a table of the sine function.

Multiple choice question *(Tick appropriate box)*

Fig 19.19

A ship is 94 m out to sea. From the top of a cliff the angle of depression is 17°. The height of the cliff, to 3 sig. figs., is:

a)   307 m   □

b)   27.5 m   □

c)   28.7 m   □

d)   28.8 m   □

e)   1598 m   □

Points to note

1) *Use of calculator*

a) Your calculator works "backwards" for the sin, cos and tan functions. Do not press the sin button before you have entered the angle.

b) Do not press the = button after the function button.

c) Leave rounding till the end of your calculation.

2) *Right-angled triangles*

The trig. ratios are defined for right-angled triangles. If there is no right-angle in your figure then the ratios cannot be used.

3) *The three ratios*

Make sure that you do not use the wrong ratio. Usually this error occurs because the triangle has been wrongly labelled.

It does not matter which way up the triangle is. The longest side, (the side farthest from the right-angle), is always the HYP. The side next to the angle we are dealing with is the ADJ, and the side opposite the angle we are dealing with is the OPP. Note that the labelling of HYP is always the same, but that the labelling of OPP and ADJ depends on the angle we are dealing with.

If you have any difficulty with these, make sure that the triangle is labelled with HYP, OPP and ADJ before you start working out the ratios.

4) *Depression*

The angle of depression is the angle which the line of vision makes with the horizontal, not with the vertical.

Cross-curriculum topic

Megaliths

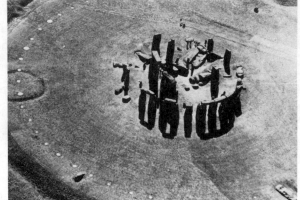

One of the most famous monuments in Britain is Stonehenge in Wiltshire. It consists of rings of huge stones, some with other stones balanced on top. It is an example of a megalithic monument, the word megalith meaning "huge stone". It was built between 2,800 and 1,600 BC, though no one knows for certain how it was built, or what purpose it had.

In fact, Stonehenge is just the most spectacular of many megalithic monuments. In the British Isles and Brittany in France there are over 1,000 stone rings. At the time of their construction writing was not known in Northern Europe, so there are no records about them, and the peoples that built them have been driven out by later invaders. Only from the stones themselves can we find out what knowledge the builders had, to enable them to construct these rings.

Shapes

The monuments are often described as stone circles. For the majority, about two thirds, the stones are laid out in a regular circle. The rest are more complicated shapes. Some are ovals, some "flattened circles", some "egg-shapes".

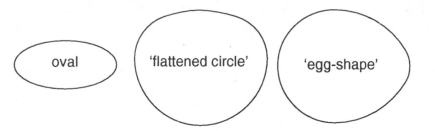

oval   'flattened circle'   'egg-shape'

The actual equations of these shapes are very complicated. But there is no reason to assume that the builders set out the stones with a lot of calculation. The shapes could have been made naturally.

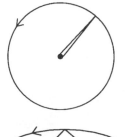

The earliest stone rings are all circles. Probably they were set out by fixing a post in the middle of a field, passing a long loop of rope over the post, and walking round scratching the earth with a stake to mark out a circle.

If there were two posts within the loop, then as the perimeter was scratched out an oval shape would be formed. This shape is known as an ellipse. Ellipses occur in many different situations. A circle seen from the side will appear to be an ellipse.

It is not known whether this happened by accident or on purpose, but there are more than 20 stone rings in the shape of an ellipse.

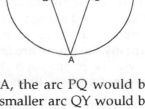

The "flattened circles" are less symmetrical than the circles or ellipses. But they are made up out of parts of circles. The arc XAY is a semicircle. Then PQ is the arc of a circle with centre A, and XP and YQ are arcs of circles with centres at B and C, with B and C dividing XY into three equal parts.

The shape could have been made by ropes. After drawing the semicircle, B and C could have been found by pacing along the diameter. Posts would have been put at B and C as well as at A. With the loop of rope based at A, the arc PQ would be scratched out. The rope would then meet B, and as the marker walked on the smaller arc QY would be made.

The "egg-shape" is also made out of arcs of circles. XAY is a semicircle. XP and YQ are arcs of circles with centres C and B, and PQ has centre D.

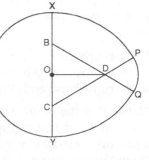

This shape could also have been made with a rope. Posts would be placed at O, B, C and D. With the rope based at O the semicircle could be traced. Then with the rope based at C, as the marker walked clockwise from X the arc XP would be drawn. When the rope met the post at D the smaller arc PQ would be scratched out.

Right-angled triangles

The "egg-shape" can be varied, between a long thin shape and one that is almost round like a circle, by varying the shape of the triangle BCD or the length of the rope loop. It seems that the triangle was built up out of two right-angled triangles, OBD and OCD, which were put back to back.

For many of the "egg-shapes", the sides OB, OD and BD are in the ratio 3:4:5. This triple of numbers is known as a Pythagorean Triad.

If a triangle is formed from these numbers, it will be right-angled. This is a special case of Pythagoras' Theorem.

> If a triangle is right-angled, then $a^2 + b^2 = c^2$.

Note that $3^2 + 4^2 = 25 = 5^2$.

Other Pythagorean Triads have been found in megalithic rings. One is designed on the ratio 12:35:37. (Check that these numbers obey the Theorem!) It seems likely that these numbers were chosen so that a right-angled triangle would be formed.

The Theorem is named after a Greek who lived a thousand years after the stone rings were constructed. Was Pythagoras' Theorem discovered many years before Pythagoras himself?

But there are also stone rings whose triangle is based on a ratio of 8:9:12. Now, $8^2 + 9^2 = 145$, and $12^2 = 144$. So Pythagoras' Theorem just fails for this triangle.

The biggest angle of a 8, 9, 12 triangle is 89.6°. This is less than 90°, but we could not tell by eye the difference between an angle of 89.6° and one of 90°. It seems likely that the sides of right-angled triangles were found by trial and error. Sometimes an exact right-angle was found, sometimes it was slightly inaccurate.

Stone graph paper

There are other megalithic monuments beside the rings. There are isolated stones and stones placed along the sides of a rectangle. In sites in Scotland and Brittany the stones are laid out in rows. The photograph shows the rows at Carnac in Brittany.

A diagram of part of the rows is on the right. Notice that the rows are not parallel. For whatever reason, they spread out in a fan-shape.

Let x represent the distance at the left-hand end of each row from the top. Let y be the amount by which this has decreased at the right-hand end. We can plot y against x as shown.

Notice that the points fall on a regular curve. It is similar to the curve of a quadratic graph. In fact the values of x and y fit the equation $y = 0.001x^2$ very closely. Is the arrangement meant to be a sort of "stone graph paper"? Did the builders plan such a regular relationship, or did it just happen because of the way the stones were laid out?

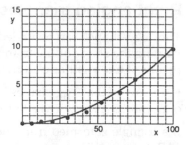

The direction of sunrise

The biggest mystery is the purpose of these great monuments, which must have required enormous amounts of labour from primitive societies. It has been known for a long time that the main axis of Stonehenge points towards where the sun will rise on midsummer day. Over the past few decades much research has been done in finding other alignments of the stones, to do with the positions of the moon and stars as well as the sun.

In Ireland there is a burial site called Newgrange. The burial chamber is at the right of the diagram, and there is a passage of length 19 m leading up to it. It was found that at dawn on midwinter's day the sun would shine down the whole length of the passage to illuminate the burial chamber.

Newgrange

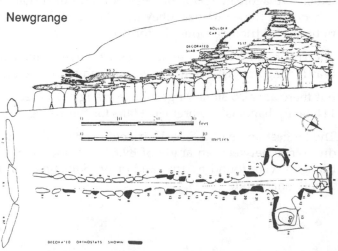

So it is very possible that Newgrange was aligned towards midwinter sunrise, though we cannot tell whether this was for religious or scientific purposes. But it is not absolutely certain – if the sun rises at any bearing between 113° and 116° then its rays will reach the burial chamber. This happens for a few days before and after midwinter, so the alignment may be coincidental.

Purpose

As there are no written records we should be very cautious when deciding the purpose of these monuments. Many stones have fallen down and been replaced, the earth itself has shifted. Any deduction based on the present position of the stones is guesswork. The people who built the monuments may have had reasons and techniques which we know nothing about.

The mathematics of megaliths

The study of these monuments raises many questions about the mathematical knowledge of their builders. Material from Chapters 7, 12, 15 and 18 has been touched upon.

Extended task. Centres of triangles

Triangles seem to be very simple objects. But there is an enormous quantity of geometric results that can be found concerning them. For this investigation you will need to construct triangles as accurately as you can.

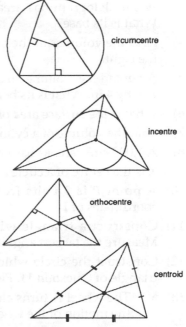

There are several centres associated with triangles. The first two appeared in Chapter 14.

A. **Circumcentre.** This is the centre of the circle which goes through the points of the triangle. It is found by constructing the perpendicular bisectors of the sides, and seeing where they intersect.

B. **Incentre.** This is the centre of the circle which touches the sides of the triangle. It is found by bisecting the angles of the triangle, and seeing where they intersect.

C. **Orthocentre.** This is found by taking perpendiculars from the points of the triangle to its sides.

D. **Centroid.** This is found by joining each corner of the triangle to the midpoint of the opposite side.

Draw several triangles on separate sheets of paper. Take a variety of triangles: your selection should include triangles which are acute-angled, obtuse-angled, right-angled, equilateral and isosceles. For each triangle construct as accurately as you can the four centres above. Things to look for are:

a) When are the centres inside the triangles?

b) When do the centres coincide?

c) Which of the centres lie on a straight line?

d) What are the distances between the centres?

e) One of these centres is the centre of gravity. Cut one of these triangles out of fairly stiff cardboard, and try to balance it on the point of a pin. Where must the point be put?

If you think you have found a relationship, investigate further by checking it with other triangles. See whether you can show why the relationship holds.

Miscellaneous exercises

Group A

1) The lines on the diagram below are 1 cm apart. Find the areas of the shapes (a), (b) and (c) shown.

2) A circle has area 3.5 cm². Find its radius and circumference.

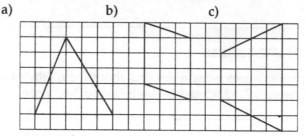

a)   b)   c)

3) A parallelogram has area 80 cm² and height 4 cm. What is its base?

4) Find the volumes of the cuboid and prism shown on the right.

a)   b)

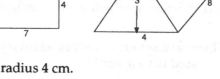

5) A cuboid has volume 36 cubic inches, and its base is 2 in by 4 in. What is its height?

6) What is the surface area of the cuboid of Question 5?

7) Find the volume of a cylinder which is 8 cm high and has base radius 4 cm.

8) A 1,000 cm³ can has base radius 6 cm. What is its height?

9) X is the centre of a circle and AB is a chord. If $A\hat{X}B = 44°$ find $X\hat{A}B$.

10) A point P is 3 units from the point (1,1), and is 2 units above the x-axis. Find the possible coordinates of P.

11) Construct a triangle with sides 6.5 cm, 5.5 cm, 4.5 cm. Measure the largest angle of the triangle.

12) Construct the circle which goes through the vertices of the triangle of Question 11. Find the radius of this circle.

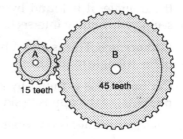

13) a) The wheel A turns clockwise twice every second. Predict the motion of the wheel B.

    b) The rope X is pulled down at $\frac{1}{2}$ m per second. Describe the motion of the pulley block Y.

14) ABCDEFGH is a cube of side 1, with ABCD and EFGH opposite faces.

    a) If A, B, C, D are placed at (0,0,0), (0,0,1), (0,1,1), (0,1,0) respectively, where could the other vertices be?

    b) If A and B are placed at (0,0,0) and (0,0,1) respectively, where could the other vertices be?

    c) If A is placed at (0,0,0), where could the other vertices be?

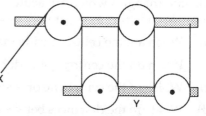

15) From where I stand, there is a mountain 10 km North and 5 km East. The mountain is 2 km higher than I am.

    a) Taking the origin at my position, what are the coordinates of the mountain top?

    b) Taking the origin at the mountain top, what are my coordinates?

16) Let $\mathbf{a} = \begin{pmatrix} 2 \\ 1 \end{pmatrix}$ and $\mathbf{b} = \begin{pmatrix} 3 \\ 4 \end{pmatrix}$.

   a)   Find $\mathbf{a} + \mathbf{b}$ and $2\mathbf{a}$.

   b)   Illustrate on a diagram the vectors $\mathbf{a}, \mathbf{b}, \mathbf{a} + \mathbf{b}$.

   c)   Where would the translation corresponding to $\mathbf{a}$ take (4,5)?

17) What vector goes from (2,7) to (5,8)? Where would the translation corresponding to this vector take (1,3)?

18) Plot the triangle with vertices at A(1,2), B(3,0), C(-1,-2). Δ ABC is enlarged by a scale factor of $\frac{1}{2}$ about (1,0). Draw the enlarged triangle and write down its coordinates.

19) The triangle ABC of Question 18 is enlarged by a factor of –2 about A(1,2). Draw the enlarged triangle and write down its coordinates.

20) In the diagram, ΔABC is similar to Δ XYZ.

   a)   If AB = 8, XY = 2 and XZ = $1\frac{1}{2}$ find AC.

   b)   If AC = 4 , BC = 3 and YZ = $1\frac{1}{2}$ find XZ.

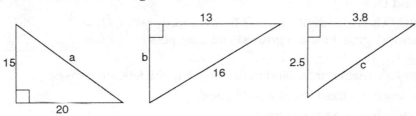

21) Find the unknown sides in the triangles below.

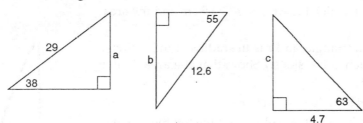

22) In Δ ABC, Â = 90°, AB = 12 m and BC = 17 m. Find AC.

23) Find the sides of the triangles below:

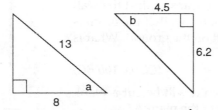

24) Find the angles of the triangles below:

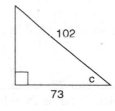

25) a)   In Δ ABC, B̂ = 90°, AB = 8 and AC = 14. Find Â.

   b)   In Δ PQR, P̂ = 90°, QR = 7, Q̂ = 53°. Find PQ.

26) On a computer screen, a line is drawn from bottom left (at (0,0)) to the point with coordinates at (230,140). What angle does this line make with the horizontal?

Group B. Challenge questions

27) In the diagram on the right, ATD and BTC are tangents to both circles. What can you say about Δ TAB and ΔTCD? What can you say about AB and CD?

28) TA and TB are tangents to a circle centre X. What sort of figure is TAXB?

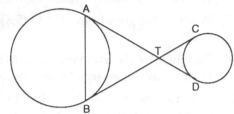

29) (For draughts players) If we take a draughts board as a coordinate grid with x-axis along the base line for White, then the moves for white are given by the vectors $\binom{1}{1}$ and $\binom{-1}{1}$.

Write down the moves for Black and for the kings.

30) (For chess players) Write in terms of vectors the moves for chess pieces.

31) In the diagram shown, $A\hat{C}B = C\hat{B}D = 90°$, $\hat{A} = 29°$, $AB = 12$ cm and $BD = 11$ cm. Find $\hat{D}$.

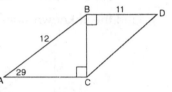

32) In triangle ABC, AB is exactly 10 cm, and $B\hat{C}A$ is exactly 90°. $C\hat{A}B = 35°$ to the nearest degree. Find the greatest and least possible values of BC.

33) P is the centre of a variable circle. Find the locus of P in the following cases:
   a) The circle touches a fixed line at a fixed point.
   b) The circle touches two parallel lines.
   c) The circle touches two non-parallel lines.

34) The base BC of a triangle ABC is fixed. If the area of the triangle is constant find the locus of A.
   Construct a triangle for which BC = 6 cm, AC = 5 cm and the area of Δ ABC is 9 cm².

35) a, b, c are the sides of a triangle, and r is the radius of the incircle. (The circle which touches the sides.) Show that the area of the triangle is $\frac{1}{2}r(a + b + c)$.

Questions 36 to 38 come from early books of problems

36) a) A bamboo is 10 *ch'ih* tall. It is broken, and the top touches the ground 3 *ch'ih* from the root. What is the height of the break?

   b) The height of a wall is 10 *ch'ih*. A beam leans against the wall so that its top is precisely at the top of the wall. If the beam is pulled 1 *ch'ih* from the wall, it lies flat on the ground. What is the length of the beam?

   (China, 100 BC)

37) A tree trunk has diameter 25 inches. From it will be cut a plank which is 7 inches thick. What is the width of the plank?

   (China, 200 AD)

156

38) On a pillar 9 cubits high is perched a peacock. From a distance of 27 cubits, a snake is coming to its hole at the bottom of the pillar. Seeing the snake, the peacock pounces upon it. If their speeds are equal, at what distance from the hole is the snake caught?

(Bhaskara, India, 1150 AD)

Group C. Longer exercises

39) Pythagoras and trigonometry

Both Pythagoras's Theorem and Trigonometry deal with right-angled triangles. In many cases the same problem can be solved in two different ways.

a)   In the diagram AB = 8, AC = 7, $\hat{C}$ = 90°.

Find $\hat{B}$ and then BC by trigonometry.

Find BC by Pythagoras. Do your answers agree?

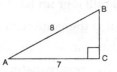

b)   Try some other triangles, and check that you do get the same answer by both methods.

c)   Your calculator gives separate buttons for sin, cos and tan. But we could get by with just one of them.

In the triangle shown, the hypoteneuse AB is 1. Find AC and BC in terms of $\hat{A}$.

What does Pythagoras tell us about the relationship between sin $\hat{A}$ and cos $\hat{A}$?

Suppose sin $\hat{A}$ = 0.7. Find cos $\hat{A}$ without using the cos button on your calculator. Put these values into the diagram above to find tan $\hat{A}$.

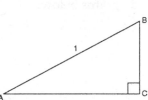

40) A Chinese Proof of Pythagoras

A proof of Pythagoras's theorem appears in a Chinese book written by Liu Hui, in about 250 AD.

a)   The tilted square is made up out of 4 triangles and a little square in the middle. What are the two smaller sides of each triangle?

What is the total area of the tilted square? What is the side of the square, and hence the longer side of the triangles?

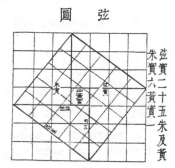

b)   The diagram given is a particular triangle. But the proof works for any right-angled triangle. Say the sides are *a*, *b* and *c* as shown.

By considering the area of the tilted square, show that

$$c^2 = 4(\tfrac{1}{2}ab) + (a - b)^2.$$

Expand out the right hand side and simplify. What do you get?

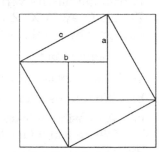

Revision exercises

Group A

1)   The lines of the grid at the top of the next page are 1 unit apart. Find the areas of the shaded shapes.

a)   b)   c)

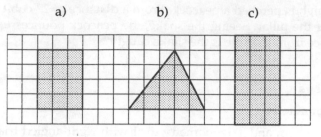

2)   Find the area and circumference of a circle with radius 4.5 cm.

3)   A parallelogram has base 4 cm and area 44 cm². What is its height?

4)   What is the volume of a cuboid which is 3 cm by 4.5 cm by 6 cm?

5)   Find the areas of the shapes on the right

  a)   by approximating with a rectangle

  b)   by tracing onto squared paper and counting the squares.

a)   b)

6)   By measurement or calculation find the angles in the diagrams below:

a

57

b

7)   Which of the diagrams below represent reflections and which rotations?

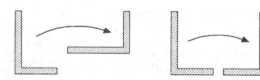

8)   On the right are some Chinese characters. Describe their symmetry.

中 田 生

9)   A triangle has its vertices at X(1,1), Y(3,1), Z(1,2). Draw Δ XYZ on graph paper, and enlarge it by a scale factor of 2.

10) The diagram on the right shows a 4 by 6 grid, lettered A to X.

  a)   What translation will take G to P?

  b)   What translation will take N to E?

  c)   A translation takes M to J. Where will this translation take G? Where will it take N?

A	B	C	D	E	F
G	H	I	J	K	L
M	N	O	P	Q	R
S	T	U	V	W	X

  d)   Describe the transformation which takes the block AGMN to the block EKQP.

  e)   Describe the transformation which takes AGMN to QKED.

  f)   Describe the transformation which takes AGMN to LKJP.

  g)   Describe the transformation which takes MST to AGMSTUV.

158

11) Find the interior angle of a regular polygon with: a) 8 sides   b) 15 sides.

12) The sum of the internal angles of a polygon is 900°. How many sides are there?

13) Each internal angle of a regular polygon is 160°. How many sides does it have?

14) The interior angle of a regular polygon is four times the external angle. How many sides does it have?

15) Which of the following could be the internal angle of a regular polygon? In each possible case give the number of sides.

   a)   175°   b)   165°   c)   145°   d)   150°   e)   130°

16) a)   You have several tiles in the shape of the isosceles triangle shown. Show how it is possible to tessellate a floor with them.

   b)   You have several tiles in the shape of the right-angled triangle shown. Show how it is possible to tessellate a floor with them.

17) a)   A map is in the scale of the map of 1 cm to 4 km. What is the real distance corresponding to 1.5 cm on the map?

   b)   The grid lines on this map are 1 cm apart. What is the distance between the points with grid references 213455 and 213480?

18) An architect's drawing of a building is 1.5 m long. The real building is 30 m long. What is the scale of the diagram?

19) The prism shown on the right has cross-section of a triangle with sides 3, 4, 5. The length of the prism is 6. Draw the plan and elevation of the prism.

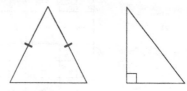

20) Draw the prism of Question 19 on isometric paper.

21) The shape on the right is called a tetrahedron. How many faces, edges and vertices does it have? Draw a net for the solid.

22) A pyramid has a square base ABCD of side 10 cm. The vertex V is 10 cm above A. Draw the plan and elevation of VABCD if it is:

   a)   resting on its base ABCD   b)   resting on a face VAB.

23) A triangle ABC has AB = 7 cm, $\hat{A}$ = 53°, $\hat{B}$ = 59°. Construct the triangle and measure BC.

Puzzles and paradoxes

1)   Suppose the wheel on the right rolls through a complete circle, so that A goes to A′ and B goes to B′.

   The point on the rim of the outer circle has gone through a distance of $2\pi R$, where R is the radius of the outer circle. Similarly the point on the rim of the inner circle has gone through $2\pi r$, where r is the radius of the inner circle.

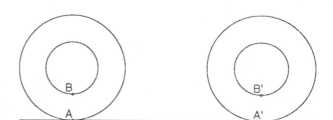

   But AA′ = BB′, so $2\pi R = 2\pi r$, giving $R = r$. What has gone wrong?

2) The square below is an 8 by 8 grid like a chessboard. It is cut up into four pieces, which are then reassembled as shown.

Try it by cutting up a piece of squared paper.

The original square is 8 by 8, so has 64 little squares. The rectangle is 5 by 13, so has 65 little squares. Where has the extra square come from?

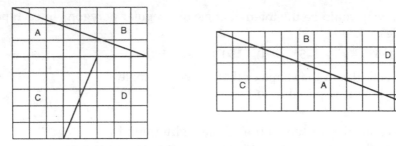

3) The rings below are called "Borromean Rings". Can they be pulled apart? If one of the rings was removed, would the remaining two be linked together?

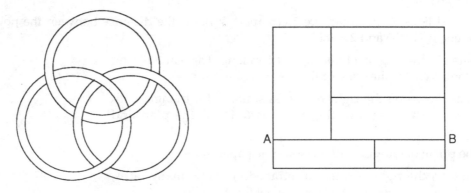

4) Suppose we dissect up a rectangle into smaller rectangles as shown (above). A dissection has a fault if there is a line crossing the rectangle, either from top to bottom or from right to left.

The dissection shown does have a fault, as there is a line going from A to B. What is the smallest possible number of rectangles in a dissection with no faults?

Chapter 20
Collecting data

You receive the leaflet shown. Is the question fair?

You are invited to reply by post. A month later it is announced that 98% of the replies were against the proposal. Does this mean that 98% of the town is against the proposal?

> Coketown Council proposes to widen the A175 access road. This will result in heavy lorries passing through Wig Green.
>
> Write to us with your opinions on the proposal.

> We received 500 letters about the Council's road proposal. Of these 490 were against.
>
> This proves that 98% of Coketown is opposed to the proposal. Think again, Councillors!

Fig 20.1

20.1 Questionnaires to test opinion

To find public opinion on a topic, a questionnaire is used. A selected number of people are asked what they think about a proposed change, or which products they prefer, and the results are then analysed.

It is important that the questionnaire is worded in an unbiased way. That is, the question must not make it easier to respond in one way rather than another.

It is also important to question a representative selection of people. The results of a questionnaire will not be reliable if all the people questioned came from the same group of society.

20.1.1 Example

The "Starlite Club" is applying for a licence to stay open until 3 a.m. Plan a questionnaire which would test public opinion on the subject.

Solution   Some people might want somewhere to go to late at night, but others might resent the extra noise caused. The wording of the questionnaire must not emphasize either of these points. It would be wrong to ask: "Would you welcome the provision of late night entertainment proposed by the Starlite Club?" or "Do you think that the Starlite's Club proposal will result in excessive disturbance?". The question asked should be as neutral as possible. It could ask:

"Do you support the Starlite Club's application for a late night licence?"

A balanced selection of people should be asked. To stand outside a local college would give too many people in favour of the proposal, and to knock on doors of nearby houses would give too many against it.

It would be better to stand in a public place, for example a nearby shopping centre on a Saturday morning. You would then be able to meet people of varied age and occupation. You would also get a reasonable balance between local residents and visitors.

20.1.2 Exercises

In each of the following design a questionnaire to test opinion or preference. Describe also how you would collect responses.

1) The local council is proposing to make the centre of your town a pedestrian precinct. Should this be done?

2) Should the metric system become compulsory for all food and drink sold?

3) What form should the rail link from the Channel Tunnel to London take?

4) Should there be a pedestrian crossing outside your school? And should it be a Zebra or a Pelican crossing?

5) Which of the popular soap-operas are watched most frequently?

6) Which sport is supported most?

7) How frequently do people go to the cinema?

8) Should temperature in weather reports be given in Fahrenheit as well as Centigrade?

9) A school is considering making recycling of paper compulsory. To test opinion a form is sent round. What would be a fair question to put on the form?

10) Is the question in the problem at the beginning of the chapter fair? Rephrase it if you think it is biased.

11) In the problem at the beginning of the chapter, opinions were found from the responses to the leaflet. Is this an unbiased way to test opinion? If you think not, devise a way by which opinion could be tested.

20.2 Finding a connection

There is often a connection or correlation between two quantities. This can be tested by collecting data, and plotting the results on a graph. The result is called a scatter diagram. If the points lie roughly on a straight line then there probably is a connection.

The best line that can be drawn through the points is the line of best fit. This line can then be used to predict other results.

Fig 20.2

20.2.1 Example

The table below gives the height and weight of 10 children. Plot the results on a scatter diagram, and draw a line of best fit. Predict the weight of a child who is 4' 9" tall.

Height	4'8"	4'6"	4'2"	5'0"	5'2"	4'6"	4'7"	4'1"	4'3"	4'5"
Weight (lb)	73	66	51	77	69	63	80	49	54	60

Solution With height along the x-axis, and weight up the y-axis, the values are plotted as shown in Fig 20.3.

Draw a line through the points. Read off from the line the weight corresponding to a height of 4' 9".

The child might weigh 70 lb

20.2.2 Exercises

1) A group of 10 pupils took tests in French and Maths. The results are below. Plot the points on a scatter diagram, and draw a line of best fit. If an eleventh pupil got 17 in French, what would you expect the Maths mark to be?

French	16	10	9	22	28	15	20	12	23	15
Maths	23	29	11	20	25	18	20	10	19	12

2) The ages and heights of 10 children are shown below. (Ages in months). Plot the values on a scatter diagram, and draw a line of best fit. Predict the height of a 12 year old child.

Age	120	105	93	130	135	120	92	80	85	90
Height	4'8"	4'6"	4'2"	5'0"	5'2"	4'6"	4'7"	4'1"	4'3"	4'5"

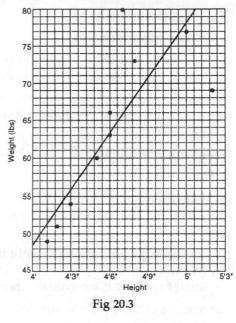

Fig 20.3

3) A group of 12 fifth-formers were asked how many hours of television they watched per week. This was then checked with their grade in Maths GCSE. The results are below:

Hours	10	0	15	12	5	9	16	8	17	23	12	8
Grade	B	C	F	A	D	C	A	G	G	D	C	A

Is there any connection?

4) The profits of a small business in the first 8 years after it was started are given below.

Year	1	2	3	4	5	6	7	8
Profit in £1,000's	12	22	24	21	28	32	39	41

Plot these points, and draw a line of best fit. What do you predict for the profit in the 9th year?

5) A car is driven at different speeds, and the fuel economy is recorded. The speed is given in m.p.h., and the economy in m.p.g.

Speed	30	40	50	60	70	80
Economy	48	44	40	33	30	25

Plot these points, and draw a line of best fit. What is the economy at 55 m.p.h.? If 70 miles must be travelled on 2 gallons, what is the maximum speed?

6) An inaccurate weighing machine was tested by various weights being put on it. The results are below.

True weight (kg)	1	1.5	2	2.5	3
Recorded weight	0.9	1.3	2.1	2.3	3.1

Plot these points, and draw a line of best fit. If an object is recorded as weighing 1.6 kg, what is its true weight?

20.3 Longer exercises

A. Using a questionnaire

In the exercises of this Chapter all the issues were decided for you. It would be more interesting to conduct an investigation about something which you have thought up.

Find some issue which you are interested in. Devise a questionnaire to find out what other people think. If you yourself feel deeply about the subject be sure that you do not let this bias the questions.

Submit the questionnaire to several people, making sure that you obtain a reasonably balanced group. Write up the results and state your conclusions.

B. Finding a connection

In all the exercises on scatter diagrams of this Chapter the figures were given for you. It would be more interesting for you to collect the information yourself, to see whether there is a connection between two quantities.

Think of two quantities which might be connected. Measure both of them in several cases, and plot the results on a scatter diagram. See whether or not they are sufficiently in a straight line for you to be confident that there is a correlation between them.

Suggestions of things to measure are:

    a) Foot size and hand size.

    b) The heights of children and their parents.

    c) Weather and sales of cold drinks in a canteen.

Multiple choice question *(Tick appropriate box)*

The scatter diagram on the right shows the English and History marks of 12 pupils.

From a line of best fit, you would expect the History mark of someone who got 40 in English to be:

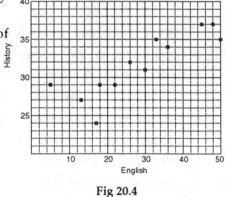

Fig 20.4

a)   33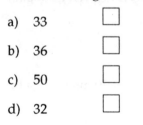

b)   36

c)   50

d)   32

Points to note

1) *Questionnaires*

   a) The question asked must not be biased, so that the people who respond are nudged towards one particular answer.

   b) The people who are asked should not come from one small section of the community.

2) *Scatter diagrams*

   a) The line you draw does not necessarily go through the origin.

   b) The line you draw does not necessarily go through the first and last points. These may be exceptional.

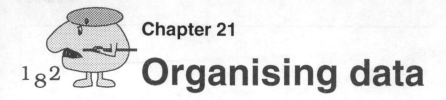

Chapter 21

Organising data

A golf club awards a cup for the best newcomer. There are two contenders, and their scores for going round the course are:

    A: 80, 83, 79, 77, 88, 80, 71, 90.

    B: 81, 82, 80, 82, 83, 78, 79, 83.

Who has the lower scores? Who is most consistent?

Fig 21.1

21.1 Averages

When presented with a whole mass of numbers it is not easy to see what the general pattern is, or to draw conclusion about the numbers as a whole. It is often useful to find a single number which summarizes all the original numbers. This number is called an average.

There are several widely used averages.

Mean

The mean of a set of numbers is what is normally meant by the word average. To find the mean of n numbers, add all the numbers together and divide by n.

The mean of 1, 1, 1, 2, 4, 6, 6 is:

$$(1 + 1 + 1 + 2 + 4 + 6 + 6) \div 7 = 3$$

Median

The median of a set of numbers is the middle number. There are as many numbers less than the median as greater than it. The median of the numbers above is 2.

With 9 numbers, the median is the 5th. With 8 numbers, the median is halfway between the 4th and the 5th.

Mode

The mode of a set of numbers is the most commonly occuring number. The mode of the numbers above is 1.

Range

The range of a set of numbers is the difference between the highest and the lowest numbers. The range of the numbers above is $6 - 1 = 5$.

21.1.1 Examples

1) 12 children took a test, and their marks out of 10 were as follows:

8, 8, 7, 7, 6, 8, 9, 5, 6, 7, 7, 6.

Find the mean, the mode and the range.

Solution   For the mean, find the sum of all the marks.

$8 + 8 + 7 + 7 + 6 + 8 + 9 + 5 + 6 + 7 + 7 + 6 = 84.$

Divide by 12 to obtain:

The mean mark is $\frac{84}{12} = 7$

The most common mark is 7, which occurs 4 times.

The mode is 7

The highest score is 9, and the lowest is 5.

The range is 4

2) In 8 successive innings, a batsman scored the following:

45, 65, 4, 0, 76, 12, 8, 30.

Find his median score.

Solution   Re-arrange the eight scores in increasing order:

0, 4, 8, 12, 30, 45, 65, 76.

The median score is between his fourth best and his fifth best. Take halfway between 12 and 30:

The median is 21

21.1.2 Exercises

1) Find the mean, mode and range of the following numbers:

5, 6, 4, 5, 10, 3, 9, 4, 9, 5.

2) Find the mean, median and range of the following numbers:

23, 38, 20, 30, 31, 19, 27, 24, 32, 26.

3) 8 children were asked to measure the width of their right hands. The results were (in cm):

6.3, 7.1, 5.8, 6.0, 5.5, 5.8, 6.2, 5.3.

Find the mean and the median of these widths.

4) A football team scored the following number of goals in 12 matches:

0, 3, 1, 0, 2, 3, 6, 3, 4, 0, 2, 0.

Find the mean and mode of these scores.

5) 8 packets of butter were weighed and found to be:

    252 g, 247 g, 253 g, 250 g, 250 g, 248 g, 247 g, 246 g.

    Find the mean weight and the median weight.

6) For the seven days of his holiday George measured the hours of sunshine. His results were:

    8.3, 7.3, 2.1, 9.0, 6.5, 7.3, 8.5.

    Find the mean and median of these figures. Find the range of values.

7) The 8 classes of a year at a school contain the following number of pupils:

    27, 28, 24, 25, 26, 25, 26, 25.

    Find the mean and median number of pupils per class.

8) Don and Ron are gardeners. Don is employed by the council, while Ron is self-employed. Over an eight week period they worked the following numbers of hours. Find the mean and range in each case. Comment on the results.

    Don: 40, 43, 38, 39, 41, 42, 42, 44

    Ron: 38, 43, 52, 21, 60, 30, 20, 40

9) Estate agents in two towns each gave the prices of 8 three-bedroom flats. Find the mean and median in each case. Comment on your results.

    Town A. Prices in £1,000's.:   150, 68, 66, 62, 69, 52, 55, 62

    Town B. Prices in £1,000's.:   73, 69, 81, 50, 56, 69, 72, 79

10) Over 10 weeks the average temperature in two places was measured. Find the mean and range in each case. Comment on your results.

    A: −4, 5, 6, 7, 7, 8, 6, 6, 9, 12

    B: 3, 5, 4, 7, 7, 10, 4, 3, 6, 4

11) Two classes each entered 9 children for a race. The results are below. Find the means and medians. Comment on your results.

    Class A: 12.4, 13.1, 13.3, 13.6, 12.9, 13.8, 13.3, 12.8, 21.4

    Class B: 13.2, 13.8, 13.9, 14.1, 12.5, 13.7, 13.6, 14.0, 13.9

12) At the beginning of this chapter there was a problem about golf scores. Find the mean and range for each golfer. Who do you think should get the cup?

21.2 Frequency tables

It is very difficult to draw any conclusions from a large amount of data. It is easier to understand if it is organized into a frequency table.

Means can be found from the frequency table, though they are often only an approximation.

21.2.1 Examples

1) A survey was made of 100 families, to investigate the number of children in each family. The results are given in the following frequency table:

Number of children	0	1	2	3	4	5	6	7	8+
Number of families	11	24	35	16	9	3	1	1	0

Find the mean number of children per family and the median number.

Solution   The total number of children is found by multiplying the numbers of children by the frequencies.

$$0 \times 11 + 1 \times 24 + 2 \times 35 + 3 \times 16 + 4 \times 9 + 5 \times 3 + 6 \times 1 + 7 \times 1 + 8 \times 0 = 206$$

There are 100 families in all, which gives:

The mean number is $\frac{206}{100} = 2.06$

The median number is the number of children such that half the families have more than that number, and half the families have less. Only an imperfect answer is possible here: 35 families have less than 2 children and 30 have more than 2. Hence:

The median number is 2

2) 48 children took an exam, and the results were as follows:

50 53 43 69 66 54 34 70 42 42 36 37

61 47 63 66 46 44 56 73 39 77 75 32

68 65 48 54 62 51 73 68 67 40 49 50

74 72 58 54 52 49 56 62 64 42 58 49

Make a frequency table for these figures, using a suitable class interval. Find the mean mark from the frequency table.

Solution   The marks go from 32 to 77. It would be appropriate to use class intervals of 10 marks. Count the number of marks in each interval and fill in the table below as shown:

Interval	30-39	40-49	50-59	60-69	70-79
Frequency	5	12	12	12	7

This table does not give the exact marks. But we will not be far wrong if we take the marks in each interval to be evenly spread. So for example in the first interval we can assume that the marks are evenly spread about the mid-interval value of 34.5. Make similar assumptions in the other intervals.

Find the total of the marks. Then divide by 48.

Total Marks $= 34.5 \times 5 + 44.5 \times 12 + 54.5 \times 12 + 64.5 \times 12 + 74.5 \times 7 = 2656$

Mean $= \frac{2656}{48} = 55.3$

21.2.2 Exercises

1) The first 500 words of a book were examined to see how many letters they contained. The results are shown in the following table:

Number of letters	1	2	3	4	5	6	7	8	9	10	11+
Frequency	15	34	45	76	106	94	79	41	6	3	1

Find the mean, the mode and the median number of letters per word.

2) A class of 24 children were asked how many books they had read in the previous week. 6 had read none, 8 had read 1, 6 had read 2, 3 had read 3 and one had read 4. Find the mean number of books read.

3) The Ministry of Transport conducted a survey in a certain area to see how many driving tests people have before they pass. The results are as follows:

Number of tests	1	2	3	4	5	6	7	8+
Frequency	131	52	25	19	11	7	4	1

Find the mean number of tests needed to pass.

4) The 50 people at a party had ages given below:

44 32 33 27 40   56 54 61 11 12   17 18 28 30 31

15 63 56 65 48   44 44 30 55 26   18 50 48 21 24

15 30 41 23 56   59 24 20 19 38   51 58 37 43 19

19 26 19 31 18

Set up a frequency table, using a class interval of 10 years. Find the mean age from the frequency table.

5) The heights in cm of 60 boys were as follows:

145 141 126 127 130 142   142 146 139 136 130 129

132 137 133 148 142 141   144 135 133 148 140 145

125 135 140 144 139 138   138 141 147 132 133 138

139 149 142 135 128 131   136 145 138 144 140 132

139 148 138 136 130 125   132 135 143 138 134 131

Set up a frequency table, using a class interval of 5 cm. Use the table to estimate the mean height.

6) The salaries in £1,000's of 50 employees of a firm were as follows:

15 16 9 35 10   28 10 8 12 18   24 47 16 13 18

14 38 21 9 29   26 25 16 14 23   18 11 9 10 19

42 27 26 12 13   19 9 19 17 13   10 14 13 9 11

29 9 11 10 18

Set up a frequency table, using an appropriate class interval. Estimate the mean salary from the table.

21.3 Longer exercises

Other kinds of mean

1) The mean we have dealt with so far is called the Arithmetic Mean. To find the Arithmetic mean of n numbers, we add up all the numbers and divide by n. Just for practice, find the Arithmetic Mean of the following 7 numbers:

    54, 55, 56, 57, 55, 57, 58 ... ... *

    What eighth number should be added to take the mean to 60?

Another sort of mean is called the Geometric Mean. To find the Geometric Mean of n numbers we multiply them together and take the n'th root.

So, for example, the Geometric mean of 8, 7 and 10 is $\sqrt[3]{8 \times 7 \times 10} = 8.24$.

2) Find the Geometric Mean of the 7 numbers * above. What eighth number should be added to take the mean to 60?

Take several groups of numbers, and find their Arithmetic and Geometric means. Which is greater?.

3) A third sort of mean is called the Harmonic Mean. To find the Harmonic Mean of n numbers, we write down the inverse of each of the numbers, and then find their (Arithmetic) mean. Invert this again to get the Harmonic Mean.

So for example the Harmonic Mean of 8, 7, 10 is given by: $\dfrac{1}{H} = \dfrac{1}{3}\left(\dfrac{1}{8} + \dfrac{1}{7} + \dfrac{1}{10}\right)$. $H = 8.16$

Find the Harmonic Mean of the 7 numbers * above. What eighth number should be added to take the mean to 60?

Multiple choice question *(Tick appropriate box)*

The number of strokes taken by 25 golfers at a certain hole is given by the following table:

Number of Strokes	3 4 5 6 7 8
Frequency	2 9 7 4 2 1

The mean number of strokes is:

a) 4   ☐

b) 20.5   ☐

c) 5   ☐

d) 3.73   ☐

e) 4.92   ☐

Points to note

1) Be sure that you know the difference between the three averages, mean, median, mode. They are often confused.

2) *Mean*

   a) If the mean of a set of values is not an integer, don't round it to the nearest whole number. Though a family must have a whole number of children, it still makes sense to say that:

      "The mean family size is 2.4 children."

   b) When finding a mean from a frequency table, be sure that you are finding the mean of the figures, not of the frequencies.

   c) When finding a mean from a frequency table, be sure that you divide by the total of the frequencies, not by the number of classes. If your frequency table is:

Number of children in family	0	1	2	3	4	5
Frequency	10	27	34	22	15	12

      Be sure that you divide by 120 (the number of families) not by 6 (the number of classes). If you do the wrong thing you will get an absurdly large answer.

   d) When the figures in a frequency table are given by a range of values, make sure that you take the middle of the range for working out the mean. It may not be perfect, but it is the best that can be done in the circumstances.

3) *Median*

   When working out the median, be sure that you take the middle value. The median of 19 numbers is not 9, it is the 9th number.

Chapter 22
Illustrating data

You are saving up to buy a computer. The amounts you save each month are shown on the right.

How could you show the total saved? When will you reach the required amount of £520?

22.1 Frequency polygons

Suppose we are given a histogram for a distribution. The line going through the centre of the top of each bar is a frequency polygon.

The shape of this polygon will tell us something about the distribution. If it is thin, then the measurements are all bunched together. If it is flat, then the measurements are widely separated. See Fig 22.2 below right.

22.1.1 Example

50 cats and 50 dogs were weighed. The results in kilograms are shown in the following frequency tables:

Weight of cats	Frequency	Weight of dogs	Frequency
1.0 - 1.5	2	1 - 2	2
1.5 - 2.0	7	2 - 3	5
2.0 - 2.5	18	3 - 4	6
2.5 - 3.0	13	4 - 5	5
3.0 - 3.5	8	5 - 6	4
3.5 - 4.0	2	6 - 7	7
		7 - 8	7
		8 - 9	6
		9 - 10	5
		10 - 11	3

On the same graph draw frequency polygons for both sets of data. What conclusions can you reach?

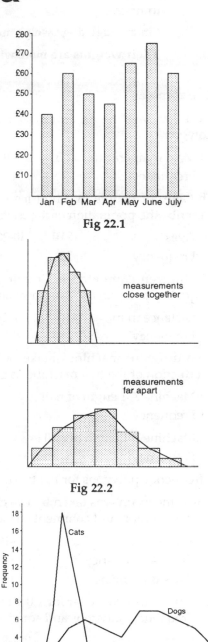

Fig 22.1

measurements close together

measurements far apart

Fig 22.2

Fig 22.3

Solution   There is no need to draw histograms. Plot points, taking mid-interval values as the *x*-coordinates and the frequencies as the *y*-coordinates. See Fig 22.3

Notice that the cat-polygon is to the left of the dog-polygon, and is much taller and thinner.

On average dogs weigh more than cats,

Their weights are more widely spread

22.1.2 Exercises

1) Over 200 days the maximum temperature was measured. The results are below. Draw a frequency polygon.

Max. temperature	0-5	5-10	10-15	15-20	20-25	25-30
Frequency	5	48	62	58	20	7

2) The ages of people in a housing estate are given in the table below. Draw a frequency polygon. Describe the population of the estate.

Ages	0-10	10-20	20-30	30-40	40-50	50-60	60-70
Frequency	53	21	38	48	21	8	3

3) 55 children competed in "putting the shot". The results are given in the table below. Plot a frequency polygon and comment on its shape.

Distance in m	0-1	1-2	2-3	3-4	4-5	5-6
Frequency	18	14	6	13	3	1

4) Two different machines make nails which are meant to be 5 cm long. The distributions of the production of the two machines is given in the tables below:

Machine A Length of nail	4.7-4.8	4.8-4.9	4.9-5.0	5.0-5.1	5.1-5.2
Frequency	5	10	38	42	5

Machine B Length of nail	4.7-4.8	4.8-4.9	4.9-5.0	5.0-5.1	5.1-5.2
Frequency	10	17	23	35	15

Draw frequency polygons for the two distributions. Comment on the difference between the machines.

5) The same exam was taken by two classes. The marks are shown below. Plot frequency polygons on the same graph and comment on the difference.

Marks	0-19	20-39	40-59	60-79	80-100
Class A frequency	5	6	8	4	2
Class B frequency	0	11	12	2	0

6) Two field guns were set for 1,000 m and were each fired 80 times. The results are shown below. Plot the frequency polygons and comment on the difference. Which is the better gun?

Distance in m	994-996	996-998	998-1000	1000-1002	1002-1004
Gun A frequency	2	36	32	10	0
Gun B frequency	12	13	21	25	9

22.2 Running totals

Suppose we have a sequence of numbers. If a total is kept at each stage this is a running total.

22.2.1 Example

In 10 matches a batsman scored 23, 14, 54, 68, 31, 101, 45, 2, 98, 76. Find the running total and illustrate it on a graph.

Solution   Find the running totals by adding the scores after each match.

The totals are 23, 37, 91, 159, 190, 291, 336, 338, 436, 512

These totals are plotted on the graph on the right.

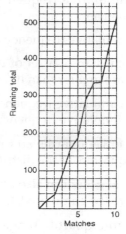

Fig 22.4

22.2.2 Exercises

1)   A church needs £25,000 for repairs to its roof. The money raised month by month is shown below. Find the running total of the money raised and illustrate it on a graph.

Jan	Feb	Mar	Apr	May	Jun	Jul	Aug	Sep	Oct
£2000	£1230	£1840	£1200	£1700	£2120	£3230	£1010	£3220	£4120

2)   The monthly sales of a book are shown below. Find the running total of the numbers sold and illustrate it.

Apr	May	Jun	Jul	Aug	Sep	Oct	Nov	Dec
1100	980	830	520	370	410	290	520	2320

3)   A driver keeps a record of how many miles he drives each week. Find the running total and illustrate it.

Week	1	2	3	4	5	6	7	8
Miles	154	273	337	184	429	381	264	381

4)   Millie owes £300. The amounts she pays off each month are shown below. Find the running total and illustrate it.

Feb	Mar	Apr	May	Jun	Jul	Aug
£35	£23	£18	£45	£29	£32	£48

5)   Look again at the problem at the beginning of the chapter. Find the running total of the amount saved. Illustrate the running total, showing when you are likely to reach the goal of £520.

22.3 Cumulative frequency

The thinness or thickness of a frequency polygon shows how widely apread the measurements are. Often it is useful to have an actual number to show the spread of measurements.

Suppose an exam is taken by 500 candidates. A histogram would give the number of candidates whose mark was between 40% and 50%. We might also want to know the number of candidates whose mark was less than 50%. This would be the total of all the frequencies up to 50%, called the cumulative frequency.

175

A cumulative frequency table gives the cumulative frequencies. It gives the running total of the frequencies.

A cumulative frequency chart gives a graph of the cumulative frequency.

The median of a set of measurements is the middle value. Half the measurements are less than it and half are greater than it.

The cumulative frequency chart can be used to find the median, by finding the point on the graph where the cumulative frequency is half the total frequency.

The lower quartile and upper quartile are defined similarly, as the points which cut off the bottom and top quarters of the distribution.

The quartiles can also be found from the cumulative frequency curve, by finding the points on the graph where the cumulative frequency is a quarter or three quarters of the total frequency.

The interquartile range is the difference between the quartiles. The interquartile range contains the "middle half" of the measurements. It is a guide to how widely spread the measurements are. If the interquartile range is small, then the middle half is bunched together in a small region. If the interquartile range is large, then the middle half is widely spread over a large region.

22.3.1 Example

A man did a survey of the prices of second-hand cars advertised in his local newspaper. The results were as follows:

Price Range	0-499	500-999	1000-1999	2000-2999	3000-4000
Frequency	7	10	27	23	13

a)   Fill up a cumulative frequency table.

b)   Draw a cumulative frequency curve.

c)   Find the median, the quartiles and the inter-quartile range.

d)   What proportion of cars cost less than £1,500?

Solution   a)   Fill in the third row of the table, adding up the frequencies as you go along:

Price Range	0-499	500-999	1000-1999	2000-2999	3000-4000
Frequency	7	10	27	23	13
Cum. Frequ.	7	17	44	67	80

b)   The horizontal axis represents price. Label it from £0 to £4,000. The vertical axis represents cumulative frequency. Label it from 0 to 80. Now draw the graph.

The points on the graph correspond to the endpoints of the intervals. 44 cars cost less than £2,000, so the point (2000,44) must lie on the graph. The graph is shown in Fig 22.5.

c) From the graph, 40 cars cost less than £1800.

The median is £1,800

20 cars cost less than £1,100, and 60 cars less than £2,600.

The lower quartile is £1,100. The upper quartile is £2,600

The interquartile range is £1,500

d) Take £1,500 on the horizontal axis. This corresponds to a cumulative frequency of 32.

The proportion of cars costing less than £1,500 is $\frac{32}{80} = \frac{2}{5}$

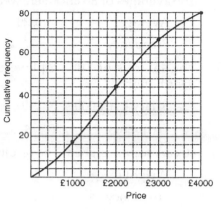

Fig 22.5

22.3.2 Exercises

1) The heights of 60 boys were measured. The results are shown on the following table:

Height in cm	150-160	160-170	170-180	180-190
Frequency	10	23	18	9

a) Fill up a cumulative frequency table.

b) Draw a cumulative frequency curve.

c) Find from your curve the median, the quartiles and the inter-quartile range.

d) What proportion of boys were more than 165 cm in height?

2) The weights of 80 eggs were found to be as follows:

Weight in grams	50-60	60-70	70-80	80-100	100-120
Frequency	7	15	28	19	11

a) Construct a cumulative frequency curve.

b) Draw a cumulative frequency graph.

c) From your graph find the median, the quartiles and the inter-quartile range.

d) What proportion of eggs lie between 60 and 90 grams?

For each of the situations in Questions 3 to 7:

a) Find the cumulative frequencies.

b) Draw a cumulative frequency chart.

c) Find the median, the quartiles and the inter-quartile range.

3) The ages of a group of 500 people at a cinema were as follows:

Age range	10-20	20-25	25-30	30-35	35-40	40-70
Frequency	74	73	104	116	67	66

4) The averages of 80 cricketers were compared. The figures are shown in the following table:

Average	0-20	20-30	30-40	40-50	50-80
Frequency	22	18	16	12	12

5) The salaries of 100 employees of a firm were analysed, and the following table shows the distribution:

Salary in £1,000's	7-9	9-10	10-11	11-12	12-13	13-16
Frequency	24	15	17	19	10	15

6) 60 cats were weighed. The results were as follows:

Weight in kg.	1-3	3-3.5	3.5-4	4-4.5	4.5-6
Frequency	20	9	15	10	6

7) 50 children ran 100 metres. Their times are given in the following table:

Time in secs.	12-14	14-15	15-15.5	15.5-16	16-17	17-20
Frequency	4	13	9	11	4	9

8) The same exam was taken by class A and class B. The results were as follows:

% Mark	0-29	30-39	40-49	50-59	60-69	70-100
Class A frequency	1	3	9	14	1	0
Class B frequency	2	5	7	7	4	3

Construct cumulative frequency tables for both the classes, and draw the cumulative frequency curves on the same sheet of graph paper. What is the difference between the curves?

Find the inter-quartile ranges for the two classes. What does the difference between the values tell you about the two classes?

9) Two golfers Lucy and Liz regularly play together over the same course. After they have each been round 40 times their scores are given by the following table:

Score	70-74	75-79	80-84	85-89	90-99	100-109
Lucy's frequency	2	3	23	7	5	0
Liz's frequency	5	8	14	5	4	4

Construct cumulative frequency tables for both players, and draw the cumulative frequency graphs on the same sheet of graph paper. Comment on the difference.

Evaluate the inter-quartile ranges for the two women. Explain the difference. Who do you think is the better player?

10) Find the interquartile ranges for the nails of Question 4 of 22.1.2. What can you conclude?

11) Find the interquartile ranges for the exam marks of Question 5 of 22.1.2. What does this tell you?

12) Find the interquartile ranges for the distances of Question 6 of 22.1.2. What does this tell you?

22.4 Longer exercise

Lies, damned lies and statistics

The point of Statistics is to summarize a mass of data, so that accurate conclusions can be drawn. But its techniques can be misused – without actually lying, presenting the data in such a way that false conclusions are drawn.

1) Look at the advertisement in Fig 22.6. Why is it misleading? How could you re-draw it so that it is honest?

2) Before an election, the opposition party puts out a pamphlet containing the diagram in Fig 22.7.

   Why is it misleading? Re-draw it so that it is honest.

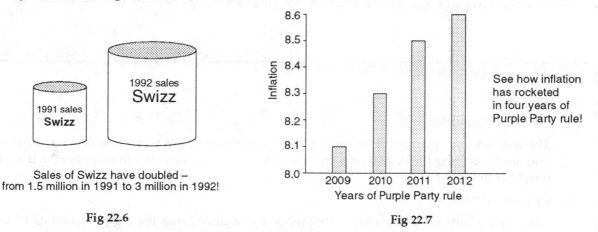

Sales of Swizz have doubled –
from 1.5 million in 1991 to 3 million in 1992!

Fig 22.6

See how inflation
has rocketed
in four years of
Purple Party rule!

Fig 22.7

3) You are the advertising manager of Miaou Catfood Ltd. Your tins, containing 100 grams, sell for 43 p, while the rival firm Purr plc makes tins of 80 grams for 32 p each. Can you present this information in a way which makes your product seem better value?

4) You are part of the campaign team for the party which has been governing for the last 4 years. The table below gives economic figures for the past 8 years: how do you present the information in a pamphlet to make it look favourable to your party?

Year	2005	2006	2007	2008	2009	2010	2011	2012
Employment 100,000's	300	301	302	305	306	308	312	311
Unemployment 1,000's	402	410	411	416	430	462	523	510

Multiple choice question *(Tick appropriate box)*

Two golfers went round the same course several times. The frequency polygons of their scores are shown in Fig 22.8. The conclusions that can be drawn are:

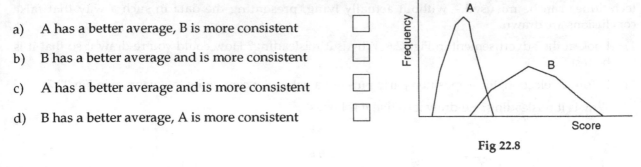

a) A has a better average, B is more consistent ☐

b) B has a better average and is more consistent ☐

c) A has a better average and is more consistent ☐

d) B has a better average, A is more consistent ☐

Fig 22.8

Points to note

1) *Median and quartiles*

   The median and quartiles must refer to the measurements, not to the frequencies. Suppose you are measuring the heights of 80 people. The lower quartile is not the number 20, it is the height of the 20th person.

2) *Cumulative frequency graphs*

   a) The points on a cumulative frequency curve must be at the right endpoints of the intervals, not at the middles.

   b) Don't join up the points on your cumulative frequency graph with straight lines. Draw as smooth a curve as you can between them.

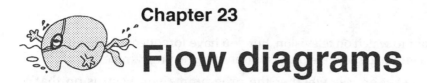

Chapter 23

Flow diagrams

A sick friend asks you to get fruit juice for him. His instructions are:

"Go to Maxwell's first, if they've got juice already chilled get that, otherwise go to Ace Grocery, if they charge less than 95p buy it there, otherwise go back to Maxwell's provided of course they've got it in stock otherwise you'll have to go to the supermarket."

These instructions are very muddling. Is there a way you could organize them so that they can be carried out easily?

Fig 23.1

23.1 Flow diagrams

A Flow Diagram or Flow Chart is a type of network diagram, used to describe the sequence of actions needed to complete a task. One important use of flow diagrams is to describe the operations we wish a computer to perform.

Flow diagrams contain orders and questions, which are put in different shaped boxes.

Orders tell us to do something. They are put in rectangles.

Questions ask us whether something is true. They are put in diamond-shaped boxes. Lines lead from the box according to the answer to the question.

The beginning and end of a flow diagram are sometimes shown by "Start" or "Stop" in circles.

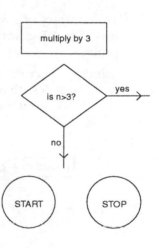

Fig 23.2

Input and output

When a number N is to be put into a flow diagram, we put "Input N", or "Read N".

When a number N is to be taken out of a flow diagram, to record a result, we put "Print N", or "Write N".

Giving values

If a number N is to be given the value 3, we put "N = 3". If N is to be given the same value as M, we put "N = M". If N is to be changed, maybe by adding 1, we write "N = N + 1".

23.1.1 Examples

1) There is a programme you want to watch on television, but you have forgotten whether it is on BBC1 or BBC2. Draw a flow diagram to show the process of finding the programme.

   Solution   After switching the set on, see whether the programme you want is on that channel. If it is stay and watch, if it isn't try the next channel. The flow diagram is below.

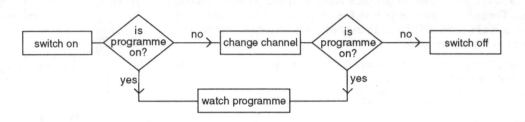

Fig 23.3

2) The accuracy of a weighing machine is decided by using it to weigh a 500 gram mass. If there is less than 1.5 gram error then it is reported as accurate. Write a flow diagram to show this process.

   Solution   Let the weight recorded be X. If X is bigger than 500, then we take X – 500, if it is less than 500 we take 500 – X. We then find whether this error is less than 1.5, and print the result accordingly. The flow diagram is below.

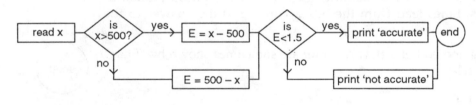

Fig 23.4

23.1.2 Exercises

1) The following instructions describe the making of toast. Re-arrange them in the correct order.

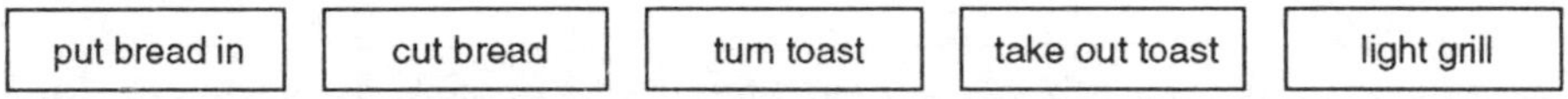

| put bread in | cut bread | turn toast | take out toast | light grill |

Fig 23.5

2) Re-arrange the following instructions to describe hand-washing.

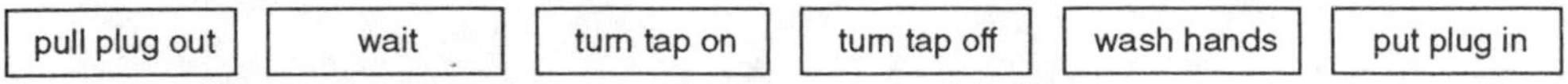

| pull plug out | wait | turn tap on | turn tap off | wash hands | put plug in |

Fig 23.6

182

3) To make a telephone call from a public call-box, you lift the receiver, put in money, dial the number, wait for an answer. Write a flow diagram to describe this process.

4) Write a flow diagram to evaluate the function $y = 3x^2 + 4$, breaking the function down into basic steps of adding, multiplying, squaring.

5) Using the same basic steps as in Question 4, write flow diagrams to evaluate the following:

   a) $y = 2x^2 - 5$ b) $y = 3(x + 4)$ c) $y = (x + 4)^2$

6) The parity function is defined by $f(x) = 1$ if x is odd, and $f(x) = 0$ if x is even. Write a flow chart to evaluate this.

7) The absolute difference of x and y is defined as $x - y$ if $x \geq y$, and as $y - x$ if $y \geq x$. Write a flow chart to evaluate this.

8) A measurement lies between 4 and 5. If it is less than 4.5 it is rounded down to 4, if it is at least 4.5 it is rounded up to 5. Write a flow diagram to describe this process.

9) Look at the problem at the beginning of the chapter. Write a flow chart which describes what to do.

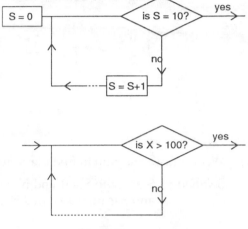

23.2 Loops in flow diagrams

Fig 23.7

In many tasks an operation has to be repeated, for a certain number of times or until a certain condition is satisfied. In these cases the flow diagram will contain a loop. Fig 23.7 (above right) shows two examples of a loop, both of which are described below.

If the operation is repeated 10 times, we have a counter which starts at 0 and is increased by 1 every time the loop is gone through. When the counter reaches 10 we move on to the next part of the flow diagram.

If an operation is repeated until a certain condition is satisfied, then before entering the loop we ask whether the condition is met. If it is then we move on to the next part of the flow diagram.

23.2.1 Examples

1) I can go to work either by train or by number 24 bus. My procedure is to go to the bus stop, and if a bus is in sight then I wait to see whether it is a number 24. If there is no bus in sight then I go to the station and take a train. Write a flow diagram to describe this procedure.

   Solution The steps of this procedure are shown in the flow diagram below. Note that if the bus which comes is not a 24, then I look to see whether there is another bus behind it.

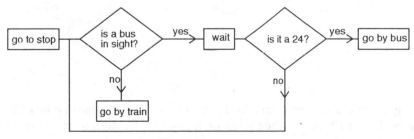

Fig 23.8

2) Every year a population is multiplied by 1.02. (This is equivalent to an annual increase of 2%). Write a flow diagram to describe the process of finding the year after which the population has doubled.

   Solution   Start off with $S = 1$, then each time we go through the loop the year increases by one and S is multiplied by 1.02. Repeat until $S > 2$, then print out the year. The flow diagram is below.

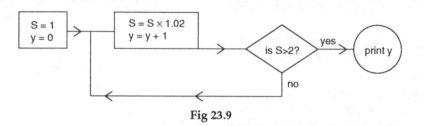

Fig 23.9

3) Write a flow diagram to find the sum of the first 100 squares.

   Solution   Start with $S = 0$, and $N = 0$. Each time the loop is gone through N is increased by 1, and S is increased by N^2. This is repeated until $N = 100$.

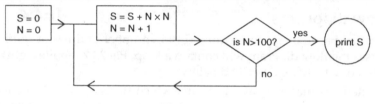

Fig 23.10

23.2.2 Exercises

1) When the score at tennis is Deuce, a player must be two points ahead to win the game. The following diagram shows the scoring: fill in the boxes.

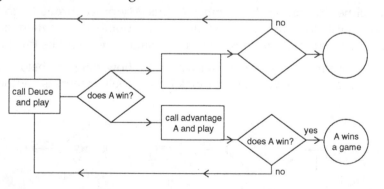

Fig 23.11

2) A gambler goes into a casino with £10. He will leave either when he has £30 or when he is broke. Each time he bets £10, and either wins or loses £10. Complete the flow diagram (Fig 23.12) to describe the procedure.

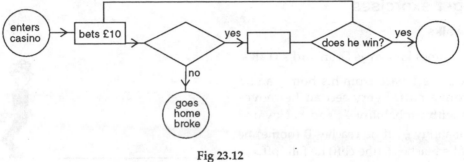

Fig 23.12

3) When a bath has been filled, I test the water, and if it is cool then I get in. If it is too hot then I wait a minute and test again. This procedure is repeated until the water is cool enough. Draw a flow diagram to describe this procedure.

4) $n!$ is defined as the product of the first n numbers, i.e. $4! = 1 \times 2 \times 3 \times 4$. The flow chart below evaluates $10!$. Fill in the boxes.

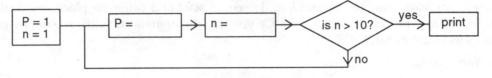

Fig 23.13

5) Amend the flow chart of Question 4 to evaluate $n!$ for any n.

6) Write a flow chart to find the sum of the first 100 numbers.

7) Write a flow chart to find the sum of the first N numbers, for any N.

8) Write a flow chart to find how many times N can be divided by 2 before it becomes a fraction.

9) If x is a positive number, it can be rounded down to a whole number. 3.75 can be rounded down to 3. Write a flow chart to round down x.

10) Write a flow chart to round x up to a whole number.

11) Write a flow chart to round x to the nearest whole number.

12) The flow chart below is meant to find the sum of the first 10 squares. There are several mistakes. Identify the mistakes and write a correct flow chart.

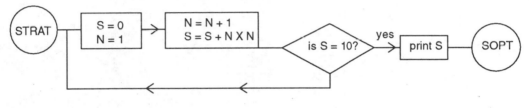

Fig 23.14

185

23.3 Longer exercises

A. Random walks

These are sometimes known as Drunkard's Walks.

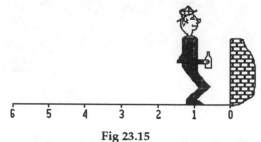

1) A drunkard is 1 pace from his home, and 5 paces from a cliff. Every second he moves forward with probability $\frac{1}{2}$, and backwards with probability $\frac{1}{2}$. If he reaches 0 (home) he is safe. If he reaches 6 (the cliff) he falls off.

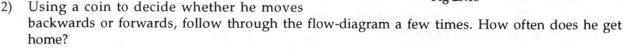

Fig 23.15

1) Write a flow diagram to describe the journey.

2) Using a coin to decide whether he moves backwards or forwards, follow through the flow-diagram a few times. How often does he get home?

3) If you can program a computer, you can repeat the flow diagram many times. What proportion of times does he get home?

4) There are many variations to the problem. He could start at a different place. He could be more likely to move forwards than backwards. Or you could eliminate the cliff, so that he could move backwards indefinitely far.

B. Noughts and crosses

If you have played noughts and crosses a few times, you probably realized that you can "play safe". If you make safe moves then you will never lose.

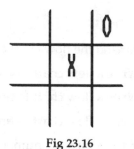

Suppose you are the first to move. Write a flow diagram which describes the safe moves which ensure that you will not lose.

Play games of noughts and crosses using your flow diagram. If your opponent makes a foolish move, will you then win?

Fig 23.16

Multiple choice question *(Tick appropriate box)*

Which of the following flow diagrams describes the procedure of finding the sum of the first 100 numbers?

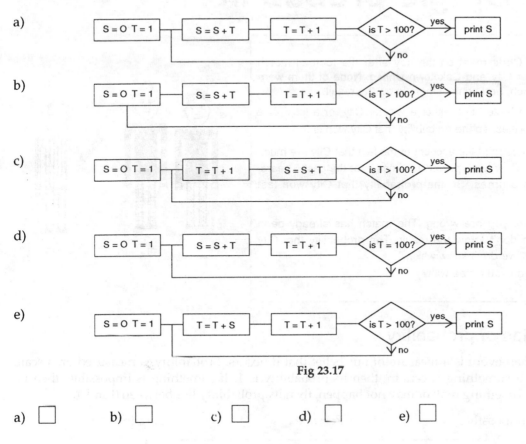

Fig 23.17

a) ☐   b) ☐   c) ☐   d) ☐   e) ☐

Points to note

1) *Flow diagrams*

   a) When a number is going through a flow diagram, its value may be changing. Make sure you use the correct value of a number.

   b) Do not be confused by the order S = S + 1. This means "Change S to S + 1" or "Add 1 to S".

2) *Loops*

   If a loop is used to increase a "counter", then do not reset the counter back to 1 each time. If you do this the loop may go on for ever.

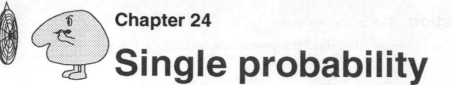

Chapter 24

Single probability

Andy, Benny and Chris meet on the day after the football match between Barchester City and Coketown United. None of them were able to see the match, and none of them know the result.

Andy says: "It must have been either a win for City, or a loss, or a draw. Three possibilities, so the probability that City won is $\frac{1}{3}$."

Benny says: "That doesn't take account of the fact that City are much better than United. They have played 15 times over the past 5 years, and City has won 8 times. So the probability that City won last evening is $\frac{8}{15}$."

Chris says: "Both of you are wrong. The match has already been played, even if we don't know the result. The probability that City won is either 0 or 1, we don't know which."

Which of the three do you agree with?

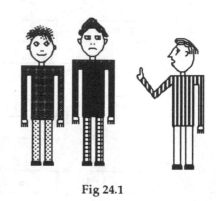

Fig 24.1

24.1 Estimation of probability

The probability of an event is a measure of our belief that it occurs. Probability is measured on a scale between 0 and 1. If something is certain, then its probability is 1. If something is impossible, then its probability is 0. If something may or may not happen, then its probability lies between 0 and 1.

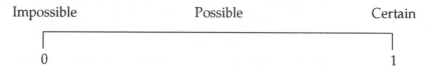

Impossible   Possible   Certain

0   1

There are various ways of finding probability, as follows:

Symmetry

If there are n possible things that could happen, and each are equally likely, then the probability of each of them is $\frac{1}{n}$. For example, a fair die is equally likely to show each of its six faces. Hence the probability that it will show a 5 is $\frac{1}{6}$.

Relative frequency

If the event is something that can be repeated, then the proportion of times that it occurs is an estimate of its probability. Suppose we have a bent coin. If it is tossed 100 times, and it comes up Heads 30 times, then the probability of Heads is about 0.3.

Subjective probability

If an event is neither symmetric nor repeatable, then we have to make a personal estimate of its probability. Suppose a football match is about to be played. We might guess that the probability of our local team winning is $\frac{2}{3}$. This would be a subjective opinion – a supporter of the other team might give a different probability.

24.1.1 Examples

1) A bag contains 5 red and 9 blue marbles. If one is drawn at random, what is the probability that it is blue?

   Solution   Each of the 14 marbles is equally likely to be drawn. The probability that one of the 9 blue ones is chosen is:

   $$\frac{9}{14}$$

2) How could we find the probability that a person chosen at random is left handed?

   Solution   It would be impracticable to test every single person. So we could test 100 people, and the proportion of the left-handed people we find would be a good guide for the proportion in the population as a whole.

3) How could you find the probability that by 2050 AD the world record for running 100 m will be under 9.5 seconds?

   Solution   There is no symmetry involved here. We are asked to find the probability of a single event – we cannot re-run history to see whether or not it occurs! We can only guess, and as training is improving all the time, it is quite likely that the 100 m race will be run in under 9.5 seconds.

   We could guess the probability to be about $\frac{3}{4}$

24.1.2 Exercises

In the following find the probability, if it can be calculated exactly, or say how you could find it by experiment or guesswork.

1) A solid in the shape of a regular tetrahedron (4 sides) has the numbers 1 to 4 on its faces. If it is thrown, what is the probability that it lands on the face labelled 2?

2) A person is picked at random from the electorate. What is the probability that he or she will vote Conservative?

3) What is the probability that it will rain tomorrow?

4) A bag contains 12 green and 18 yellow marbles. A child draws one at random. What is the probability that the marble is yellow?

5) What is the probability that England will win the next World Cup?

6) A multiple choice question has 5 possible answers. If a candidate picks the answer at random, what is the probability that it is correct?

7) A die is thought to be biased. What is the probability that it will show a 6?

8) The letters of the word MATHEMATICS are each written on squares of cardboard, which are then shuffled. If one is picked at random, what is the probability that the letter is:

   a) S   b) T?

9) A drawing pin is thrown in the air. What is the probability that it will land point upwards?

10) What is the probability of a manned landing on Mars by 2010?

11) What is the probability that by 2020 the world chess champion will be a computer?

12) What is the probability that you will pass your driving test at the first attempt?

13) Look at the problem at the beginning of the chapter. Criticize the three arguments.

24.2 Expected numbers

Suppose an event has a probability of 0.1. If it is repeated 100 times, we would expect the event to happen $100 \times 0.1 = 10$ times.

24.2.1 Example

A fair die is rolled 600 times. How many sixes would you expect?

Solution   For each roll, the probability of six is $\frac{1}{6}$. Multiply this by 600:

We would expect 100 sixes

24.2.2 Exercises

1) If I spin a fair coin 100 times, how many heads do I expect to get?

2) A sack contains a large number of nuts. One nut in four is a walnut. If I draw out 40, how many walnuts do I expect to get?

3) About 10% of the population is left-handed. How many left-handers would you expect to find in a group of 200 people?

4) At a school in January, it is found that 150 of the 600 pupils have colds. What is the probability that a pupil has a cold? How many colds would you expect to find in a class of 24?

5) In a period of 35 years, how many times do you expect Christmas Day to fall on a Saturday?

6) Mr Smith has probability $\frac{1}{40}$ of being late for work. How many times would you expect him to be late in 240 days?

7) A jar contains toffees and chocolates in the ratio 5:3. If I draw out 16, how many toffees do I expect to get?

8) A club contains twice as many men as women. If 30 people are picked, how many men would you expect?

24.3 Possible outcomes

When we calculate a probability by symmetry, we must know all the equally likely things which could happen. In some cases this is straightforward. If a die is rolled, each of the six faces is equally likely. If a card is taken from a pack, each of the 52 cards is equally likely to be chosen.

In some more complicated cases, it is a good idea to write down all the possible outcomes of an experiment. This can be done by a list or a table.

24.3.1 Examples

1) Two fair dice are rolled. What is the probability that the total score is 8?

   Solution   The total score could be anything from 2 to 12. But these are not equally likely. A total of 7 is more likely than a total of 12. Make a table showing the scores on both dice, and find the total in each case.

   Score on first die

		1	2	3	4	5	6
	1	2	3	4	5	6	7
Score	2	3	4	5	6	7	8
on	3	4	5	6	7	8	9
second	4	5	6	7	8	9	10
die	5	6	7	8	9	10	11
	6	7	8	9	10	11	12

   There are 36 squares, which are equally likely. In 5 of the squares the total is 8.

   The probability of a total of 8 is $\frac{5}{36}$

2) Three fair coins are tossed. What is the probability that there are exactly 2 heads?

   Solution   There will be 0, 1, 2, or 3 heads. But these are not equally likely. Letting H represent heads and T represent tails, the possible outcomes can be listed alphabetically as follows:

   HHH   HHT   HTH   HTT   THH   THT   TTH   TTT

   Of these 8 outcomes, 3 have two H's.

   The probability of 2 heads is $\frac{3}{8}$

24.3.2 Exercises

1) A 4-sided die and a 6-sided die are thrown together. Fill in the following table with the total scores.

   Find the probabilities that the total is:

   a) 10

   b) 7

   c) less than 4

   Score on 6-sided die

		1	2	3	4	5	6
Score on	1					6	
4-sided	2		4				
die	3						9
	4						

2) Two fair 4-sided dice are thrown. Complete the table for the total score:

   Find the probability that the total is

   a) 2

   b) 7.

   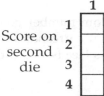

   Score on first die

		1	2	3	4
Score on	1		3		
second	2				6
die	3				
	4			7	

3) Two fair 6-sided dice are rolled. Use the table of Example 1 to find the probabilities of the following:

    a) The total is 7

    b) The total is 3

    c) The dice show the same number

    d) The total is less than 5

    e) The second die is the higher

    f) The total is at least 7

    g) The higher number showing is 4

    h) Both dice are less than 3

4) Three fair coins are tossed. What is the probability of:

    a) no tails

    b) exactly 2 tails?

5) Two fair 4-sided dice are rolled. The score is the greater of the numbers obtained. (So if a 4 and a 3 are rolled, the score is 4). Draw a table like that of Question 2 to show the possible scores. Find the probability that the score is:

    a) 1   b) 3   c) less than 3   d) more than 2

6) A spinner has three sides, labelled A, B, C, which are equally likely. It is spun twice. List all the possible outcomes, and hence find the probability that:

    a) There are no A's

    b) The same letter comes up twice

7) There are 4 children, Amanda, Brian, Cheryl and Damien. Two will be chosen for (identical) prizes. List all the possible selections of two children. Find the probability that both girls will be chosen.

8) Len, Maurice and Nathan take the same exam. List the orders in which they could be placed. (There are no tied places). If the places are decided at random, find the probability that:

    a) They are placed in alphabetic order

    b) Nathan is placed before Len

9) A bag contains 4 marbles, which are red, orange, yellow and green. Two marbles are picked out together. List the possible outcomes, and find the probability that the red and green marbles are chosen.

10) The situation of Question 9 is repeated, but this time the first marble is drawn and returned to the bag before the second is drawn. List the possible outcomes, and find the probability that:

    a) The same marble is chosen twice

    b) The red and the green marbles are chosen, in either order

24.4 Longer exercise

Simulation

1) Example 2 of 24.3.1 showed that if 3 fair coins are tossed, the probability of two heads is $\frac{3}{8}$. We shall verify this experimentally.

Experiments involving tossing coins are time-consuming and noisy. You can use a calculator to simulate the coins.

When you press the random number generator button (RAN#)of your calculator, a 3-digit number appears. Each digit corresponds to a coin. If the digit is odd, then the coin is Heads, and if the digit is even then it is Tails. So 0.458 corresponds to THT.

Press ⎡RAN#⎤ 100 times, and fill in the following tally chart:

0 heads	
1 head	
2 heads	
3 heads	

From your result find the probabilities of 0 Heads, 1 Head etc. How do your results compare with the theoretical results?

2) The ⎡RAN#⎤ button can simulate the rolling of a die. Divide the interval from 0 to 1 into 6 equal parts, from 0 to 0.167, from 0.167 to 0.333 and so on. If the random number is in the first interval then a 1 was rolled on the die and so on.

Press the ⎡RAN#⎤ button 60 times, and record the frequency with which you got each number. Are all the probabilities roughly equal to $\frac{1}{6}$?

Multiple choice question *(Tick appropriate box)*

A die is in the shape of a regular dodecahedron. (12-sided). Two of the sides are labelled 1, three are labelled 2, three are labelled 3, four are labelled 4. If it is rolled the probability that the top number is less than 4 is:

a) $\frac{3}{4}$ ☐

b) $\frac{2}{3}$ ☐

c) $\frac{1}{3}$ ☐

d) $\frac{1}{4}$ ☐

e) None of these   ☐

Points to note

1) *Single probability*

   If there are n outcomes to an experiment, then the probability of each outcome is $\frac{1}{n}$ only if the outcomes are equally likely.

2) *Possible outcomes*

   a) When counting possible outcomes, be sure not to count the same thing twice. If two dice are rolled, then you could get a 2 and a 3 in two ways, as 2,3 or as 3,2. But there is only one way to get double 3.

   b) When listing possible outcomes, don't miss any. Try to list them in a systematic way, for example alphabetically.

Chapter 25

Probability of combined events

There are 3 reels on a fruit machine, each of which has 20 pictures. There are 2 cherries on the first reel, 3 on the second and 1 on the third. If the reels are spun at random what is the probability of a "Jackpot" of three cherries?

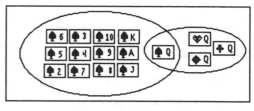

Fig 25.1

25.1 Adding probabilities

Often we need to find a probability connected with more than one event. This could be called a combined probability.

Exclusive events

For example, suppose we have backed two horses in the same race. The probability that we win one or other of our bets is found by adding the individual probabilities.

Of course, the two horses cannot both win the race. In cases like this, when two events cannot happen together, they are said to be exclusive. (Because they exclude each other).

If events are exclusive, the probability of one or other of them happening is the sum of their individual probabilities.

$$P(A \text{ or } B) = P(A) + P(B)$$

Non-exclusive events

Suppose we are playing a card game in which we will win if we draw either a Spade or a Queen. What is the probability of this?

The probability of a Spade is $\frac{1}{4}$. The probability of a Queen is $\frac{1}{13}$. But the card could be both a Spade and a Queen, i.e. it could be the Queen of Spades.

So if we add together the probabilities we will have counted twice the probability of the Queen of Spades. Subtract away this probability.

Fig 25.2

P(Queen or Spade) = P(Queen) + P(Spade) – P(Queen of Spades)

P(Queen or Spade) = $\frac{1}{13} + \frac{1}{4} - \frac{1}{52} = \frac{4}{13}$

In general: $P(A \text{ or } B) = P(A) + P(B) - P(A \& B)$

The "inclusive or"

Note that in Mathematics the "inclusive or" is used. That is, "A or B" means "A or B or possibly both".

25.1.1 Examples

1) Joe reckons that Brazil has probability $\frac{1}{10}$ of winning the next World Cup, and that Argentina's chance is $\frac{1}{15}$. What is the probability of either of them winning?

   Solution   Clearly the teams cannot both win the Cup. Hence the events are exclusive. The probabilities can be added:

   The probability of either winning is $\frac{1}{10} + \frac{1}{15} = \frac{1}{6}$

2) Two fair dice are rolled. What is the probability that either of them will be a 5?

   Solution   For each single die, the probability of a 5 is $\frac{1}{6}$. But a double 5 could be thrown, with probability $\frac{1}{36}$. Hence the events are not exclusive. Use the formula above for the probability of A or B:

   The probability that either will be a 5 is $\frac{1}{6} + \frac{1}{6} - \frac{1}{36} = \frac{11}{36}$

25.1.2 Exercises

1) A fair die is rolled. What is the probability of either a 2 or a 3?

2) A roulette wheel has the numbers 1 to 36. What is the probability that the number which comes up will be either 10 or 30?

3) An icosahedral (20 sided) die has its faces numbered 1 to 20. If it is rolled what is the probability that it lands on a face numbered 5 or 17?

4) A card is drawn from a standard pack. (Without jokers).

   a)   What is the probability that it is either a Spade or a Diamond?

   b)   What is the probability that it is either black or a Heart?

   c)   What is the probability that it is either an Ace or a King?

   d)   What is the probability that it is either a 2 or a picture card? (The picture cards are the Kings, Queens and Jacks.)

5) Two fair dice are rolled. What is the probability that either the first is a 2 or the second is a 3?

6) Two fair coins are spun. What is the probability that either the first is a Head or the second is a Tail?

7) A card is drawn from a standard pack. (Without jokers).

   a) What is the probability that it is either a Spade or an Ace?

   b) What is the probability that it is either a Heart or a picture card?

8) A poker hand consists of 5 cards. The first four cards I receive are the 6, 7, 8, 9 of hearts. If the fifth card is another heart, then I shall have a flush. If the fifth card is a 5 or a 10, then I shall have a straight. Find the probabilities that I get:

   a)   A flush.   b)   A straight.

   c)   A straight flush.   d)   Either a flush or a straight.

9) Out of 30 boys, 18 play soccer and 12 play rugger. 8 play both. if a boy is picked at random, find the probability that he plays either of the two games.

10) The probability that chips are on the menu for dinner is $\frac{2}{3}$, and the probability of beans is $\frac{1}{4}$. The probability of both is $\frac{1}{5}$. Find the probabilities that either chips or beans will be on the menu.

25.2 Multiplying probabilities

Independent events

A coin is spun and a die is rolled. I bet on the coin showing Heads and on the die showing a six. The probability that I win both of my bets is found by multiplying the individual probabilities.

If events do not affect each other in any way, they are said to be independent. If two events are independent the probability of them both happening is the product of their individual probabilities.

$$P(A \ \& \ B) = P(A) \times P(B)$$

Tree diagrams

When we have successive experiments, a good way to illustrate the possible outcomes is by a tree diagram. Consider the example of spinning a coin and rolling a die. See Fig 25.3.

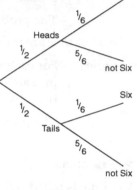

The first fork corresponds to whether the coin is Heads or Tails. The second forks correspond to whether the die shows a six or not. The top branch then corresponds to the coin showing Heads and the die showing a six. Its probability is found by multiplying the probabilities along the branch.

Fig 25.3

25.2.1 Examples

1) Three fair dice are rolled. What is the probability that they will all be sixes?

   Solution   The probability that each single die gives a six is $\frac{1}{6}$. The probability that all three are sixes is therefore:

   $$\frac{1}{6} \times \frac{1}{6} \times \frac{1}{6} = \frac{1}{216}$$

2) A third of the pupils at a school have blue eyes, and a tenth are left-handed. These qualities are not connected. If a pupil is picked at random, draw a tree-diagram to show all the possibilities, and find the probability that the pupil is blue eyed and right-handed.

   Solution   Let the first fork show whether the pupil is blue eyed or not. Label the branches and put the probabilities alongside. Do the same to show whether the pupil is left-handed or not.

   The second branch corresponds to blue-eyed right-handed pupils. Multiply the probabilities:

   The probability is $\frac{1}{3} \times \frac{9}{10} = \frac{3}{10}$

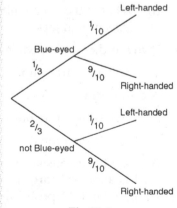

Fig 25.4

25.2.2 Exercises

1) A fair coin is spun three times. What is the probability of three heads?

2) Three fair dice are rolled. What is the probability that none will show a 6?

3) I draw a card from the standard pack and roll a die. What is the probability that I draw a Heart and roll a 6?

4) A coin is spun and a die is rolled. What is the probability that the coin gives Heads and the die gives a six?

5) The holes of a roulette wheel are numbered 1 to 36. I always bet on the number 17. What is the probability that in two spins of the wheel:

   a) I shall win both my bets   b) I shall lose both my bets?

6) A darts player always aims at the "treble 20", which will give a score of 60. His chance of hitting the treble 20 is $\frac{1}{3}$. What is the probability that in 3 darts he will score 180?

7) A roulette wheel has the numbers 1 to 36. For the first spin I bet that an even number will come up, and for the second I bet that a number divisible by 3 will come up. What is the probability that I win both my bets?

8) Every day the probability that I shall be late for work is $\frac{1}{10}$. What is the probability that I shall be late on two successive days?

9) The probability that I am late for work on Monday is $\frac{1}{5}$, and the probability for Tuesday is $\frac{1}{15}$. Draw a tree diagram to show the possibilities for both days, and hence find the probabilities that:

   a) I am late on both days   b) I am on time on both days

10) A football team has probabilities $\frac{1}{2}, \frac{1}{3}, \frac{1}{6}$ of winning, losing, drawing respectively. The team plays two matches. Draw a tree diagram to show the possible outcomes, and hence find the probabilities that:

   a) Both matches were won   b) Neither match was lost

11) At the beginning of the chapter there was a problem about a fruit machine. What is the probability that you will get a Jackpot?

25.3 Longer exercises

A. Cameroons

This is a game played with 5 dice. Another name for it is *Yahtzee*. The players try to get various combinations of the dice, such as "Five of a kind" (all dice the same number), "Full House" (3 dice the same and 2 the same), "High Cameroon" (2, 3, 4, 5, 6), "Low Cameroon" (1, 2, 3, 4, 5).

1) What is the probability of throwing "Five of a kind" in one go?

2) You have thrown 3, 3, 3, 5, 6. You are allowed to throw some of the dice again. If you throw the 5 and the 6, what is the probability you get

   a) "Five of a kind"   b) "Full House"?

3) Suppose instead you throw two of the 3's. What is the probability you get "High Cameroon"?

4) You have 4, 4, 5, 6, 6. You have one more go, to get either Full House or High Cameroon. Which are you more likely to get?

5) You have 1, 1, 2, 3, 4. You want to get Low Cameroon, and have two more throws. What is the probability you get it?

B. The Chevalier de Méré

The study of probability developed in the 17th century, when the Frenchman Blaise Pascal solved problems given to him by a gambler friend, the Chevalier de Méré. Below is an extract from a letter written by Pascal.

> If one wagers on the throwing of a six with a single die, it is advantageous to wager that the six will come up in 4 throws. But if one wagers on throwing 12 with two dice, it is disadvantageous to wager that it will happen in 24 throws. But 24 is to 36 as 4 is to 6. To Chevalier de Méré this was a great scandal, and it made him say loudly that arithmetical theorems are not always true, and that arithmetic contradicts itself.

1) If a die is thrown four times, what is the probability of no sixes? What is the probability of at least one six? Have you shown that: "It is advantageous to wager that the six will come up in 4 throws"?

2) If two dice are rolled, what is the probability of a double six?

3) If two dice are rolled 24 times, what is the probability that we do not get a double six? What is the probability we do get a double six? Have you shown that: "It is disadvantageous to wager that it will happen in 24 throws"?

4) What is meant by "24 is to 36 as 4 is to 6"?

5) How many times would we have to throw 3 dice, before there was a 50% chance of a triple six?

Multiple choice question *(Tick appropriate box)*

When Mr and Mrs Berman go out, Mr Berman remembers to take his house key with probability $\frac{4}{5}$, and Mrs Berman remembers her copy of the key with probability $\frac{9}{10}$. The probability that they won't be able to get back in again is:

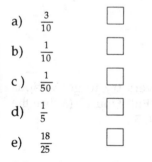

a) $\frac{3}{10}$

b) $\frac{1}{10}$

c) $\frac{1}{50}$

d) $\frac{1}{5}$

e) $\frac{18}{25}$

Points to note

1) *Addition of probabilities*

Probabilities are only added together if the events cannot happen together. If events A and B can happen together, then it is not true that P(A or B) = P (A) + P(B).

If your answer gives a probability of more than 1, then you must have made a mistake of this sort.

2) *Multiplying probabilities*

a) You can only multiply probabilities if the events do not affect each other.

b) Suppose you are drawing a tree diagram to see whether *A* and *B* occur. The branches of the first fork should be labelled *A* and not *A*. Do not label them *A* and *B*.

c) Read the question carefully, to make sure you do not confuse *or* with *and*.

Cross-curriculum topic

Population

Stoney Creek
Population 1½

The population of a country is the number of people who live in it. The study of population is called Demography.

Governments want to know facts about population. Every few years (10 years in the U.K.) a census is held, from which the government finds out how many people there are, what ages they are, how many children they have and so on. A lot of attention is given to the way the form is written. Questions on the form must be phrased so that people answer honestly.

There are two ways by which the population of a country can rise – through birth and through immigration. There are also two ways by which it can fall – through death and through emigration. For most countries the numbers involved in immigration and emigration are fairly small compared with those born and dying. But in Ireland the size of the population has been greatly affected by people leaving, and in Australia the number of immigrants is very substantial.

As far as the whole world is concerned, population is only affected by birth and death. This will remain the situation until space-travel becomes commonplace.

Population increase

Even today no one is quite sure what the total world population is. We can only guess what the population was in the past. Estimates of the population in millions are given below.

	BC	AD						
Date	5000	0	1750	1800	1930	1960	1974	1987
Popn.	5-10	300	800	1000	2000	3000	4000	5000

We see that though it took all of human history to reach the first billion in 1800, the second billion was reached 130 years later. The rate of growth has increased since then – it took only a further 44 years for the population to double again from 2 to 4 billion.

Though the total grew very slowly for thousands of years, during this century world population has been growing rapidly. On the right is a graph of world population.

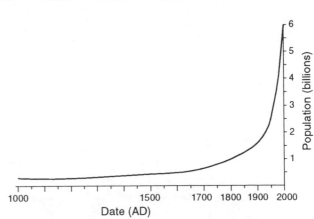

Obviously this increase cannot continue indefinitely. Suppose the world's population is increasing at 2% each year. This means that every year the population is multiplied by $\frac{102}{100} = 1.02$. A sequence in which each number is a multiple of the one before is an exponential sequence. If the multiple is 1.02, as above, then the population will double every 35 years.

Recently the proportional rate of increase has slowed down slightly, but as there are so many more people the absolute rate continues to rise.

The rate of increase differs between countries. In particular, the developed countries in Europe, North America, Australia, Japan and so on have a slow rate of increase. The less developed countries in Africa, South America have high rates of increase.

Mortality and fertility

Population growth is affected by mortality and fertility. These are usually measured in deaths or births per thousand. So a fertility rate of 25 per thousand means that 25 people are born for every thousand of population.

If a country contains a large number of elderly people, then its mortality rate will be misleadingly high. Similarly if a country has a lot of people in the age range 20-30, then its fertility rate will also be misleadingly high. The "crude" death and birth rates are often adjusted to take account of this.

Of course, Britain is one of the most densely populated countries in the world. But now the growth rate of the population is very low indeed. Let us see what has happened over the past few hundred years.

In the past the death rate was very high, because of disease, poverty and so on. The birth rate was also very high: so many children died in childhood that a couple had to have many children to ensure that some survived.

When the industrial revolution started in 1750 or so, the death rate fell, through increased prosperity and medical advances. But large families were traditional, and so the birth rate remained high. The population grew rapidly throughout the nineteenth century.

In this century the birth rate has fallen to be roughly equal to the death rate, and so the population has become stable.

This pattern was followed in countries in Europe and North America. The graph below shows death and birth rates following this pattern. The death rate falls at point A, while the birth rate remains high. The birth rate falls to join the death rate at B. Between A and B the population grows rapidly.

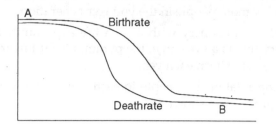

It is expected that other countries, which at present have a wide gap between birth and death rates, will show the same pattern.

Life expectancy

No one can tell for how long he or she will live. One may live to a safe old age, or one could have a fatal accident tomorrow. Each person can only make a guess for the probability that he or she will reach 100.

But one can make an estimate for the time one expects to live. This is called life expectancy.

A newborn child has a probability of, say, p_1 of living to be 1 year old. It has a probability p_2 of living to be 2 years old, and so on. p_{40} is the probability that this newborn child will live to 40.

When these probabilities are added up we find the number of years the child expects to live.

$$\text{Life Expectancy} = p_1 + p_2 + \dots + p_{40} + \dots$$

For rich countries in Europe, North America and Japan life expectancy is over 70 years. For poorer countries it might be below 40. When the prosperity and health-care of a country increases its life expectancy increases also.

Population pyramids

Population growth is affected not just by the numbers of people, but also by their ages. A population which contains a high proportion of people aged 20 to 30 will be increasing more than one with a lot of older people. A diagram which shows the proportions of the different age groups is called a population pyramid. Two are illustrated below.

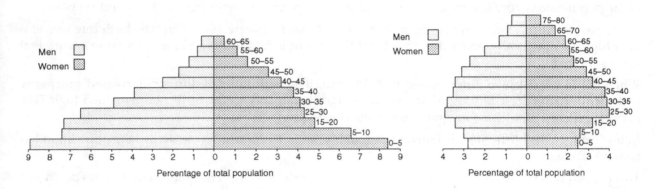

On the left is the pyramid for a country with low life expectancy and a high rate of increase of population. Notice how quickly the pyramid narrows. This is because many people die fairly young, and also because there are many more people in the younger generations.

On the right is the pyramid for a country with a high life expectancy and a declining population. Because people in this country live to a great age, the pyramid is fat towards the top. It is narrow at the base, because fewer people are being born each year.

Suppose we add up a running total of the people in each generation. Graphs of these running totals, called cumulative frequency graphs, are shown below.

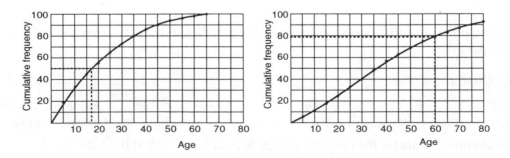

In the left graph, notice that about half the population is under 17. This is called the median age. If everyone stayed on at school until 17, then half the population would be either a child or in school! It would be impossible for the working population to support them.

In the right graph, notice that more than 20% of the population is over 60. So the working population will have to support this very high proportion of elderly people.

Zero population growth

The present rapid increase of population cannot continue. Eventually world population must stay almost constant. This situation is called Zero Population Growth.

Let us suppose that life expectancy levels off at 70, and that the birth rate levels at approximately 2 children per woman. Then in a while the population of the World will level off at a fixed number. The pressure on land and resources will not continue to grow, and environmental problems will be more easy to control.

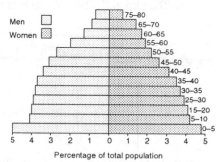

A population pyramid for Zero Population Growth could be like that on the right. The median age is about 30. About 30% of the population is under 16, about 10% is over 65.

Under these circumstances about 60% of the population is in the working age range. The world will be able to afford full-time education for everyone under 16, and will be able to allow everyone over the age of 65 to retire.

The mathematics of population

The study of population involves a lot of mathematics and statistics. Here material from Chapters 5, 20, 21, 22 and 24 has been touched upon.

Extended task. Predicting population

What will the population be in 20 years time? Obviously we cannot know exactly, as there are so many uncertainties. But we can make a prediction for what the population will be, based on the numbers in each age group, the survival rate from one year to the next, and the rate at which different age groups produce children. In this project you make a model of population change over 20 years.

Spreadsheets

The arithmetic involved in calculating 20 years ahead is horrendous. This project is best done with a spreadsheet.

You could investigate a situation of your own, or you could follow through the suggestion below, which deals with population growth in a particular situation.

Fish farming

We will take a simplified situation, in which there are only 4 generations. Newly-hatched fish are introduced to a lake in year 1. None of them lives more than 4 years. In each year a fixed proportion of each age group survives. When the fish are a year old they become fertile, and a fixed proportion of each age group gives birth to new fish. The figures might be:

Age	Survival rate	Fertility rate
0-1	0.9	0
1-2	0.7	0.65
2-3	0.4	0.55
3-4	0	0.45

This mean that in the age range 1-2, for example, 70% of them survive to the next year. The fertility rate is such that on average each fish in this age group gives birth to 0.65 live offspring.

Suppose that initially 100,000 fish are introduced. Set up the spreadsheet as below.

	A	B	C	D	E
2					
3	100000	+0.65*A4+0.55*A5+0.45*A6			
4	0	+0.9*A3			
5	0	+0.7*A4			
6	0	+0.4*A5			

The numbers in column A show the original population, of 100,000 newly-hatched fish. There are no older fish.

The entries in B4, B5, B6 show what happens after 1 year. 90% of the new fish survive to become 1 year-old fish. So the entry in B4 is 0.9 times the entry in A3.

The entry in B3 shows how fish are born. 65% of the 1 year-old fish give birth to a new fish, and 55% of the 2 year-olds, and 45% of the 3 year-olds.

Now copy the formulas in B3 to B6 across the page so that we can see the generations for 20 years.

You should find that the populations are given for each generation for a total of 20 years.

Extra calculations

We would be interested in other things about the population. For example, we might want to know the following:

a) The total population for each year.

b) The percentage increase from one year to the next.

c) The proportion of each age group in the population as a whole.

You could calculate these things yourself, but it is much easier to use the facilities of the spreadsheet to do the hard work for you. For (a), in A7 enter the formula which adds up the entries in A3 to A6. Copy this formula all the way across to T7.

Questions to answer

Important questions concerning the population are as follows:

a) Does the total population grow, or shrink, or stay the same?

b) Does the proportion of each age-group settle down to a fixed value, or does it fluctuate?

Changing the rates

Try the effect of changing either the fertility rates or the survival rates. See if you can find rates for which the total population remains roughly constant over the years.

Advanced Use of spreadsheets

To change the rates, as described above, involves rewriting the formulas in B3 to B6 and in recopying them across the columns. If you are expert at spreadsheet use, you can arrange it so that the population figures will change the moment you change the rates. You must be careful to distinguish between relative addresses and absolute addresses.

Miscellaneous exercises

Group A

1) Should the voting age be lowered to 16? Or should it be raised to 25? Devise a questionnaire to test opinion on this point.

2) The table below shows the prices and number of pages of 5 books. Plot the points, and draw a line of best fit. Predict the cost of a 400 page book.

Number of pages	200	250	350	320	300
Cost in £	4.50	5.99	6.99	6.49	5.49

3) Find the mean, median, mode and range of the following numbers:

$$45 \quad 54 \quad 76 \quad 56 \quad 45 \quad 45 \quad 34 \quad 55 \quad 63 \quad 45$$

4) Two groups of pupils took a test. The results are below. Find the mean and range in each case; what can you conclude?

Group A: 5, 6, 7, 8, 5, 6, 5, 7, 6, 8, 6, 7, 5, 7
Group B: 5, 2, 9, 9, 8, 9, 3, 1, 4, 7, 5, 8, 2, 9

5) The ages of 60 cars advertised in a CarMart magazine were as below. Record this information in a frequency table. Use your table to find the mean age of the cars.

Age in years:	3	4	3	5	2		6	4	7	10	4		3	6	5	2	5
	6	4	10	11	3		1	12	8	5	6		4	3	12	13	1
	2	1	4	3	6		5	3	5	6	13		2	15	1	2	5
	3	5	4	7	8		1	10	11	12	3		5	8	6	9	10

6) The weights of 100 portions of chips in a canteen were investigated. Results are in the table below. Draw a frequency diagram to show the results.

Weight of portion (grams)	10–15	15–20	20–25	25–30	30–35	35–40
Frequency	5	12	23	38	16	6

7) Find the cumulative frequencies for the figures in Question 6. Draw a cumulative frequency chart, and find the median and the interquartile range.

8) Draw a flow-diagram to evaluate the function $5x + 3$.

9) Amend the flow-diagram of Question 8 so that it finds the first x for which $5x + 3 > 82$.

10) In the following situations describe how you would find the relevant probability:

   a) That a card drawn from a pack will be a Club.

   b) That the next president of the United States will be a Democrat.

   c) That you will hit the bulls-eye when you throw a dart at a dartboard.

11) A player in Scrabble has the letters A, T, E left. List the possible orders in which these three letters could be placed. How many of these orders are an actual English word? If the letters are put down at random what is the probability that they form a word?

12) In a horse race, the probability that Grey wins is $\frac{1}{8}$, and the probability that Skewbald wins is $\frac{1}{12}$. What is the probability of either of them winning? What is the probability that neither will win?

13) The chance that a car has defective lights is $\frac{1}{10}$, and the chance of defective brakes is $\frac{1}{20}$. The probability of both is $\frac{1}{40}$. What is the probability that a car will have neither defect?

Group B. Challenge questions

14) The mean of 5, 6, 7, x, 6, 4 is 5.5. Find x.

15) The series $\frac{1}{2} + \frac{1}{3} + \frac{1}{4} + \frac{1}{5} + \dots$ grows as big as we like. Design a flow-chart to find the term by which it passes 4.

16) In a certain country the car number plates contain 2 letters. How many possible combinations of letters are there? What is the probability that the letter is repeated?

17) Think up some situations in which you might wish to find the probability of an event. In each case decide whether you would find the probability by calculation, by experiment or by guesswork.

18) When an archer fires at a target the probability that he hits the gold (the centre) is $\frac{1}{8}$. If he shoots 10 arrows, find the probability that he gets at least one in the gold.

19) In order to start at a certain game it is necessary to roll a 6 with a die. What is the probability that a player starts:

   a) on the first roll   b) on the second roll   c) on the third roll.

20) A bag contains red, white and blue marbles. The probability of a red one being drawn is $\frac{1}{7}$, and the probability of a white one is $\frac{3}{8}$. What is the probability of a blue one? What is the least number of marbles the bag could contain?

21) A floor is covered by boards which are 10 cm wide. A disc of radius 4 cm is thrown on the floor. What is the probability that the disc does not cross a crack between floorboards?

22) Three dice are rolled. How many possible outcomes are there? List the ways in which the total could be 17, and find the probability of this score.

23) Three dice are rolled. What is the probability that the *product* of the numbers is prime? (1 does not count as a prime).

24) The wheel at roulette gives a black or red number with equal probability $\frac{1}{2}$. Ron operates a system known as a Martingale: he puts £1 on red, and if he wins he goes home. If he loses he doubles the stake and plays again. The procedure is repeated until either he has won or has lost all his money. What is the probability that he wins after 3 goes? If he starts with £31, what is the probability that he loses all his money?

Group C. Longer exercises

25) **Spreadsheet menus**

When you use a spreadsheet, there is a sequence of menus which allow you to do things like copying cells, drawing graphs and so on. These menus are arranged in an order, so that one menu follows on from another.

Investigate the menus on the spreadsheet which you have available. Make up a diagram which shows the order in which menus follow from one another.

26) **Craps**

This is a dice game very popular in America.

a) Two dice are rolled and the total found. Make up a table showing the probability of each total. This can be done from the table of Example 1 of 24.3.1.

b) If the total is 7 or 11, the thrower wins immediately. If the total is 2, 3 or 12 (craps) the thrower loses immediately. Find the probability of winning immediately and of losing immediately.

c) If the total is 4, 5, 6, 8, 9 or 10, the thrower tries again, until either that total is repeated or 7 is obtained. If the total comes first the thrower wins, if 7 comes first the thrower loses.

Suppose the total was 4. The probability of 4 is $\frac{1}{12}$, and the probability of 7 is $\frac{1}{6}$. 7 is twice as likely as 4, so the probability that 4 is obtained before 7 is $\frac{1}{3}$. Find the probability that the thrower gets a total of 4 and then gets 4 again before 7.

d) Find the probabilities that the thrower gets a total of 5, 6, 8, 9 or 10 and then repeats this total before getting 7.

e) By adding up all your answers find the probability that the thrower wins. Is craps a fair game?

Revision exercises

1) Design an observation sheet to investigate the number of pages in the books on your shelves.

2) The glove sizes of 40 men are shown in the table below. Draw a histogram to illustrate the figures.

Size	7	$7\frac{1}{2}$	8	$8\frac{1}{2}$	9	$9\frac{1}{2}$	10	$10\frac{1}{2}$
Frequency	1	3	5	5	12	7	4	3

3) The sales of different sorts of milk in a shop are shown in the table below. Draw a pie chart to illustrate the figures.

Type	skimmed	semi-skimmed	full-cream	UHT
Sales in 100 pints	13	6	12	5

4) Find the shortest route round the road map on the right, beginning and ending at A and covering each road at least once.

5) Find the shortest route round the road map shown, beginning at A and ending at B, and visiting each town at least once.

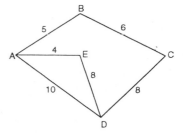

6) A dodecahedral die has 12 sides. It is rolled once. What is the probability that it shows:

a) a '7'   b) a number bigger than 3   c) an even number

207

7) Two dice like that of Question 6 are rolled. The total score is found. What is the probability that:

   a) The total is 24   b) the total is more than 2

   c) the dice show the same number.

8) How could you find the probability of the following events?

   a) It will snow on February 7th of next year.

   b) This book, if opened at random, will show a page number of at least 100.

Puzzles and paradoxes

1) Three coins are spun. From the calculations in Example 2 of 24.3.1 the probability that all are Heads is $\frac{1}{8}$, and that all are Tails is $\frac{1}{8}$. So the probability that all are the same is $\frac{1}{4}$. But what is wrong with the following?

   We know that at least two of the coins must be the same. Say two are Heads. Then the third coin could be either Heads or Tails, with equal probability. The probability of Heads is $\frac{1}{2}$, so the probability that all coins are the same is $\frac{1}{2}$.

2) Two people do not know how much money the other is carrying. It is suggested that they exchange their wallets or purses.

   Jane says to herself: "I have £10. If Joan has less than £10, I shall lose an amount less than £10. If Joan has more than £10, then I shall gain an amount more than £10. So as I stand to gain more than I can lose, it is worth my while to swap."

   Joan can argue in exactly the same way, however much money she is carrying. How can it be advantageous for both of them to swap?

3) Three people quarrel, and have a three-way duel. Each fires in turn at either of the others, until there is only one survivor.

   Smith is the best shot. He is certain of hitting the person he fires at. Brown has probability 0.8 of hitting his target. Jones has probability 0.6 of hitting his target.

   Though he is the worst shot, Jones has the best chance of survival. (Regardless of who fires first). Why is this so?

Mental test 1

1) Write twenty thousand and fourteen in figures.

2) What is the least number 2, 3 and 5 will all divide into?

3) Multiply together $\frac{2}{3}$ and $\frac{4}{5}$.

4) A span is four inches. How many spans in three feet?

5) What is 7.15 p.m. in the 24 hour clock?

6) A car does 33 miles per gallon. How far will it get on 5 gallons?

7) Write twenty thousand in standard form.

8) Ballpoint pens cost 16p each. How much do 20 cost, in pounds and pence?

9) A legacy of £6,000 is shared between Lorna and Martha, so that Lorna gets twice as much as Martha. How much does Lorna get?

10) A weight is given as 5 kg, to the nearest whole number. What is the least possible value of the weight?

11) A rectangle is 40 metres by 30 metres. What is its perimeter?

12) A television programme begins at 5.45 and lasts 70 minutes. When does it finish?

13) Continue the sequence 4, 7, 10, 13 for two more terms.

14) x is multiplied by 3 and 4 is added. What is the result?

15) Simplify $5x + 7x^2 + 3x - 2x^2$

16) How many edges does a cube have?

17) The circumcentre of a triangle is the intersection point of three lines. What are these lines?

18) In a pie chart showing the result of an election, the wedge for the Crimson Party was 90°. What was their percentage share of the vote?

19) What is the average of 10, 11, 12, 13, 14?

20) A spinner has the numbers 1 to 5 on its edges. If it is spun twice, what is the probability that 1 comes up both times?

Mental test 2

1) A car is driven for 120 miles at 40 m.p.h. How long does it take?

2) Add 1.32 to 2.47.

3) The temperature rose from –5° to 18°. What was the rise?

4) What is the result after squaring 4 and adding 3?

5) What is the square root of 10,000?

6) A man earns £15,000 per annum. How much will he earn after a 10% pay rise?

7) Seven out of twenty voters support the Purple Party. What is this as a percentage?

8) Add $\frac{3}{10}$ to $\frac{1}{10}$ and simplify your answer.

9) Multiply together 2×10^4 and 3×10^6.

10) A business man started with £1,000 and doubled his money each year. How much did he have after 5 years?

11) To convert Reaumur temperature to Fahrenheit, divide by 4, multiply by 9, add 32. Convert 40° in Reaumur to Fahrenheit.

12) What is the largest number which will divide into 30 and 25?

13) F9 is an address of a cell in a spreadsheet. How many cells are adjacent to it?

14) Evaluate $x^2 + x + 3$ when x is –2.

15) Convert x metres to centimetres.

16) Describe the rotational symmetry of a regular pentagon.

17) A rectangle whose sides are 4 cm and 6 cm is enlarged by a factor of $1\frac{1}{2}$. What are the new sides?

18) The following scores are the runs made by a batsman in 10 innings, in increasing order. Find the median score. 0, 10, 12, 15, 20, 22, 25, 31, 33, 47.

19) The proportion of left-handed people is 1 in 10. How many left-handers would you expect to find in 180 people?

20) Britain has two entrants in an Olympic race, and their chances of winning are $\frac{1}{10}$ and $\frac{1}{20}$. What is the probability of either of them winning?

Revision test 1

Do not use a calculator for this test

1) Without writing down anything except the answers, find the values of:

   a) 20×400 b) $1{,}200 \div 60$

2) What is the total cost of 17 books at £4.95 each?

3) You buy items costing £8.75 and £6.20. Round each price to the nearest £. Roughly how much change do you expect to get from a £20 note?

4) A rod is x metres long. What is its length in centimetres?

5) On the right is a cuboid and the net from which it is made. Make a copy of the cuboid, and label its vertices with the letters A, B, C, D, E, F, G, H.

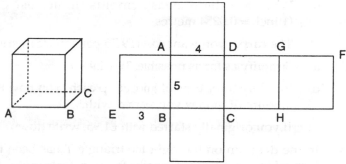

6) Draw the plan and elevations of the cuboid of Question 5. Your diagrams need not be to scale, but the lengths of the sides should be indicated.

7) The numbers 1 to 5 were written on five cards. These cards were shuffled and two were drawn out. The table on the right gives the total of the two cards. Copy and complete it.

   What is the probability that the total is

   a) 3   b) even?

		Number on first card			
	1	2	3	4	5
1	X	3			6
2		X			
3	4		X	7	
4		6		X	
5		8			X

Number on second card

Revision Test 2

Calculators may be used for this test

1) You want to cover the floor of a room with a carpet. The floor is a rectangle, and you measure its length as 167 inches and its width as 134 inches.

   a) What are these measurements in feet and inches?

   b) What are these measurements in metres? Give your answers to two decimal places. (1 inch = 0.0254 metres).

   c) The carpet you want costs £9.75 per square metre. What will be the cost of carpeting the room?

2) a) Simplify as far as possible: $3x + 2y + x - 5y$.

   b) You buy three cans of juice at xp each. You now have 45p left. Write down an expression for the amount of money you started with.

   If you originally started with £1.95, write down an equation in x and solve it.

3) In the diagram on the right the triangle T has been transformed in three ways. Describe the transformations which have taken T to:

   a) P   b) Q   c) R

4) A sandwich bar sells either sandwiches or rolls, in brown or white bread. One lunchtime it sold 100 sandwiches and 80 rolls. Half the sandwiches were of white bread. 40% of the rolls were of white bread.

   Find how many of each were sold. Construct a pie-chart to show the information.

Revision Test 3

Calculators may be used for this test

1) What fraction of the shape on the right is shaded?

2) Half of the dwellings in a borough are owned by the council. Of these dwellings three fifths are flats.

   What fraction of the dwellings are council-owned flats?

3) Arrange the following in increasing order:

   $$0.7 \qquad \frac{2}{3} \qquad -1 \qquad 0 \qquad \frac{4}{5} \qquad -0.2 \qquad -\frac{1}{7}$$

4) y is given in terms of x by $y = 3x - 2$. Find the value of y when $x = 5$.

5) On the right is a graph for conversion from Canadian dollars to £. Find how much £16 is worth in Canadian $.

6) Find the rough area of the shape on the right by approximating it by a rectangle.

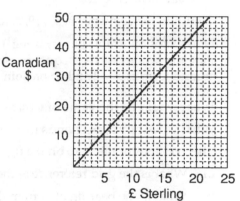

7) The foreign languages spoken by a group of four people are given in the table below.

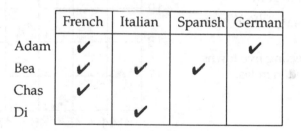

	French	Italian	Spanish	German
Adam	✔			✔
Bea	✔	✔	✔	
Chas	✔			
Di		✔		

   a) Who spoke most languages?

   b) Which language was spoken by most people?

8) One of the four people of Question 7 is picked at random. What is the probability that he or she speaks Spanish?

213

Revision Test 4

Calculators may be used for this test

1) Ms Bennett has a total income (before tax) of £24,260. Her tax-free allowance is £4,512.

   a) On what income is she taxed?

   b) If the tax rate is 25%, how much tax does she pay?

   c) What percentage of her total income does she pay in tax? Give your answer to 1 decimal place.

   d) Ms Bennett has a mortgage of £35,000, for which the annual repayments are £105 per £1,000. How much does she repay each year?

   e) What proportion of her income after tax goes on mortgage repayments? Give your answer to 3 significant figures.

2) Continue the sequence 3, 5, 7, 9, ... for 3 more terms.

   Draw axes on graph paper, using 1 cm per unit and taking the origin near the centre of the paper. Plot the values of the sequence, so that the first term of the sequence corresponds to $x = 1$, the second term to $x = 2$ and so on. Join the points up with a straight line.

   What would be the value of y corresponding to $x = 2\frac{1}{2}$? What value corresponds to $x = -2$?

   What value of x corresponds to $y = 4$?

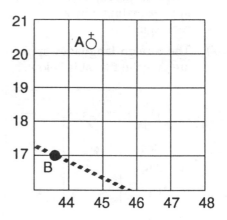

3) The gridlines of the map on the right are 2 km apart.

   a) What is the grid reference of the church at A?

   b) What is the bearing of A from the station at B?

   c) I arrive at B and walk 5 km on bearing of 050°. What is the grid-reference of where I end up?

4) The network below shows the roads connecting five towns. It is not to scale. The distances are measured in miles.

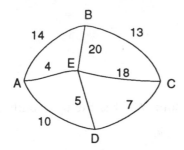

   a) What is the shortest distance from A to C?

   b) A salesman starts at A and has to visit B, C, D, E, in any order, before returning to A. What is the shortest route?

214

Formula sheet

When you sit the GCSE exam, you will be given a sheet of formulas similar to this to refer to when answering the questions.

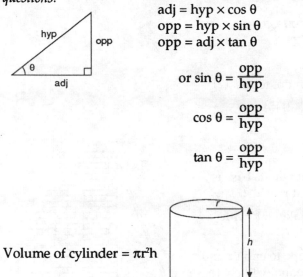

$$adj = hyp \times \cos \theta$$
$$opp = hyp \times \sin \theta$$
$$opp = adj \times \tan \theta$$

$$\text{or } \sin \theta = \frac{opp}{hyp}$$

$$\cos \theta = \frac{opp}{hyp}$$

$$\tan \theta = \frac{opp}{hyp}$$

$$\text{Area of triangle} = \frac{base \times height}{2}$$

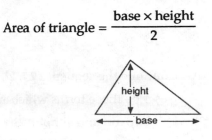

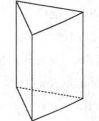

Volume of cylinder = $\pi r^2 h$

Quadratic equations

The solutions of $ax^2 + bx + c = 0$ where $a \neq 0$, are given by

$$x = \frac{-b \pm \sqrt{(b^2 - 4ac)}}{2a}$$

Area of parallelogram = base × height

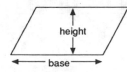

Volume = area of base × height

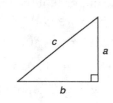

Area of trapezium = $\frac{1}{2}(a + b)h$

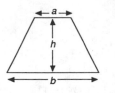

Pythagoras' Theorem

$$a^2 + b^2 = c^2$$

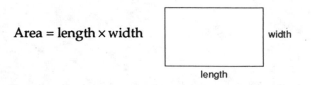

Volume of cuboid = height × width × length

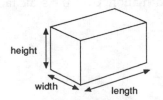

Area = length × width

Exam 1

Answer all the questions.
Time: 2 hours

1) Continue the sequence $2^{\frac{1}{2}}, 2^1, 2^{1\frac{1}{2}}, 2^2, \ldots$ for two more terms. (2)

   Describe those terms which are whole numbers. (3) [5]

2) a) Expand and simplify $3(x-2) - 4(x-8)$ (2)

   b) Factorize $2x^2y^2 + 4xy^2 + 6x^2y$ (2) [4]

3) A ladder of length 4 m leans against a wall as shown. Its base is 1.5 m from the wall. How high up the wall does it reach? (3)

   The base of the ladder is pulled back so that it makes 60° with the ground. How far has it been pulled back? (4) [7]

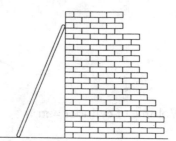

4) In a fairground game, balls are rolled down a slope to end up in one of the slots shown on the right. If the ball is equally likely to land in any of the slots, find the probabilities that:

   a) The ball lands in the slot labelled 8. (1)

   b) The score with one ball is less than 6. (1)

   c) The score with two balls is 16. (2)

   d) The score with three balls is 3. (2) [6]

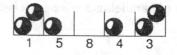

5) Certain paint costs £12 per litre. How much does one millilitre cost? (2)

   How many millilitres are bought for £1? (2)

   1 litre is 1.76 pints. What is the cost of 1 pint of the paint? (2) [6]

6) Evaluate the function $y = \frac{3}{x}$, at $x = \frac{1}{2}, 1. 1\frac{1}{2}, 2, 2\frac{1}{2}, 3$. (3)

   Plot the graph of the function, using a scale of 1 cm per unit. (3)

   On the same paper plot the graph of $y = x + 1$. Show that where the graphs cross x obeys the equation $x^2 + x - 3 = 0$. Write down the solution to this equation. (4) [10]

7) Triangle T has vertices at (1,1), (1,3), (4,1). Triangle S has vertices at (6,7), (10,7), (6,1).

   Draw T and S on graph paper. Explain briefly why T and S are similar. (4)

   Explain briefly why T cannot be transformed to S by an enlargement. (2)

   T can be transformed to S by an enlargement and one other transformation. Give the scale factor of the enlargement and the name of the transformation. (2) [8]

8) The national colours of Ruritania are crimson, purple and emerald. They must all appear on the national flag. Adjacent regions of the flag must be coloured differently.

   Three designs are suggested.

   a) A tricolour. List all the different ways in which the flag could be coloured. (3)

   b) In the second design, the flag must be symmetrical about the horizontal line through the centre. How many possible designs are there? (4)

   c) The third design is square. The flag must have rotational symmetry of order 4 about its centre. How many designs are there? (3) [10]

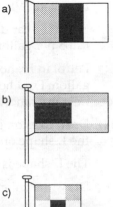

a)

b)

9) A trade union asks for a pay rise of 9% for all the employees of a factory. If the total wage bill is now £11,500,000, what will it be if the company agrees to the increase? (2)

   Instead the company grants a 6% increase and a reduction of the working week from 40 to 39 hours. What is the percentage increase in the average hourly rate? (4) [6]

c)

10) a) On the right is a graph showing the distances of Karen and Peter from Peter's house.

   How far from Peter's house did they meet? How long did they spend together? (2)

   What were their speeds when returning home? (2)

   b) Next day Peter leaves home and walks at 4 mph. for 30 minutes. He spends 20 minutes at a library and then walks home at 3 mph. Draw a travel graph showing his distance from home. (4) [8]

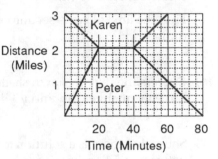

11) A machine makes steel washers which should be 1 cm in radius. It had been adjusted incorrectly, and ten washers that it produced had radii:

   1.10 1.20 1.15 0.95 1.04 1.12 0.96 1.03 1.22 1.08

   Find the mean and median radius. (3) [3]

12) The lengths of 100 novels were found. The results are in the frequency table below.

Number of pages	0-99	100-199	200-299	300-399	400-499	500-600
Frequency	5	15	31	28	13	8

Find the mean number of pages. (2)

Guess the median number of pages. Give reasons for your guess. (3)

Draw a frequency polygon to illustrate the data. (4) [9]

13) Mr Bull takes his car across the Channel to Calais and drives along the autoroute. The graph on the right shows the distance travelled. What was his speed? (2)

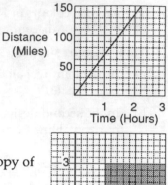

Mr Bull's car does 32 miles per gallon. If petrol in England costs £2.05 per gallon find the cost of travelling one mile. (2)

Petrol in France costs 5.7 FF per litre. There are 4.55 litres in a gallon. Find how much in Francs it costs Mr Bull to drive for a mile in France. (3) [7]

14) Draw axes on graph paper, using a scale of 1 cm per unit. Make a copy of the L-shape on the right.

The L-shape is enlarged by a factor of $2\frac{1}{2}$ from the point (1,1).

Draw the enlarged shape on your graph. (4) [4]

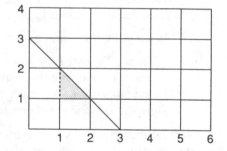

15) The diagram shows the cross-section of a horizontal drain. The length of the drain is 100 m and the radius of cross-section is 10 cm.

Find the area of cross-section and the volume of the drain. (4) [4]

16) Express the region shown shaded on the right in terms of three inequalities in x and y. (3) [3]

17) Show that there is a solution to the equation $x^2 + 3x = 5$ between $x = 1$ and $x = 2$. (2)

By trial and improvement find this solution to one decimal place. (3) [5]

18) A college wished to find how how well its ex-students were doing financially. It contacted ten of them and asked them what their annual salaries were. The responses were as below:

£9,500   £11,600   £48,000   £8,900   £12,000

£10,500   £8,600   £13,100   £9,900   £11,500

Find the mean salary. (2)

Find the median salary. (2)

Which of these averages is a better guide for the future prospects of the college's students? (2) [6]

19) What are the names for the triangles which have the following properties?

a)   Two angles are each 60°. (1)

b)   One angle is 40° and another is 70°. (1)

c)   The sides are 6 cm, 8 cm and 10 cm. (1) [3]

20) May buys items worth £6.38, £2.77 and £1.95, and pays for them with a £20 note. She does not have a calculator with her. Show how she can work out the approximate amount of change she should get. (3) [3]

21) The gravitational force between two objects is given by $F = \dfrac{GmM}{r^2}$.

Express G in terms of F, m, M and r. (3) [3]

Exam 2

Answer all the questions.
Time: 1 hour 30 minutes

1) Before decimal currency, there were 20 shillings in the pound and 12 pence in the shilling. Each penny was divided into 2 halfpence or 4 farthings.

Write $5\frac{3}{4}$ (fivepence three-farthings) as a fraction of a shilling. (2)

Suppose the price of potatoes is $5\frac{3}{4}$ per pound.

Find the cost in shillings and pence of 12 pounds of potatoes. (4) [6]

2) Write 6 as a product of primes. (1)

$6^2 = 36$. Write 36 as a product of primes. (1)

Without evaluating it, write the square root of $2^2 \times 3^4 \times 5^4$ as the product of primes. (2)

Write down as a product of primes a number bigger than 1,000,000 which is a perfect square. (3) [7]

3) In a raffle, the prizes cost a total of £250. The tickets, which cost nothing to produce, are sold for 20p each.

If 2,000 tickets are sold, what is the profit? What percentage of the receipts is profit? (2)

How many tickets must be sold to ensure that 50% of the receipts is profit? (2) [4]

4) Evaluate $1^2, 11^2, 111^2$. (1)

Continue this number sequence for three more terms. (2)

Guess the value of 111111111^2. (2) [5]

5) Snow falls to a depth of 1 metre over an area of 80 km². Find the volume of snow in m³, giving your answer in standard form. (3) [3]

6) Two friends pool their money.

Michael says: "We could buy three buns and have 95p left over".

Sandra says: "We could buy five buns and have 25p left".

If each bun costs xp, form an equation in x. Show that it simplifies to $3x + 70 = 5x$. (3)

Solve this equation. (1) [4]

7) Simplify the following:

a) $2x + 3y - x - 2y$ (1)

b) $3p^2q^4 \times 4pq^2$ (1)

c) $6r^3s^2 \div 2rs^4$ (1)

d) $\frac{1}{2}x^2 + \frac{1}{3}x^2 + \frac{1}{6}x^2$ (1)

e) $(3xy)^2$ (1) [5]

220

8) A stone is thrown up in the air, so that t seconds later its height h metres is given by $h = 40t - 5t^2$.

Fill in the table:

t	0	1	2	3	4	5	6	7	8
$40t$		40					240		
t^2		1					36		
$5t^2$		5					180		
h		35					60		

(3)

Plot a graph of this function. (3)

What was the greatest height reached? When was it reached? (2)

At what times was the stone 70 m above the ground? (3) [11]

9) Let $\mathbf{a} = \begin{pmatrix} 3 \\ 1 \end{pmatrix}$ and $\mathbf{b} = \begin{pmatrix} 1 \\ 2 \end{pmatrix}$. Find $3\mathbf{a}$ and $2\mathbf{a} + 3\mathbf{b}$. (2)

Suppose x and y are such that $x\mathbf{a} + y\mathbf{b} = \begin{pmatrix} 14 \\ 3 \end{pmatrix}$.

Form simultaneous equations in x and y and solve them. (3)

Draw on a graph the vectors $\mathbf{a}$, $\mathbf{b}$ and $\mathbf{a} + \mathbf{b}$, showing the connection between them. (3) [9]

10) x and y represent lengths in cm, A represents area in cm^2, V represents volume in cm^3. Write down the units of the following:

a) $A + xy$

b) $\dfrac{V}{A}$

c) $\dfrac{xyA}{V}$ (3)

11) Mark points on graph paper at A(0,1), B(4,5), C(6,0). These represent three towns A, B, C, where each unit on the graph paper represents 10 miles. (1)

By measurement, find the distance between A and B. (1)

By measurement, find the bearing of A from C. (2)

A radio transmitter is sited at (3,2), and it can be received within 20 miles. A car drives from A to B along a straight road. How far from A will the driver be able to receive the radio signals? (4) [8]

12) A slide in a children's playground is 3 m long, and the top is 2 m higher than the bottom.

a) Find the angle of slope of the slide. (2)

b) Find the horizontal distance between top and bottom. (2)

New EEC regulations require that all slides in playgrounds must have an angle of between 33° and 37°. If the length of the slide is unchanged, find the range of possible heights of the slide. (3) [7]

13) The units of a 3-dimensional coordinate system are 1 cm apart. A cuboid is placed so that the corners of its lower face are at (2,0,0), (2,3,0), (6,3,0), (6,0,0). If the cuboid is 1 cm high, find the coordinates of the corners of the top face. (2)

Find the volume of the cuboid. (2) [4]

14) A college offers 10 art classes, 7 language classes, 4 history classes, 8 science classes, 2 mathematics classes and 4 literature classes. An inspection team picks 10 different classes at random to be visited. Find the probabilities that:

a) The first class to be chosen will be a language class. (2)

b) The last class picked will be either maths or science. (2)

c) The second class picked will not be an art class. (2) [6]

15) The mileages of 60 second-hand cars were found to be as follows. (In 1,000s of miles.)

$$
\begin{array}{cccccccccc}
53 & 43 & 48 & 51 & 67 & 21 & 43 & 19 & 9 & 71 \\
21 & 28 & 42 & 31 & 80 & 37 & 43 & 27 & 19 & 64 \\
5 & 41 & 84 & 32 & 49 & 30 & 51 & 47 & 32 & 64 \\
16 & 19 & 63 & 34 & 27 & 53 & 27 & 82 & 39 & 70 \\
19 & 36 & 72 & 57 & 93 & 74 & 48 & 74 & 34 & 60 \\
29 & 37 & 42 & 75 & 45 & 63 & 32 & 54 & 23 & 7
\end{array}
$$

Group these data into a frequency table, using intervals of width 10,000 miles. (3)

From the frequency table find the average mileage. (3)

Plot a frequency polygon to show your results. (3) [9]

16) A tourist authority questioned 10 visitors to find out how long they were staying in a town and how much they planned to spend. The results are below.

Length of stay (days)	2	3	4	3	7	4	1	2	4	3
Amount to be spent (£)	80	100	180	90	220	90	30	60	190	110

Plot these points on a graph, taking the length of stay along the x-axis and the amount up the y-axis. (3)

Draw a straight line through the middle of the points. Find the gradient of this line. (4)

If someone plans to stay 5 days, how much would you expect him to spend? (3) [10]

Exam 3

Answer all the questions in both sections
Time: 2 hours 30 minutes

Section A

1) An atom of a certain substance weighs 0.0000000000000000000000004 grams.

   a) Write this number in standard form. (2)

   b) How many atoms are there in 12 kilograms of the substance? (3) **[5]**

2) a) Solve the inequality $3x + 7 < x - 11$ (2)

   b) Illustrate the inequality $-2 < x \leq 3$ on the number line. (2)

   c) List the integers x for which $x^2 < 7$. (2) **[6]**

3) The angles of an isosceles triangle are $3x$, $6x + y$, $3x + 3y$. Find two simultaneous equations in x and y and solve them. (6) **[6]**

4) Azaeez and Neville play a game by each rolling a die. If the dice show the same number, Azaeez pays Neville 40p. If they show different numbers Neville pays Azaeez 10p.

   By considering the table on the right, or otherwise, find the probability that Neville wins a game. (3)

   They play this game 60 times. How many times would you expect Neville to win? (3)

   Who will gain overall when they play 60 times, and by how much? (4) **[10]**

		A					
		1	2	3	4	5	6
N	1						
	2						
	3						
	4						
	5						
	6						

5) a) Evaluate $3.24 \times 2.17 + 4.21 \times 1.23 - 1.94 \times 3.16$. (2)

   b) Evaluate $\dfrac{2.17 - 1.43}{2.35 + 1.95}$ to 3 decimal places. (3)

   c) If $y = x^2 - 7x - 2$, find y when x is

   i) -3 ii) $\frac{2}{3}$ (3)

   d) Write down possible sequences of calculator buttons to evaluate:

   i) $3 + 4 \times 5$ ii) $(3 + 4) \times 5$ (3) **[11]**

6) A paved area is to be made so that it is a rectangle 2 m longer than it is wide. If the width is x m find an expression for the length. Find an expression for the perimeter. (3)

   Show that the area can be expressed as $A = x^2 + 2x$. (2)

   Fill in the table shown. Plot a graph of this function. (7)

   For what x is the area equal to 23 m²? (3)

   With this value of x what is the perimeter of the rectangle? (3) **[18]**

x	0	1	2	3	4	5
x^2			4			
$2x$			4			
A			8			

7) A is 20 miles from B, on a bearing of 355°. C is 15 miles from B, on a bearing of 055°. Make a drawing of A, B and C, to a scale of 1 cm per 5 miles. Find the distance of A from C. (6)

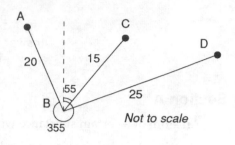

D is 25 miles from B, on a bearing of 085°. What is the angle ABD? By calculation, find the distance of A from D. (5) [11]

8) Over a period of 8 years the average price in p of a pint of milk was calculated. The results are below.

Year	1	2	3	4	5	6	7	8
Price	23	25	26	29	30	33	36	40

Plot these values on a graph, taking the year along the x-axis and the price up the y-axis. Draw a straight line through the points. (4)

From your line, what do you expect the average price to be in year 9? When will the price reach 45p? (4) [8]

9) A Pythagorean Triad consists of three whole numbers a, b and c for which $a^2 + b^2 = c^2$. They can be found by taking numbers r and s, with $r < s$, and putting $a = 2rs$, $b = s^2 - r^2$, $c = s^2 + r^2$.

Find a, b, c in the cases

i) $r = 1$, $s = 2$ and (ii) $r = 1$, $s = 4$.

In both cases check that a, b, c form a Pythagorean Triad. (4)

What values of r and s will give the Pythagorean Triad 5, 12, 13? (4) [8]

10) Let **a** be the vector which has translated T to T' in the diagram shown. Write down **a** in coordinate form. (2)

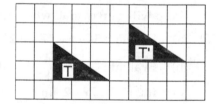

Let S be the triangle with vertices at A(2,2), B(0,1), C(1,0). Plot S on graph paper. Apply the translation defined by **a** to S. Plot the translated triangle and write down the coordinates of its vertices. (6) [8]

11) Triangle T has vertices at A(1,1), B(1,5), C(4,1). Plot T on graph paper. (1)

T is enlarged from the origin (0,0) by a factor of $2\frac{1}{2}$. Draw the enlarged triangle and write down the coordinates of its vertices. (4)

Another enlargement leaves A fixed and takes B to B'(1,7). What is the scale factor of this enlargement? Where does the enlargement take C? (4)

On a certain size of graph paper the distance AB is 3 cm. What is the distance AB'? (2) [11]

12) The ages of 160 members of a squash club are given in the frequency table below.

Age	15-19	20-24	25-29	30-34	35-39	40-44	45-49	50-54
Frequency	24	42	28	24	18	10	8	6

Find the cumulative frequencies. Plot a cumulative frequency graph. (5)

Find the median and the interquartile range. (4)

Two members are picked at random. What is the probability that they will both be under 25? (3) [12]

13) a) The basic cost of a computer is £300. Calculate the cost after VAT at 15% has been added. (1)

b) The VAT rate rises to $17\frac{1}{2}$%. Calculate the new price. (1)

c) What multiplying factor will take you from the old price to the new price? (2)

d) A printer costs £372.60, including VAT at 15%. Use your answer to (c) to find the price when VAT is raised to $17\frac{1}{2}$%. (2) [6]

Section B

Using and Applying Mathematics

14) Make a tracing of the dots on the right. Use the dots to draw four pairs of lines, (a), (b), (c), (d), which are:

a) Parallel, but not horizontal or vertical. (2)

b) Perpendicular, but not horizontal or vertical. (2)

c) At 45° to each other. (2)

d) At an angle of $\tan^{-1}2$ to each other. (2)

If the dots can be extended as far as we like, what other angles could be constructed by lines joining pairs of dots? (7) [15]

15) In factored form, a number N is $2^3 \times 3^2 \times 7^2$.

a) Evaluate N. (1)

b) Which of the following could be factors of N? in each case give reasons.

   i) 5   ii) $2^2 \times 3$ iii) 3^3 (3)

c) Write 150 in factored form. (1)

d) There are 12 factors of 150, including 1 and 150 itself. Write down the other 10 in factored form. (4)

The number N above is in factored form. How many factors does it have? (6) [15]

225

Exam 4
Using and Applying Mathematics

Attempt as many of the questions as you can.
Time: 2 hours 30 minutes

1) How many people, laid end to end, would stretch around the equator? (3)

   (The radius of the Earth is 6,400,000 metres) [3]

2) "A survey shows that 66.7% of doctors think that spicy food is dangerous for health."

   Is there anything about this announcement which makes you suspicious? (3) [3]

3) In the game of Noughts and Crosses, players put either a O or a X on a grid. The winner is the first person to get three O's or three X's in a line.

   Suppose Noughts and Crosses is played on a grid which stretches in all directions. Show that the person who starts can always win. (8) [8]

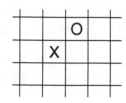

4) You have a collection of cubes, which can be joined together face to face.

   a) Show that with two cubes only one shape can be formed. (1)

   b) Show that with three cubes two different shapes can be formed. (2)

   c) See how many shapes you can form out of four cubes. (7) [10]

5) A cuboid is to be made out of a net. The net is to be cut from a square of side 12 inches, as shown.

   How do you cut the net so that the volume of the cuboid is as large as possible? (8) [8]

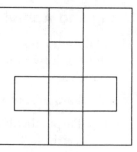

6) Suppose a fair coin is spun many times. The "Gambler's Fallacy" is that after a long run of Tails a Head is more likely to appear.

   Design an experiment which would investigate whether this is true. (8) [8]

7) The flow diagram below evaluates whether or not an odd number N is prime.

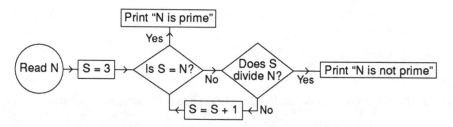

   Suggest ways in which the diagram could be made more efficient. (10) [10]

Solutions

Chapter 1

1.1.2 *Page 1*

1) (a) $2 \times 3 \times 5$ (b) $2 \times 2 \times 5 \times 5$ (c) $2 \times 2 \times 2 \times 7$
   (d) $2 \times 5 \times 11$ (e) $2 \times 2 \times 13$ (f) $2 \times 2 \times 2 \times 2 \times 3 \times 3 \times 5$
2) If it ends in 0, 2, 4, 6, or 8 3) If it ends in 0 or 5 4) a, b, c
5) 15 6) 8

1.2.2 *Page 2*

1) (a) 2 (b) 2 (c) 3 (d) 6 (e) 1
2) (a) 30 (b) 28 (c) 45 (d) 60 (e) 210
4) 10 p 5) 15 pints 6) 24 seconds
7) 15 February 8) 30 cm square

1.3.2 *Page 4*

1) (a) $\frac{5}{3}$ (b) $\frac{13}{5}$ (c) $\frac{33}{10}$ (d) $\frac{9}{7}$

2) (a) $2\frac{2}{5}$ (b) $2\frac{6}{7}$ (c) $3\frac{7}{8}$ (d) $7\frac{9}{13}$

3) (a) $\frac{8}{21}$ (b) $\frac{1}{9}$ (c) $\frac{9}{10}$ (d) $\frac{10}{21}$ (e) $\frac{2}{15}$

   (f) $1\frac{33}{35}$ (g) $4\frac{19}{42}$ (h) $1\frac{1}{6}$ (i) $\frac{5}{6}$ (j) $\frac{5}{27}$

   (k) 22 (l) $2\frac{11}{12}$ (m) $\frac{5}{42}$ (n) $\frac{27}{49}$

4) (a) $\frac{7}{12}$ (b) $\frac{23}{30}$ (c) $\frac{17}{21}$ (d) $\frac{4}{15}$

   (e) $1\frac{3}{4}$ (f) $5\frac{13}{36}$ (g) $1\frac{43}{70}$

5) $1\frac{5}{12}$ yd 6) $12\frac{3}{4}$ 7) $\frac{1}{20}$ 8) 40 9) 24 10) 6 hrs

11) $\frac{1}{2}$ mile 12) 6 13) $\frac{7}{30}$ 14) $\frac{11}{240}$ lb

15) $\frac{1}{3} + \frac{1}{15}, \frac{1}{3} + \frac{1}{5} + \frac{1}{15}, \frac{1}{2} + \frac{1}{6} + \frac{1}{10} + \frac{1}{30}$.

Chapter 2

2.1.2 *Page 8*

1) (a) 105.6 (b) 1.294 (c) 70.902 (d) 13.95 (e) 0.741
   (f) 1.8 (g) 0.327 (h) 6.702
2) 52.6 m². (a) £28.93 (b) £44.71
3) £336.92. £342.83
4) (a) 36,175.44 pts. (b) 50,013.04 esc.
5) 2.92 hours. 2.16 hours.

2.2.2 *Page 9*

1) (a) 28, 29.6 (b) 4, 4.37 (c) 100, 113 (d) 200,000, 219,000
   (e) 20, 21.5 (f) 0.01, 0.0113 (g) 100, 99.7 (h) 0.002, 0.00156
2) £450 3) 24 kg 4) £70 5) 1.5 hours
6) 260,000 L 7) 200 hours. 25 days. £2,600 8) 400

Chapter 3

3.1.1 *Page 12*

1) 800,000
2) 1,500,000
3) 14,000,000
4) 20
5) 30
6) 100
7) 11,000,000
8) 18,000,000
9) 660,000
10) 250
11) 500
12) 1500
13) 90
14) 1,200
15) 48,000
16) 20,000
17) 200,000
18) 30,000
19) 200 m
20) 60 grams
21) £14,000
22) 1,200 inches
23) 2,000 cm^3
24) 180 hours
25) 500

3.2.2 *Page 14*

1) (a) 2.3×10^4 (b) 8.76×10^8 (c) 1.23×10^{-4} (d) 5×10^{-6}
2) (a) 2,000,000 (b) 93,000,000,000 (c) 0.00000042
3) (a) 4.5×10^9 (b) 9.92×10^{13} (c) 9.35×10^6 (d) 3×10^8
   (e) 3.4×10^{22} (f) 4×10^{21} (g) 5.5×10^{-7} (h) 8.362×10^{-10}
   (i) 6.5×10^{-7}
4) $£5 \times 10^8$ 5) 1.5×10^8 km 6) 5×10^4 tons 7) 3×10^9 years
8) 4×10^7 m 9) 2.5×10^8

3.3.2 *Page 15*

1) (a) 3×10^5 (b) 8×10^8 (c) 6×10^{17} (d) 1.5×10^9 (e) 1.04×10^{14}
   (f) 2×10^3 (g) 1.5×10^6 (h) 5×10^3 (i) 2.5×10^4
2) 6.696×10^8 miles. 5.87×10^{12} miles 3) 2.5×10^{30} 4) 4×10^7 metres
5) 2.2×10^9 6) 3×10^7 7) 5×10^9. 3.81×10^{12}. 762 cm^2.

3.4.2 *Page 15*

1) (a) 9×10^8 (b) 6×10^6 (c) 1.75×10^6
   (d) 3.2×10^7 (e) 1.2×10^9 (f) 2×10^{11}
2) 7×10^7 kg 3) 1.6×10^9years 4) 2.58×10^8 km. 4.2×10^7 km
5) 2.3×10^7 6) $\$2.6 \times 10^9$

Chapter 4

4.1.2 *Page 19*

1) (a) 32 (b) 81 (c) 343 (d) 54 (e) 216 (f) 63
   (g) 441 (h) 108 (i) 72 (j) 8 (k) 4
2) (a) x^{11} (b) y^{13} (c) z^6 (d) w^5 (e) t^8 (f) $8x^7$
   (g) $12y^{11}$ (h) $49z^8$ (i) $8t^9$ (j) $4w^5$ (k) $3t^4$ (l) $\frac{1}{4}s^4$
3) (a) 729 (b) 1,024 (c) 3.375 (d) 104.8576
4) x^2. $2x$. $4x^2$ 5) y^3. $3y$. $27y^3$
6) (a) 2^{14} (b) 2^{18} (c) 2^{25}

4.2.2 *Page 20*

1) (a) 8 (b) 10 (c) 10 (d) 5 (e) 3 (f) 7
   (g) 6 (h) 4 (i) 15 (j) 6 (k) 20 (l) $\frac{5}{3}$
   (m) $\frac{2}{3}$ (n) $\frac{1}{2}$ (o) $\frac{2}{3}$ (p) $\frac{2}{10}$
2) (a) x^4 (b) y^5 (c) x^2 (d) $2x$ (e) yz^2 (f) $3x^2$
   (g) s^2t^2 (h) $4x^2$
3) 64 4) 8 cm 5) 6 m 6) $6z$ inches 7) $10y^2$cm

4.3.2 *Page 21*

1) (a) $\frac{1}{2}$ (b) $\frac{1}{4}$ (c) $\frac{4}{3}$ (d) $\frac{7}{5}$ (e) 4 (f) 12

(g) $\frac{4}{5}$ (h) $\frac{6}{7}$ (i) $\frac{7}{16}$ (j) $\frac{1}{x}$ (k) x (l) $\frac{y}{x}$

Chapter 5

5.1.2 *Page 24*

1) (a) 11, 13 (b) 27, 32 (c) −1, −4 (d) −11, −13 (e) $2\frac{3}{4}$, 3 (f) $1\frac{2}{3}$, $1\frac{1}{3}$

(g) 48, 96 (h) 16, $10\frac{2}{3}$ (i) $\frac{5}{6}$, $\frac{6}{7}$ (j) $\frac{31}{32}$, $\frac{63}{64}$

2) (a) start 1, add 2 (b) start 2, add 5 (c) start 11, subtract 3

(d) start −3, subtract 2 (e) start $1\frac{1}{2}$, add $\frac{1}{4}$ (f) start 3, subtract $\frac{1}{3}$

(g) start 3, multiply by 2 (h) start 81, multiply by $\frac{2}{3}$

(i) start $\frac{1}{2}$, add 1 to top and bottom

(j) start $\frac{1}{2}$, double bottom, for top subtract 1 from bottom.

3) (a) 3, 7, 11, 15 (b) 4, 7, 10, 13 (c) 7, 6, 5, 4

(d) $1\frac{1}{2}$, 2, $2\frac{1}{2}$, 3 (e) 2, 5, 10, 17 (f) 4, 11, 22, 37

(g) 2, 1, $\frac{2}{3}$, $\frac{1}{2}$ (h) $\frac{2}{3}$, $\frac{3}{5}$, $\frac{4}{7}$, $\frac{5}{9}$ (i) 0, $\frac{1}{2}$, $\frac{2}{3}$, $\frac{3}{4}$

4) (a) start 2, add 10 (b) start 30, add 1 (c) start 0, add 11 (d) start 9, add 9

5) 1, 3, 6, 10 6) 5, 8, 11, 14, 17. 20, 23. 77, 100

5.2.2 *Page 25*

1) (a) $2n - 1$ (b) $3n - 1$ (c) $5n + 5$ (d) $11 - n$ (e) $9 - 2n$ (f) $1\frac{1}{2} + \frac{1}{2}n$

(g) $1 + \frac{1}{3}n$ (h) n^3 (i) $\frac{1}{n}$ (j) $1 - \frac{1}{n}$

2) (a) 99 (b) 149 (c) 255 (d) −39 (e) −91 (f) $26\frac{1}{2}$

(g) $17\frac{2}{3}$ (h) 125,000 (i) $\frac{1}{50}$ (j) $\frac{49}{50}$

3) $2n + 1$ 4) $13 - 3n$ 5) 2 6) $a = -1, b = 2$ 7) $a = 1\frac{1}{2}, b = \frac{1}{2}$

5.3.2 *Page 26*

1) a & d true 2) true 3) true 4) true

5) false 6) false 7) true 8) (a) false (b) false

Chapter 6

6.1.2 *Page 30*

1) (a) $2n + 3$ (b) $0.5n + 1.5$ (c) $11 - 3n$

2) (a) +A3+2 (b) +A3+5 (c) +A3−2

3) (a) $k=1, c=2$ (b) $k=4, c=3$ (c) $k=\frac{1}{2}, C=2$

6.2.2 *Page 31*

1) (a) $x=3, y=2$ (b) $x=3, y=5$ (c) $x=7, y=4$

2) (a) $x=3, y=2$ (b) $x=9, y=4$ (c) $x=8, y=3$

3) (a) $3^2 + 3^2 + 2^2 + 1^2$ (b) $8^2 + 1^2 + 1^2 + 1^2$

(c) $13^2 + 6^2 + 5^2 + 1^2$ (d) $14^2 + 13^2 + 5^2 + 1^2$

6.3.2 *Page 32*

1) 4   2) 4   3) 5   4) 4

Chapter 7

7.2.2 *Page 37*

1) $34.25° - 34.35°$ 2) $905 - 915$ kg   3) $75,000 - 85,000$ 4) $0.535 - 0.545$ kg
5) $235 - 245$ miles   6) 30 grams   7) 0.7 inches   8) $40,000,000$ metres

7.3.2 *Page 38*

1) a & d & f correct.   (b) 2,000 square yards
    (c) 8 m   (e) 2 square feet
2) (a) area   (b) volume   (c) area
    (d) length   (e) area   (f) length
3) (a) 10,000   (b) 1,000,000   (c) 1,000,000,000
    (d) 144   (e) 27
4) £240   5) 1,000 kg   6) 2 grams
7) £9,000,000   8) £4   9) yes

Chapter 8

8.1.2 *Page 53*

1) $8x$ 2) $5y$ 3) $4z$ 4) $4b - 6a$
5) $4x + 10y$ 6) $2p + q$ 7) $3xy$ 8) $6ab + 2a$
9) $mn + m + n$ 10) $-x^2$ 11) $3y^2$ 12) $3x^2 + 2x$
13) $11 + 3z^2 - 2z$ 14) $4x^2 - x - 6$ 15) $3a^2 + 2b^2 + 7a + 2b$
16) $2xy + 7yz - zx$ 17) $2pq^2 + 10qp^2$ 18) $ab^3 + 3ba^3 - 3a^3 b^3$

8.2.2 *Page 54*

1) $6x^2y^2$ 2) $12xyz$ 3) $6a^3b^3$ 4) $12a^2b$
5) $-2a^2$ 6) $-8ab^2$ 7) xy 8) $6x^2y$
9) $30m^3n^3$ 10) a^3b 11) $-x^3$ 12) x^3y^2z
13) 2 14) $3.5x$ 15) $\dfrac{x}{2}$ 16) $2ab$
17) $\dfrac{3m^2}{n}$ 18) $-2a$ 19) $\dfrac{-3x}{y}$ 20) 4
21) $\dfrac{2}{x}$ 22) $\dfrac{2.5}{r}$ 23) $\dfrac{4rt}{s}$ 24) $\dfrac{3}{2b}$

8.3.2 *Page 55*

1) $5x + 35$ 2) $4a - 4b$ 3) $14x + 7y$ 4) $6x - 10y$
5) $8x + 18$ 6) $5y - 27$ 7) $-2z + 22$ 8) $37w - 21$
9) $7x - y$ 10) $8a + 11b$ 11) $2x + 2y$ 12) $c - 14d$
13) $11r$ 14) $2p + 14q$ 15) $x^2 + 6x + 5$ 16) $y^2 + 10y + 21$
17) $p^2 - p - 12$ 18) $z^2 + 2z - 24$ 19) $w^2 - 18w + 77$ 20) $q^2 - 7q + 10$
21) $x^2 - y^2$ 22) $4x^2 - y^2$ 23) $x^2 + 6x + 9$ 24) $y^2 - 6y + 9$
25) $x^2 + 4xy + 4y^2$ 26) $9z^2 - 12zw + 4w^2$ 27) $3x^2 + 19x - 40$ 28) $6y^2 + 13y - 28$
29) $ac + ad + bc + bd$ 30) $xz + xw - yz - yw$

8.4.2 *Page 56*

1) $(y + z)$ 2) $q(p - 3)$ 3) $s(3 + r)$ 4) $t(q + r)$
         6) $x(3y - 4z)$ 7) $2(x + 2y)$ 8) $3(t - 3r)$

9) $2r(s + 2q)$ 10) $3y(3x - z)$ 11) $3f(2g + 3h)$ 12) $7t(1 + 3q)$

13) $a(a + b)$ 14) $z(1 - z)$ 15) $5x(x - 3)$ 16) $7y(3y - 2)$

17) $4z(2z + c)$ 18) $3d(1 + 3cd)$ 19) $a(b + c + d)$ 20) $3x(y + 2z + 5w)$

21) $p(p + q + 4)$ 22) £10

Chapter 9

9.1.2 *Page 60*

1) $10 - x$ m   2) $T° - d°$ 3) xy 4) LB m². $2L + 2B$ m

5) $68t$ 6) £$(n - m)$ 7) $180°n - 360°$ 8) $120 + x$

9) $2N + 5$ 10) $6x + 4y + z$ 11) $2x$ cm, $2x^2$ cm², $6x$ cm

12) CA   13) $\dfrac{xP + yQ}{x + y}$ 14) $\dfrac{850x}{y^2} - 1$

9.2.2 *Page 61*

1) (a) 11   (b) $3\frac{1}{2}$ (c) -1

2) (a) 4   (b) $2\frac{1}{2}$ (c) $2\frac{1}{4}$ (d) 1

3) (a) 3   (b) -5 (c) 5   (d) 15

4) (a) 10   (b) -4 (c) $6\frac{1}{2}$ (d) $-\frac{1}{2}$

5) 42   6) 216

7) (a) 11   (b) 2   (c) -15

8) (a) 4   (b) $\frac{7}{12}$

9) (a) 108   (b) 3   (c) 36

10) (a) 6   (b) $\frac{3}{4}$ (c) 0

11) (a) 12   (b) 0   (c) $-\frac{1}{4}$ (d) 6

12) (a) 4   (b) $\frac{1}{2}$ (c) 24   (d) -6

13) (a) 9   (b) 144   (c) 4

14) 4   15) 13   16) 2.236   17) 12.042   18) 14%

9.3.2 *Page 63*

1) $\dfrac{x - 2}{3}$ 2) $a - b + c$ 3) $\dfrac{5}{9}(F - 32)$ 4) $\dfrac{rt}{3p}$

5) $\dfrac{y}{3x^2}$ 6) $\dfrac{59 - j}{n}$ 7) $2b - c$ 8) $2a(d + 3)$

9) $\dfrac{3V}{4r^3}$ 10) $20Y - 2Z$ 11) $2z - y$ 12) $\dfrac{7}{q - r}$

13) $\sqrt{\dfrac{2y}{a}}$ 14) $\sqrt{\dfrac{A}{4\pi}}$ 15) $\sqrt{T + R + 3}$ 16) $\sqrt{L^2 - 4r^2}$

17) $(h + 3)^2$ 18) $\dfrac{gt^2}{4}$ 19) $a(b - 3) - 1$ 20) $\dfrac{v}{w}$

Chapter 10

10.1.2 *Page 67*

1) 6   2) 5   3) 25   4) 2   5) 1   6) 1

7) 13   8) -3 9) -6 10) 3   11) 1.414   12) 2

13) 3   14) 1.817   15) $2x + 3 = 37. 17$ 16) $x^2 + 8 = 33. 5$

17) $2x + 12 = x + 30$. 18   18) £26   19) £30   20) 26.5 cm   21) 10 cm
22) 2 cm

10.2.2 Page 68

1) 3.1   2) 2.2   3) 0.6   4) 3.6   5) 4.8   6) 0.2
7) 6.8 m   8) 2.9   9) 2.8   10) 4.5 m

10.3.2 Page 70

1) $x = 5, y = -2$ 2) $z = 6, w = -9$ 3) $x = 2, y = -1$ 4) $x = 1, y = 4$
5) $p = 4, q = 3$ 6) $x = 27, y = -37$ 7) $z = 6, w = 2$ 8) $q = 5, p = 5$
9) $x = 4, y = 1$ 10) $x = 3, y = -2$ 11) $x = 2, y = 7$ 12) $s = 4, r = -3$
13) $x = 2, y = 3$ 14) $p = 8, q = 7$ 15) $x = 12, y = 18$ 16) $m = 8, n = 7$
17) $3x + 4y = 384, 5x + 7y = 648$. $x = 96, y = 24$ 18) 38   19) 320
20) 85 p   21) 21

Chapter 11

11.1.2 Page 74

1) $a \& d \& e$

2) $4.45 < \frac{9}{2} < 4.6 < \frac{14}{3} < \frac{19}{4}$

3) $0.2 > \frac{1}{8} > 0 > -\frac{1}{8} > -\frac{3}{17} > -\frac{1}{4} > -\frac{1}{2}$

4) 4 or 5   5) −4 or −3
6) (a) 1, 2, 3, 4, 5   (b) 2, 3, 4, 5, 6, 7   (c) 14, 15, 16, 17
    (d) 7, 8, 9
7) (a) −1, 0, 1   (b) −7, −6, −5, −4, −3 (c) −4, −3, −2, −1   (d) −2, −1, 0, 1, 2, 3
9) (a) $x < 3$ (b) $x \leq 2$ (c) $x \geq -1$ (d) $x > -2$
11) $h \geq 180$ 12) $w < 60$ 13) $-5° < T < 25°$ 14) £3,000 $< I <$ £22,000
15) $a > 17.5$ $16 < b < 17$ $c < 18$ $d > 17$ $e > 17$ $f \geq 17$

11.2.2 Page 76

1) (a) $x < 3$ (b) $x \geq 2$ (c) $x \geq 5$
    (d) $x < 3$ (e) $x > 12$ (f) $x < 3$
    (g) $x < 6$ (h) $x \leq 13$ (i) $x \geq -1$
    (j) $x > 33$
2) (a) $-3 < x < 3$ (b) $-10 \leq x \leq 10$ (c) $x < -2$ or $x > 2$
    (d) $-\frac{1}{2} \leq x \leq \frac{1}{2}$ (e) $-\sqrt{2} < x < \sqrt{2}$ (f) $x < -\sqrt{3}$ or $x > \sqrt{3}$
3) $25x < 400$. $x < 16$ 4) $10x \leq 100$. $x \leq 10$ 5) $25y < 150$. $y < 6$
6) $30z \geq 120$. $z \geq 4$ 7) $\frac{m}{5} \leq 50$. $m \leq 250$ 8) $21x + 2 \times 25 < 900$. $x < \frac{900}{71}$
9) $15 + 0.05x < 50$. $x < 700$ 10) $2x + 2(x + 2) < 60$. $x < 14$
11) no

11.3.2 Page 78

2) (a) $x + y \leq 3$ (b) $y \geq 1, x + y \leq 3$
    (c) $x \geq 1, y \geq 1, x + y < 3$ (d) $x \leq 3, y \leq 3, x + y > 3$
3) (1,1), (1,2), (2,1)   4) (1,1), (1,2), (2,1)

Chapter 12

12.1.2 Page 82

7) (2,5)   8) $x = 1, y = 4$

12.2.2 *Page 83*

1) 4 lb   2) £105   3) 280   4) 8 miles   6) £24,000
7) (a) £250   (b) £1,750   (c) £3,000   (d) £6,250   (e) £8,250,£23,000
8) over 100 miles. 9) under £24,000

12.3.2 *Page 84*

1) (a) 1 mile. 20 min   (b) 11 miles. 30 min (c) 3 m.p.h., 22 m.p.h.

2) (a) $\frac{1}{2}$ mile   (b) 35 mins   (c) 2 m.p.h., 6 m.p.h., 6 m.p.h.

3) (a) 1 hour, $\frac{1}{2}$ hour, $1\frac{1}{2}$ hours   (b) 30 miles, 40 miles, 30 miles

     (c) 30 m.p.h., 80 m.p.h., 20 m.p.h.
4) (a) 10 mins, 10 mins   (b) 4 miles   (c) 24 m.p.h.
8) After 2 hours. 8 miles

12.4.2 *Page 87*

1) 1.3, −2.3   4) 4.1 seconds

Chapter 13

13.1.2 *Page 101*

1) (a) 1,890 sq ft, 186 ft   (b) £7.56   (c) £65.1
2) 30 cm   3) 25 m, 625 m^2 4) 12 ft   5) 10 cm
6) 6, 10   7) 6   8) 8 m^2 9) 576 sq ft
10) 759 cm^2
11) (a) 6 sq units
12) (a) 4   (b) 3   (c) 9   (d) 6
13) 3   14) 3.5   15) 14 cm^2

13.2.2 *Page 103*

1) 100 m. 314 m   2) 25.1 cm   3) 7.85 cm   4) 9.42 cm
5) 9.42 in   6) 127 m. 64 m   7) 3.18 cm   8) 1,634 cm
9) (a) 2,827 cm^2 (b) 12.6 sq ft   (c) 452 m^2 (d) 0.196 sq in
10) (a) 3 cm   (b) 1.91 in   (c) 1.69 m   (d) 1.26 ft
11) 31.4 cubits

13.3.2 *Page 105*

1) 120   2) 120,000 kg 3) 4 cm   4) 0.4 m   5) 512. 5.06 g
6) (a) 7   (b) 162
7) 48.8 m^2 8) 54 cm^2 9) 3.28 m^2
10) (a) 2.625 m^2 (b) 7.875 m^3
11) 1,000 cm. 125
12) (a) 628   (b) 308   (c) 70.7
13) 1.16 cm   14) 1.05 cm

Chapter 14

14.1.2 *Page 107*

1) (a) diameter (b) radius   (c) chord   (d) tangent
2) (a) segment   (b) sector   (c) semicircle
4) (a) 2   (b) 0   (c) 1   (d) 1
5) (a) circle   (b) straight line. Tangent to the circle
6) (a) 4   (b) 3   (c) 2   (d) 1   (e) 0

14.2.2 *Page 110*

1) (a) 100°   (b) 55°   (c) 60°   (d) 30°
2) 90°. congruent   3) both 60°

14.3.2 *Page 111*

1) (a) 82°   (b) 76°   (c) 90°
2) (a) 6.6   (b) 6.3   (c) 9.5
3) (a) 3.6   (b) 4.1   (c) 4.2
4) 40°   5) 14 m

14.4.2 *Page 113*

3) (a) 4   (b) 6.7   (c) 8.5
4) (a) 1.7   (b) 3.1   (c) 3

Chapter 15

15.1.2 *Page 117*

9) (a) 2   (b) 0   (c) 3, 13
10) (2,2.2), (2,–2.2)   11) (3,2.6) (3,–2.6)   12) (4,4) (–4,4)

15.2.2 *Page 118*

11) 0.45 hours   13) no

15.3.2 *Page 120*

1) (a) 60 r.p.m. acw   (b) 240 r.p.m. acw   (c) 120 r.p.m. cw
2) 10 cm
3) up, $\frac{1}{4}$ m/sec

4) (a) 1 m/sec   (b) $\frac{1}{4}$ m/sec   (c) $\frac{1}{3}$ m/sec

Chapter 16

16.1.2 *Page 123*

1) (0,0,20), (0,30,20), (40,30,20), (40,0,20)   2) (5,4,3). (2.5,2,3)   3)   40. 40, 30
4) (3,3,5), (3,–3,5), (–3,–3,5), (–3,3,5)   5) (0,0,±1), (1,0,±1), (1,1,±1), (0,1,±1).
6) cuboid. 6   7) prism. 30
8) (1,1,0), (–1,1,0), (–1,–1,0), (1,–1,0), (0,0,3). (Many others)
9) (0,0,5), (1,0,5), (0,1,5) or (0,0,–1), (1,0,–1), (0,1,–1)
10) (2,1,1)

16.2.2 *Page 125*

1) (a) (3,1)   (b) (4,–2)   (c) (–2,–2)
3) (–1,10), (–12,12)
5) (a) (3,3)   (b) (4,2)   (c) (4,–2)   (d) (–4,–3)
6) (a) (2,–1)   (b) (9,–6)   (c) (0,1)
8) (4,–4)   9) (2,5)
10) $x = 4, y = -3$
12) (a) (2,3)   (b) (3,0)   (c) (4,–5)   (d) (–5,7)
13) (a) (5,9)   (b) (3,5)   (c) (–1,–1)
14) (1,2). 3

Chapter 17

17.1.2 *Page 129*
4) (1,–1), (6,–1), (11,–6) 5) (0,2), (4,2), (4,–6), (0,–6)
6) (1,1), (2,1), (3,0) 7) (2,0), (4,0), (4,–4), (2,–4)

17.2.2 *Page 130*
6) (5,–2), (–1,–2), (–7,4) 7) (–2,–8), (–8,–8), (–8,4), (–2,4)
8) (–1,–2), (–3,–2), (–5,0) 9) (1,1), (0,1), (0,3), (1,3)

17.3.2 *Page 131*

1) (a) 2 (b) –1 (c) $\frac{1}{2}$

2) 2, (1,2) 3) 3, $(1\frac{1}{2},1)$ 4) –2, (2,0) 5) $\frac{1}{2}$, (1,0)

6) yes. –2, (2,2) 7) at the pinhole. $-\frac{1}{4}$

17.4.2 *Page 133*
1) a & c 2) ALM, ABC
3) ABC, ALN, NMC, LBM, MNL. 4) AEG, ADC, CBA, CFG
5) (a) 3 (b) 4 (c) 6 (d) 1
6) 1.5 m. 1 m. 7) 1:4 8) ABC, AQP. 2:3
9) ABD & BCA. (a) 5 (b) 4

Chapter 18

18.1.2 *Page 137*
1) (a) 5 (b) 12 (c) 9.22 (d) 12.7
2) 10.6 cm 3) 7.94 m 4) 5.83 miles 5) 13.6 cm
6) 93.0 ft 7) 8.20 cm 8) 5.66 cm 9) 40 m. 40.05 m
10) 4 ft 11) 199.75 cm. 0.25 cm
12) no 13) yes
14) (a) 2.83 (b) 3.61 (c) 6.40

18.2.2 *Page 138*
1) 4.58 cm, 9.17 cm^2 2) 7.62 m 3) 50 cm, 50.4 cm 4) 3.46 cm. 6.93 cm^2
5) 19.8 6) 3 in. 5.29 in 7) 1.85 m

18.3.2 *Page 139*
1) (a) 2.24 (b) 5.83 (c) 7.21
   (d) 5.39 (e) 6.08 (f) 12.2
3) rhombus 4) 5, 5, 7.07. right–angled
5) 5, 5. rectangle 6) 2.24, 4.47, 6.71. In a straight line

Chapter 19

19.1.2 *Page 143*
1) (a) 0.515 (b) 0.731 (c) 19.1
2) (a) 11.8 (b) 23.6 (c) 7.13
3) (a) 10.1 (b) 4.64 (c) 4.20 (d) 11.4
4) 10.3 cm, 17.1 cm 5) 35.9 cm, 27.1 cm
6) 21.2 cm, 33.9 cm 7) 32.7 cm 8) 36.7 cm

19.2.2 *Page 145*
1) (a) 53° (b) 66° (c) 67°
2) (a) 25° (b) 50° (c) 56°

3) (a) 34°   (b) 26°   (c) 53°   (d) 30°
4) 71°   5) 58°   6) 41°   7) 42°   8) 60°

19.3.2 *Page 146*

1) 89.0 m   2) 1°   3) 1.64 m   4) 31.0°
5) 26.0 ft   6) 27°   7) 8°   8) 153 m
9) 163 m   10) 21.2 m   11) 6°, 9.95 m   12) 195 m/sec
13) 22°   14) 35 m

Chapter 20

20.2.2 *Page 163*

1) 19   2) 5' 2"   4) £44,000   5) 37 m.p.g. 58 m.p.h.   6) 1.7 kg

Chapter 21

21.1.2 *Page 167*

1) 6, 5, 7   2) 27, 26.5, 19   3) 6, 5.9   4) 2, 0
5) 249.125, 249   6) 7, 7.3, 6.9   7) 25.75, 25.5
8) Don: 41.125, 6   Ron: 38, 40   9) A: 73, 64   B: 68.625, 70.5
10) A: 6.2, 16   B: 5.3, 7   11) A: 14.1, 13.3   B: 13.6, 13.8   12) A: 81, 19   B: 81, 5

21.2.2 *Page 170*

1) 5.184, 5, 5   2) 1.375   3) 2.076   4) 34.9 years   5) 137.6 cm   6) £17,500

Chapter 22

22.3.2 *Page 177*

1) (c) 169, 163, 177, 14 (d) $\frac{2}{3}$
2) (c) 77, 69, 89, 20   (d) 0.7
3) (c) 30, 24, 36, 12
4) (c) 30, 19, 43, 24
5) (c) £10,600, £9,100, £12,000, £2,900
6) (c) 3.5, 2.7, 4.1, 1.4
7) (c) 15.4, 14.7, 16.1, 1.4
8) A:11 B:19   9) Lucy: 4 Liz: 10   10) A: 0.12 B: 0.18   11) A:37 B:13
12) A: 2.3 B: 3.2

Chapter 24

24.1.2 *Page 189*

1) $\frac{1}{4}$ 4) $\frac{3}{5}$ 6) $\frac{1}{5}$

8) (a) $\frac{1}{11}$ (b) $\frac{2}{11}$

24.2.2 *Page 190*

1) 50   2) 10   3) 20   4) 6
5) 5   6) 6   7) 10   8) 20

24.3.2 *Page 191*

1) (a) $\frac{1}{24}$ (b) $\frac{1}{6}$ (c) $\frac{1}{8}$

2) (a) $\frac{1}{16}$ (b) $\frac{1}{8}$

3) (a) $\frac{1}{6}$ (b) $\frac{1}{18}$ (c) $\frac{1}{6}$

    (d) $\frac{1}{6}$ (e) $\frac{5}{12}$ (f) $\frac{7}{12}$

    (g) $\frac{7}{36}$ (h) $\frac{1}{9}$

4) (a) $\frac{1}{8}$ (b) $\frac{3}{8}$

5) (a) $\frac{1}{16}$ (b) $\frac{5}{16}$ (c) $\frac{1}{4}$ (d) $\frac{3}{4}$

6) AA AB AC BA BB BC CA CB CC.   (a) $\frac{4}{9}$ (b) $\frac{1}{3}$

7) AB AC AD BC BD CD. $\frac{1}{6}$

8) LMN LNM MLN MNL NLM NML.   (a) $\frac{1}{6}$ (b) $\frac{1}{2}$

9) RO RY RG OY OG YG. $\frac{1}{6}$

10) RR RO RY RG OR OO OY OG YR YO YY YG GR GO GY GG.

(a) $\frac{1}{4}$ (b) $\frac{1}{8}$.

Chapter 25

25.1.2 *Page 195*

1) $\frac{1}{3}$ 2) $\frac{1}{18}$ 3) $\frac{1}{10}$

4) (a) $\frac{1}{2}$ (b) $\frac{3}{4}$ (c) $\frac{2}{13}$ (d) $\frac{4}{13}$

5) $\frac{11}{36}$ 6) $\frac{3}{4}$

7) (a) $\frac{4}{13}$ (b) $\frac{11}{26}$

8) (a) $\frac{3}{16}$ (b) $\frac{1}{6}$ (c) $\frac{1}{24}$ (d) $\frac{5}{16}$

9) $\frac{11}{15}$ 10) $\frac{43}{60}$

25.2.2 *Page 196*

1) $\frac{1}{8}$ 2) $\frac{125}{216}$ 3) $\frac{1}{24}$ 4) $\frac{1}{12}$

5) (a) $\frac{1}{1296}$ (b) $\frac{1225}{1296}$

6) $\frac{1}{27}$ 7) $\frac{1}{6}$ 8) $\frac{1}{100}$

9) (a) $\frac{1}{75}$ (b) $\frac{56}{75}$

10) (a) $\frac{1}{4}$ (b) $\frac{4}{9}$

11) $\frac{3}{4000}$

Mental tests

Test 1 *Page 209*

1) 20,014
2) 30
3) $\frac{8}{15}$
4) 9
5) 19.15
6) 165 miles
7) 2×10^4
8) £3.20
9) £4,000
10) 4.5 kg
11) 140 m
12) 6.55
13) 16, 19
14) $3x + 4$
15) $8x + 5x^2$
16) 12
17) bisectors of sides
18) 25%
19) 12
20) $\frac{1}{25}$

Test 2 *Page 210*

1) 3 hours
2) 3.79
3) 23°
4) 19
5) 100
6) £16,500
7) 35%
8) $\frac{2}{5}$
9) 6×10^{10}
10) £32,000
11) 122°
12) 5
13) 8
14) 5
15) $100x$ cm
16) order 5
17) 6 cm, 9 cm
18) 21
19) 18
20) $\frac{3}{20}$

Index